MATHEMATICS FOR BUSINESS

Mathematics

Business

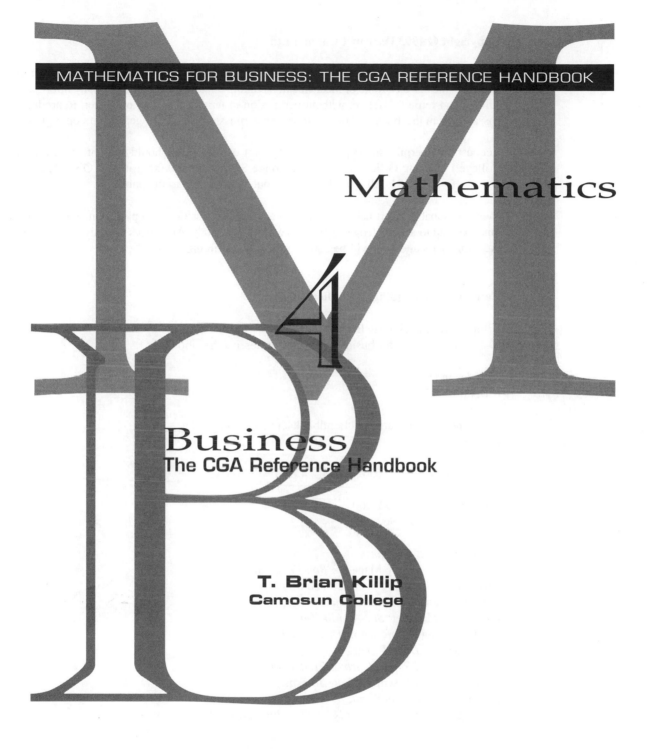

Mathematics

Business
The CGA Reference Handbook

T. Brian Killip
Camosun College

Certified General
Accountants

Canadian Cataloguing in Publication Data

Killip, T. Brian (Thomas Brian), 1946 –
    Mathematics for business: the CGA reference handbook

Includes index.
ISBN 0-03-922960-2

1. Business mathematics — Handbooks, manuals, etc.
I. Title.

HF5691.K53 1993   650'-01513   C93-093848-8

ISBN-13: 978-0-03-922960-3
ISBN-10: 0-03-922960-2

Publisher: *Scott Duncan*
Editor and Marketing Manager: *Ron Fitzgerald*
Director of Publishing Services: *Jean Lancee*
Editorial Manager: *Marcel Chiera*
Production Manager: *Sue-Ann Becker*
Manufacturing Co-ordinator: *Denise Wake*
Cover Design: *Dave Peters*
Interior Design: *Robert Garbutt Productions*
Typesetting and Assembly: *True To Type*
Technical Art: *Louisa Schulz*
Printing and Binding: *Edwards Brothers Incorporated*

Harcourt Canada
55 Horner Avenue, Toronto, ON, Canada M8Z 4X6
Customer Service
Toll-Free Tel.: 1-800-387-7278
Toll-Free Fax: 1-800-665-7307

This book was printed in The United States of America.
8   08 07

Preface

This is a basic business mathematics reference handbook designed for use in the program of studies of the Certified General Accountants' Association of Canada (CGA-Canada), a six-level program of professional accounting education. The handbook is designed as a study aid that students can turn to at any time in their program for purposes of reference or review.

In order to meet the special needs of CGA students, the author and publishers developed this handbook from material originally published under the title *Mathematics for Business* (Dryden, 1992). A chapter on statistics was added to provide students with a foundation of skills for the quantitative methods presented in CGA courses.

The handbook has been written to provide a balance in the presentation of topics, recognizing the difficulty some students have in understanding arithmetic and algebraic operations, while providing sufficiently challenging material for those students who find mathematics relatively straightforward. To accomplish this balance, the presentation of the material is different from a traditional mathematics text.

The approach taken in the handbook is to provide two methods of presenting mathematical material. The first method uses word explanations about why or how we undertake a particular operation. These explanations will be used by those students who best learn with written explanations. The second approach is by example, and, where possible, a business example. Both approaches, the written and the solved examples, allow students to learn the material in the manner most suited to their learning style.

One element that is emphasized throughout the book is that students should use an approach to solving a problem that they best understand, providing, of course, that it incorporates all the necessary elements to finding the correct solution. That is, since there are different ways to solve a problem, students are encouraged to use the method with which they are most comfortable. In many examples more than one method to solve the problem is presented.

Special Features

Some features of the book that are designed to help the student and assist in the instruction of the material are:

- The text commences with an overview of arithmetic and algebra to allow for students who may need to review their knowledge of basic arithmetic and algebra before turning to the topics on the mathematics of finance.

- All topics are presented in an easy-to-read style and are followed by solved examples to reinforce the understanding of the material.

- Every effort has been made to incorporate Canadian business examples, whether the topic is in algebra or in the mathematics of finance. Many of the examples are based on actual business situations. All examples use a step-by-step approach to solving the problem.

- Each chapter concludes with a glossary of terms and a summary of the formulas, which includes a brief explanation of where each formula is used.

The essential elements of arithmetic and algebra are presented in Chapters 1 to 4, with markup and markdown being explained in Chapter 5. The topics on mathematics of finance are covered in Chapters 6 through 11. Chapter 12 presents the basic concepts and skills required for work with business statistics.

Use of the financial calculator

Professional competence in the financial accounting field requires you to be proficient in the use of financial formulas, tables, electronic calculators, and microcomputer software. The CGA program of studies requires the use of all these methods of computation.

As many of the calculations required in contemporary business are more efficiently performed on financial calculators, the use of such a model is strongly recommended in the CGA program. While it is your responsibility to become thoroughly familiar with the operation of whatever calculator you use, the following suggestions and precautions are offered for guidance

- Before using the calculator for critical work in your studies, spend some time becoming familiar with each of the keys and the tasks they perform. Use the reference documentation and work through any simple examples that are provided.

- Know the correct order to enter data and press function or operation keys. Know which keys to press (and in which order) to obtain the required solutions.

- Know the difference between similar function keys such as − and +/−.

- Know how to select the various modes of operation and know which mode is current. Typically, a financial calculator will have a financial and a statistical mode.

- The financial mode may include one or more special indicators for annuity calculations; if so, you must know how to activate them and clear them.

- Know how to clear the memory of the calculator in any situation. For instance, you must know how to clear a single entry, all entries, the mode registers, and any data that have been stored in memory. Often, you may need to press more than one key to clear the calculator completely. It's best to completely clear your calculator at the beginning of any computation session.

- Batteries last a long time but not for ever. Keep a spare and take it to any examination.

- Finally, a golden rule for calculators, spreadsheets, and human analysts alike: estimate in advance what the answer should look like. Never accept an electronic answer at face value. Verify!

Contents

CHAPTER 1

Basic Arithmetic Operations

In this chapter, we will review elementary concepts. If you find that the material is second hand to you, move on to the chapters on decimals, percentages, and the rules of algebra (Chapters 2 and 3).

1.1 Operations with 0 and 1, Signing of Numbers, and Grouping with Brackets

There are some special properties for calculations involving 0 and 1. The understanding of these properties is essential to performing many arithmetic calculations and algebraic operations.

Not only is the use of 0 and 1 important, but also the use of signed numbers — using negative (–) and positive (+) signs. To provide an understanding of each, we shall work through a series of examples. These examples are designed to highlight how each sign affects the basic arithmetic operations.

In the last part of this section, we shall examine how we can group numbers using brackets (), as well as determine the order in which arithmetic computations must occur when using brackets.

It is important to be able to use these concepts easily since they are significant to our understanding of the later topics that apply arithmetic and algebraic methods to business and finance problems.

A. Operations with 0 and 1

To ensure that you have a clear understanding of how 0 and 1 influence computations, the following examples summarize the major rules that must be understood.

(i) Addition and Subtraction Involving 0

When 0 is added to a number, the resulting sum is not changed. For example, $5 + 0 = 5$. Another way of thinking about this is to remember $0 + 0 = 0$.

In subtraction, a similar result occurs. If you subtract 0 from any number, the difference is the same number. However, if you subtract a number from 0 the result is quite different — this type of problem will be examined when we look at the signing of numbers in the next section.

EXAMPLE 1.1

Find the sum of 35, 46, 13, and 0; from this sum subtract 55 and 0.

Solution

STEP 1   Addition

$$
\begin{array}{r}
35 \\
46 \\
\underline{13} \\
94 \\
\underline{0} \\
94
\end{array}
$$

94 ◄——— Sum without zero.

94 ◄——— Addition of zero does not change the sum.

STEP 2   Subtraction

$$
\begin{array}{r}
94 \\
\underline{-\ 55} \\
39 \\
\underline{-\ 0} \\
39
\end{array}
$$

94 ◄——— The sum from above.

39 ◄——— The difference without zero.

39 ◄——— Subtracting zero does not change the difference.

(ii) Multiplication and Division with 0 and 1

Multiplication Involving 0 or 1
When multiplying **different** numbers where **one** of the numbers is 0, the resulting product will always be 0. For example, $5 \times 0 = 0$. No matter what the situation, if 0 enters into the multiplication as one of the distinct numbers being multiplied then the product of the numbers will be 0 — there are no exceptions to the rule.

In the multiplication of numbers where one of the numbers is 1, the multiplication with 1 does not change the product. Consider the product of $5 \times 6 \times 1 = 30$, which is the same as 5×6.

Division Involving 0 or 1
Division, on the other hand, offers us a slightly different problem. For example, $5 \div 0$ will give us a very large number, so large that we say it is not defined. You can see the logic if you think about the following:

$$\frac{4}{4} = 4 \div 4 = 1; \quad \frac{4}{2} = 4 \div 2 = 2; \quad \frac{4}{1} = 4 \div 1 = 4$$

What you should notice is that as the number that is being divided stays constant, and the number being used as the divisor (in our example 4, 2, and 1) gets smaller, the resulting quotient gets larger. At 0 the size of the quotient is so large that we say it is undefined. The symbol for the quotient with 0 is ∞, called infinity — strictly, division with 0 is referred to as an undefined operation.

However, if 0 is divided by a number then the quotient is 0. For example:

$$\frac{0}{4} = 0 \div 4 = 0; \quad \frac{0}{2} = 0 \div 2 = 0; \quad \frac{0}{1} = 0 \div 1 = 0$$

Division with 1 has no consequence to the quotient. For example:

$$\frac{4}{1} = 4 \div 1 = 4; \quad \frac{6}{1} = 6 \div 1 = 6$$

SUMMARY OF THE RULES WITH 0 AND 1

Multiplication by 0:	Number $\times$ 0 = 0	e.g., $(3 \times 0 = 0)$
Division by 0:	Number $\div$ 0 = undefined	e.g., $(3 \div 0 =$ undefined$)$
0 divided by a number:	0 $\div$ Number = 0	e.g., $(0 \div 3 = 0)$
Multiplication by 1:	Number $\times$ 1 = Number	e.g., $(3 \times 1 = 3)$
Division by 1:	Number $\div$ 1 = Number	e.g., $(3 \times 1 = 3)$

B. Operations with Signed Numbers: Positive (+) and Negative (–) Numbers

Signing of numbers refers to the sign in front of the number. For example, the number 5 is said to have a positive sign in front of it, even though it is not written. Its presence is assumed. Whereas, a negative number will always have the negative sign (–) in front of it.

Visually this can be seen by using a number line with 0 as the centre point.

Exhibit 1.1

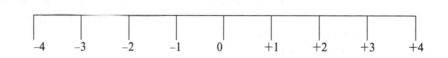

Consider the following examples:

–6 means negative 6; the sign of the number is said to be negative.

+6 means positive 6, and is the same as 6.

(i) Signed Numbers: Addition and Subtraction

The addition and subtraction of signed numbers will require one to do the operation as indicated by the sign. If all the numbers have the same sign, even if they are all negative, then we always add the negative numbers, for example, $-2 + -3 + -5 = -10$. When there are a number of additions involving both negative and positive numbers, it is best to perform the addition of the numbers with the same sign first, then perform the final operation on the two sums. For example, if we had $-2 + -3 + -5 + 4 + 3 + 5$, then the easiest way is to deal with the negative numbers separately from the positive numbers and then bring the two results together to complete the operation. In this example, $-2 + -3 + -5 = -10$ and $4 + 3 + 5 = 12$, bringing the two sums together for the final operation gives us $12 + -10 = 2$. Example 1.2 uses this procedure.

EXAMPLE 1.2

Find the sum of -365, -460, $1,355$, and 0.

Solution The sum of the positive numbers is:

$$
\begin{array}{r}
1,355 \\
0 \\
\hline
1,355
\end{array}
$$

The sum of the numbers with the negative sign is:

$$
\begin{array}{r}
-\ 365 \\
-\ 460 \\
\hline
-\ 825
\end{array}
$$

Now taking this sum we subtract it from the sum of the positive numbers:

$$
\begin{array}{r}
+\ 1,355 \\
-\quad 825 \\
\hline
+\quad 530
\end{array}
$$

Everything could have been done in one step, but by breaking up the process it made the procedure easier to follow.

One other rule that must be understood is where a negative sign is applied to a number that already has a negative sign, for example, $-(-5)$. To handle this situation the rule you must use is that a "negative, negative number" is a positive number.

Consider the following example.

EXAMPLE 1.3

Find the sum of $-(-365)$; -460; $1,355$; and 0.

Solution
$$
\begin{array}{r}
-(-365) = +\quad 365 \\
0 \\
+\ 1,355 \\
\hline
1,720
\end{array}
$$
Note the change in sign.

Now taking this sum we subtract the sum of the negative numbers — here there is only one negative number rather than a sum of negative numbers.

$$
\begin{array}{r}
+\ 1{,}720 \\
-\ \ \ \ 460 \\
\hline
+\ 1{,}260
\end{array}
$$

As can be seen, the negative sign in front of the negative number $-(-365)$ causes the sign of the number to change to a positive sign. This is an important rule and will be used often during later topics in the finance sections.

(ii) Multiplication and Division with Signed Numbers

When we are multiplying with numbers that are signed, the resulting product also will have a sign. The following rules illustrate how the signing of the product works.

Signed Numbers and Multiplication

Rule 1. If both numbers are negative, the resulting product will be a positive number. For example, $-5 \times -6 = +30$.

Rule 2. If one of the numbers is negative and the other is positive, the resulting product will be negative. For example, $-5 \times 6 = -30$.

Rule 3. If both the numbers are positive, the resulting product will be positive. For example, $5 \times 6 = 30$.

Rule 4. When multiplying more than two numbers, all with different signs, the best way to remember how to sign the final product is to group the numbers into pairs and then use rules 1, 2, or 3 when multiplying each pair. This is a little confusing, so consider the following example:

$$
\begin{aligned}
5 \times -6 \times -7 \times -8 \times 3 &= -30 \times 56 \times 3 \\
&= -1{,}680 \times 3 \\
&= -5{,}040
\end{aligned}
$$

Where:

$5 \times -6 = -30$ The product of the first pair.

$-7 \times -8 = 56$ The product of the second pair (note the positive sign in the product, from rule 1).

3 This is the last term in the original expression.

(iii) Signed Numbers and Division

The process of dividing signed numbers is similar to multiplication. To understand how division is affected by signed numbers, the following rules must be remembered.

Division Rules

Rule 1. When dividing two numbers where either the divisor or the dividend is negative, the resulting quotient is negative. For example, $6 \div -3 = -2$ and $-10 \div 5 = -2$.

Rule 2. When dividing two numbers where both have negative signs, the quotient will always give a positive number. For example, $-10 \div -5 = 2$.

Rule 3. Dividing two positive numbers always yields a positive quotient, in our example, $10 \div 5 = 2$.

C. Order of Operations and Grouping of Numbers Using Brackets

Often calculations in business involve many sets of numbers and it is important that one understands the order of operations to perform. By order of operations, we mean which is done first: addition, subtraction, multiplication, or division. To help us determine which operation to use, we often group operations by using brackets. In fact, there are many instances when there are many groupings that require more than one set of brackets. The general sequence is $\{[()]\}$, where () are used first, [] if a second set of brackets is needed, and finally {} if a third set is used.

When a group of numbers requires more than one operation, the operations are performed in the following order:

ORDER OF OPERATIONS

1. Perform all operations within the brackets. If there are more than one set of brackets, start at the "innermost" set (see Example 1.4).
2. After the operations in brackets are completed and the brackets removed, perform the necessary multiplication and division, moving from left to right.
3. Complete the operations by performing the necessary addition and subtraction, again moving from left to right.

EXAMPLE 1.4

Find the answer to $\{45 + [5 \times (4 + 5)]\} \div 10$.

Solution

STEP 1 First go to the "innermost brackets", the () type, and perform the calculations necessary. In our example we have:

$$(4 + 5) \text{ or } 9$$

Which gives: $\{45 + [5 \times 9]\} \div 10$

STEP 2   Second, perform the operation to be done on the term inside the [] brackets.

$$[5 \times 9]$$

$\uparrow$

This gives: $\{45 + 45\} \div 10$

STEP 3   Now we can remove the square brackets, [], leaving us with $\{45 + 45\} \div 10$;

STEP 4   Work the final operation inside the last set of brackets, {}, which is to add 45 to 45. This gives 90, and then,

STEP 5   Perform the last operation, 90 divided by 10, or $\{90\} \div 10 = 9$.

Therefore, the final answer is 9.

EXAMPLE 1.5

Find the answer to $25 + [18 + 16 \times (4 + 5)]$.

Solution

STEP 1   Work out the sum inside the () brackets, or $4 + 5 = 9$, which gives us:

$$25 + [18 + 16 \times (9)]$$

STEP 2   Perform the multiplication of $16 \times (9)$, or 144, which gives us:

$$25 + [18 + 144]$$

STEP 3   Perform the addition inside the [] brackets, or $18 + 144$, which gives 162, leaving the expression:

$$25 + [162]$$

STEP 4   Complete the final addition, $25 + 162$, or 187, the final answer.

The last example in this section on brackets (Example 1.6) is to show how to apply a negative sign when it is outside a group of numbers in brackets, where some numbers inside the brackets are also negative numbers. As you will see, it is critical to make sure the correct sign is applied, since the results change dramatically if the negative sign is incorrectly used.

Another purpose of Example 1.6 is to demonstrate a way of writing multiplication — without using the $\times$ sign. For example, $3 \times (4 + 5)$ could be written as $3(4 + 5)$. In the second case, $3(4 + 5)$, the $\times$ sign is understood. In each case, the product is the same, 27. Work through Example 1.6 carefully to make sure you understand that we drop the $\times$ (multiplication) sign, as well as incorporating the influence of a negative sign for the operations within the brackets.

EXAMPLE 1.6

Find the answer to $-3(-45) + -2(40 - 60)$.

Solution

STEP 1   Work out the computations inside the brackets:

$$-3(-45) = 135 \quad \text{Note the sign change.}$$

and

$$-2[40 - 60] = -2[-20]$$
$$= 40$$

STEP 2   Add the two numbers: $135 + 40 = 175$.

The final answer is 175.

1.2 Fractions

In business, fractions are commonly used. A fraction is a number that represents a portion of another number. Numbers such as 2, 3, and 467 are what we call **whole numbers**. A fraction refers to part of one of these numbers and always implies a division. When we discussed division earlier, we learned that there are three terms — dividend, divisor, and quotient. In a fraction, the dividend is called the **numerator** and the divisor is known as the **denominator**. For example, $\dfrac{1}{4}$ is a fraction, read as one-quarter, where 1 is the numerator and 4 is the denominator. Another way this fraction could have been written is $1 \div 4$. The term quotient is not used with fractions since a fraction will always be specified in terms of a numerator and a denominator.

Before we turn to the addition, subtraction, multiplication, and division of fractions, there are some new terms that we must understand. These new terms are: **reduced fractions, proper fractions, improper fractions, complex fractions,** and **mixed fractions (numbers)**.

A. Reduced Fractions — Fractions in Their Lowest Terms

If one had a fraction such as $\dfrac{4}{12}$, we would say that the fraction is not in its lowest terms — that is, not in a reduced form. A reduced form means that the numerator and denominator cannot be made smaller by dividing each by the same number evenly and still yield the same fractional value. To reduce $\dfrac{4}{12}$ we could divide both the numerator and denominator by 4. This would give $\dfrac{1}{3}$, which is the same as $\dfrac{4}{12}$, and is referred to as the **reduced form of the fraction**. Sometimes the expression "reducing a fraction to its lowest term" is used to describe the reduced form. Let's look at a couple of examples.

EXAMPLE 1.7

Reduce $\dfrac{3}{9}$ to its lowest terms.

Solution To reduce each term of the fraction we must divide both the numerator and the denominator by the same term. One number that will divide evenly into each is 3. Therefore dividing each by 3 gives:

$$\frac{3}{9} = \frac{3 \div 3}{9 \div 3} = \frac{1}{3}$$

Performing the indicated division gives the fraction:

$\dfrac{1}{3}$, which is the reduced form of $\dfrac{3}{9}$.

Another way of referring to the reduction of a fraction is through **cancellation**. Cancellation refers to the process of reducing the numerator and denominator to reach the reduced form of the fraction. In our example, $\dfrac{3}{3}$ cancels to 1, and $\dfrac{3}{9}$ cancels to $\dfrac{1}{3}$.

EXAMPLE 1.8

Reduce $\dfrac{45}{105}$.

Solution Examining both the numerator and denominator, we can see that 5 can be divided evenly into each term.

$$\frac{45}{105} = \frac{45 \div 5}{105 \div 5}$$

$$= \frac{9}{21}$$

Now can we reduce the fraction further? If we examine both the numerator (9) and the denominator (21), we see that there is one number that will divide into both — 3.

Consequently, the reduced form is $\dfrac{3}{7}$.

B. Proper, Improper, Complex Fractions, and Mixed Numbers

A **proper fraction** is a fraction where the numerator is less than the denominator. For example, $\dfrac{2}{3}$ is a proper fraction. On the other hand, when the numerator is greater than or equal to the denominator we say the fraction is an **improper fraction,** for example, $\dfrac{6}{6}, \dfrac{6}{4},$ and $\dfrac{16}{5}$ are examples of improper fractions.

Complex fractions are fractions where one or more fractions are found in the numerator or denominator. Examples of complex fractions are $\dfrac{\frac{1}{4}}{5}$ and $\dfrac{\frac{1}{2}}{17}$. A complex fraction can be converted to a proper or improper fraction by dividing the numerator by the denominator — we will return to this when we discuss the division with fractions.

Sometimes fractions consist of both whole numbers and fractions, for example, $2\frac{1}{2}$ or $5\frac{1}{4}$. When both a whole number and a fraction are present we say the fraction is a **mixed number**. Mixed numbers can be expressed as an improper fraction by using the following procedure.

We convert $3\frac{1}{2}$ to an improper fraction by multiplying the denominator (2) by the whole number (3) and adding this product to the numerator as follows:

$$3\frac{1}{2} = \frac{(2 \times 3) + 1}{2}$$
$$= \frac{7}{2}$$

On the other hand, an improper fraction may be expressed as a mixed number. For example, $\dfrac{19}{5}$ can be written as $3\frac{4}{5}$, a mixed number. This mixed number comes from dividing 19 by 5 (this gives the 3) and placing the remainder of 4 over 5, giving the $\dfrac{4}{5}$ portion of the mixed number.

C. Addition and Subtraction with Fractions

(i) Addition of Fractions

The addition of fractions requires that the denominator for each fraction be the same. For example, adding $\dfrac{3}{4}$ and $\dfrac{2}{4}$ can be handled by adding the numerators and putting this sum over the common denominator, 4, giving us $\dfrac{5}{4}$, which can be expressed as the mixed number $1\frac{1}{4}$. **The rule you must follow is to make sure the denominators are the same, then add the numerators and place this sum over the common denominator.** For example, $\dfrac{2}{3} + \dfrac{3}{4}$ requires us to find a common denominator (by common denominator we mean finding a denominator that is the same for both fractions). The first number that is common to each denominator, 3 and 4, is 12. Therefore, we change each fraction to a fraction that has 12 as the denominator. For this example, $\dfrac{2}{3}$ becomes $\dfrac{8}{12}$ (found by multiplying the numerator and the denominator by 4), and $\dfrac{3}{4}$ becomes $\dfrac{9}{12}$ (found by multiplying the numerator and denominator by 3).

Now we have:

$$\frac{8}{12} + \frac{9}{12} = \frac{17}{12}$$

This gives us $1\dfrac{5}{12}$, a mixed fraction. Let's consider two examples:

EXAMPLE 1.9

Find the sum of $\dfrac{1}{2}$, $\dfrac{3}{4}$, and $\dfrac{1}{8}$.

Solution   To do this addition, we must change each fraction so that the fractions have the same denominator — while still keeping the original value of the fraction. To do this, we look at the denominator to see if there is a common term into which each will divide evenly. The first number that all denominators will divide evenly into is 8.

$\dfrac{1}{2}$ can be rewritten as $\dfrac{4}{8}$, which is found by multiplying the numerator and denominator by 4.

$$\text{That is: } \frac{4 \times 1}{4 \times 2} = \frac{4}{8}$$

$\dfrac{3}{4}$ can be rewritten as $\dfrac{6}{8}$, which is found by multiplying the numerator and denominator by 2 giving us:

$$\frac{2 \times 3}{2 \times 4} = \frac{6}{8}$$

$\dfrac{1}{8}$ already has a denominator of 8.

Now that all the denominators are the same, we add the numerators and place this sum over the common denominator, 8. Therefore, adding the numerators and placing the sum over the common denominator gives:

$\dfrac{4 + 6 + 1}{8} = \dfrac{11}{8}$, which is a mixed number and can be written as $1\dfrac{3}{8}$.

EXAMPLE 1.10

Find the sum of $2\dfrac{1}{2}$, $5\dfrac{1}{4}$, and $\dfrac{1}{12}$.

Solution First we convert the mixed numbers into improper fractions, which gives:

$$2\frac{1}{2} = \frac{(2+2)+1}{2} = \frac{5}{2}$$

$$5\frac{1}{4} = \frac{(4 \times 5)+1}{4} = \frac{21}{4}$$

And the other fraction in the sum is $\frac{1}{12}$.

Next, we must find a common denominator for each fraction. Since 12 can be evenly divided by each denominator (2, 4, and 12), we can use it as a common denominator. In fact, 12 is the smallest term that is common to 12, 4, and 2, into which each can divide evenly.

Finally, we must convert all the improper fractions to fractions with 12 as the denominator — the common denominator. Therefore:

$$\frac{5}{2} = \frac{30}{12}$$ This is done by multiplying the numerator and denominator by 6.

$$\frac{21}{4} = \frac{63}{12}$$ This is done by multiplying the numerator and denominator by 3.

$$\frac{1}{12} = \frac{1}{12}$$ This already has a denominator of 12 and therefore nothing needs to be done to this fraction.

Now adding the numerators and placing this sum over the common denominator of 12 yields:

$$\frac{30+63+1}{12} = \frac{94}{12}$$

$\frac{94}{12}$ should be written as $7\frac{10}{12} = 7\frac{5}{6}$.

(ii) Subtraction of Fractions

The process of subtraction uses the same procedure as addition: first find the common denominator and subtract the numerators. Consider the following examples:

EXAMPLE 1.11

Subtract $\frac{7}{32}$ from $\frac{1}{2}$.

Solution As with addition of fractions, we must first find a common denominator. The first number that comes to mind is 32, since 2 divides evenly into 32 — that is, 32 is the lowest common multiple of the two numbers.

$$\frac{7}{32}$$ Since 32 is already in the denominator there is no need to do anything to this fraction.

$$\frac{1}{2} = \frac{16}{32}$$

Found by multiplying the numerator and denominator by 16.

The last step is to subtract the values of the numerators and place this difference over the common denominator of 32. This is done as follows:

$$\frac{16 - 7}{32} = \frac{9}{32}$$

EXAMPLE 1.12

Subtract $\frac{5}{16}$ from $\frac{7}{12}$.

Solution As with Example 1.20, the first step is to determine the lowest common denominator. What you must ask yourself is, into what number will both 16 and 12 divide evenly? 32 will not work, since 12 cannot divide evenly into 32. The next number that 16 will divide evenly into is 48. As it turns out, 12 will divide evenly into 48. Now we have our lowest common denominator. Converting the two fractions to their lowest common denominator gives:

$$\frac{5}{16} = \frac{15}{48}$$

Found by multiplying numerator and denominator by 3.

$$\frac{7}{12} = \frac{28}{48}$$

Found by multiplying the numerator and denominator by 4.

Subtracting the numerators with the common denominator:

$$\frac{28 - 15}{48} = \frac{13}{48}$$

D. Multiplication and Division of Fractions

(i) Multiplication of Fractions

In business, there are many examples of the use of fractions. If you look in the financial pages of your daily newspaper, you will find the stock price quotations on the Toronto and Vancouver stock markets. You will see the price quotations include fractions. For example, $58\frac{1}{2}$ would suggest the price of the stock is $58.50, where the fraction is used to describe the number of cents.

Multiplication involving fractions is also common in business and government. For example, how often have you heard someone say that almost a third of every tax dollar goes to pay the interest on the debt of the government? If the government receives 100 billion in tax dollars, how much of this goes to pay the interest? To answer this question, we could use the method of multiplication of fractions.

When multiplying fractions, you will be pleased to know that there is no need to worry about finding a common denominator. In fact, all that we must do is to ensure that the denominator of one fraction is multiplied by the denominator of the other fraction, and that the two numerators are multiplied together.

For example, if you wanted to determine how many tax dollars are used for interest payments, we would take $\frac{1}{3}$ of the 100 billion as follows:

$$\frac{1}{3} \times \$100 \text{ billion} = \frac{1}{3} \times \frac{100}{1}$$

$$= \frac{100}{3}$$

$$= \$33\frac{1}{3} \text{ billion}$$

That's right: if the federal government collects $100 billion, and if a third of the tax dollars goes to interest payments, then $33\frac{1}{3}$ billion is the interest expenditure.

Let's turn to an example involving the multiplication of fractions.

EXAMPLE 1.13

Multiply the following fractions and express the answer in the reduced form.

(a) $\frac{2}{3} \times \frac{3}{4}$

(b) $\frac{5}{16} \times \frac{3}{10}$

(c) $\frac{15}{23} \times \frac{7}{12}$

Solution

(a)
$$\frac{2}{3} \times \frac{3}{4} = \frac{2 \times 3}{3 \times 4}$$

$$= \frac{6}{12}$$

$$= \frac{1}{2}$$

(b)
$$\frac{5}{16} \times \frac{3}{10} = \frac{5 \times 3}{16 \times 10}$$

$$= \frac{15}{160}$$

$$= \frac{3}{32}$$

(c)
$$\frac{15}{23} \times \frac{7}{12} = \frac{15 \times 7}{23 \times 12}$$
$$= \frac{105}{276}$$
$$= \frac{35}{92}$$

When one is multiplying fractions, the order of the fractions is not important. For example, $\frac{1}{2} \times \frac{3}{4}$ is the same as $\frac{3}{4} \times \frac{1}{2}$.

One last thing to note in the multiplication of fractions is to realize that the process may be speeded up if there are common terms in both fractions, thus permitting us to cancel terms before multiplying. Consider Example 1.14, which uses cancellation of terms before multiplying:

EXAMPLE 1.14

Multiply the following fractions using cancellation where possible.

$$\frac{3}{7} \times \frac{2}{3}$$

Solution

$$\frac{3}{7} \times \frac{2}{3} = \frac{\cancel{3} \times 2}{7 \times \cancel{3}}$$
$$= \frac{2}{7}$$

The 3's cancel because they are common to both expressions.

The last three examples show the uses of fractions in three simple business situations:

EXAMPLE 1.15

John and Irene both own a small business worth \$75,000. If John owns $\frac{2}{5}$ of the business and Irene wants to buy him out so that she will own the business, how much would she need to pay John for his interests?

Solution   The solution to this problem can be found by using multiplication of fractions. To perform the solution, all that we need do is multiply \$75,000 by $\frac{2}{5}$ to find John's portion, which Irene would need to pay to John if she wishes to be the sole owner.

Therefore we have:

$$\frac{2}{5} \times \$75,000 = \frac{2 \times \$75,000}{5} = \$30,000$$

Irene would need to pay John \$30,000 for his share of the business.

EXAMPLE 1.16

A share (share refers to common stock, a form of ownership in a company) in a company called Arctic Services Ltd. is trading (selling) on the Toronto Stock Exchange at $32\frac{1}{2}$ ($32.50). If you wanted to purchase 15 shares of Arctic Services Ltd., how much would it cost you?

Solution
As you can see, we have a mixed fraction, so the first thing we must do is to convert this fraction to an improper fraction. Therefore:

$$\$32\frac{1}{2} = \frac{\$65}{2}$$

Multiplying this times the number of shares we are purchasing will give us the purchase price — not including any fees to the broker who acts for you in the purchase.

Thus:

$$\frac{\$65}{2} \times 15 = \frac{65 \times 15}{2}$$

$$= \frac{975}{2}$$

$$= \$487.50 \text{ is the price for the shares.}$$

Sometimes it will be necessary to multiply mixed fractions. When this is required we simply convert each fraction to an improper fraction and multiply the numerators and denominators of the improper fractions. Example 1.17 shows how to multiply mixed fractions:

EXAMPLE 1.17

Multiply $43\frac{1}{2} \times 31\frac{1}{4}$.

Solution

$$43\frac{1}{2} \times 31\frac{1}{4} = \frac{87 \times 125}{2 \times 4}$$

$$= \frac{10,875}{8}$$

$$= 1,359\frac{3}{8}$$

(ii) Division with Fractions

The rule for division of fractions is quite straight forward. The rule to remember is: **when dividing two fractions, invert the second fraction (the divisor) and multiply.** Consider Example 1.18:

EXAMPLE 1.18

Divide $\frac{1}{2}$ by $\frac{1}{4}$.

Solution The rule is to invert the second fraction ($\frac{1}{4}$) and multiply. Therefore, if we invert and multiply we get:

$$\frac{1}{2} \times \frac{4}{1} = \frac{1 \times 4}{2 \times 1}$$

$$= \frac{4}{2}$$

$$= 2$$

Another way of thinking about this example is to remember that there are two quarters in a half!

Complex fractions (for example, $\frac{\frac{1}{2}}{5}$) require us to perform a division. However, a much easier way is to undertake a multiplication. For example, $\frac{\frac{1}{2}}{5}$ can be expressed as a proper fraction by multiplying the denominator and the numerator by 2, which causes the $\frac{1}{2}$ in the numerator to become 1 and the 5 in the denominator to become 10, giving us the fraction $\frac{1}{10}$. If we had $\frac{5}{\frac{1}{2}}$ we would multiply the numerator and denominator by 2; this would give 2×5 or 10 in the numerator and $2 \times \frac{1}{2}$, or 1, in the denominator. Therefore, the final answer is $\frac{10}{1}$, or 10, a whole number.

EXAMPLE 1.19

Find the answer to the following complex fractions.

(a) $\frac{\frac{1}{2}}{4}$

(b) $\frac{\frac{1}{4}}{8}$

(c) $\frac{15}{\frac{1}{2}}$

Solution

(a) $\frac{\frac{1}{2}}{4} = \frac{\frac{1}{2} \times 2}{4 \times 2}$

$= \frac{1}{8}$

We multiplied the numerator and the denominator by 2 to remove the fraction in the numerator. To keep the value of the fraction this also must be done to the denominator.

(b) $\dfrac{1/4}{8} = \dfrac{1/4 \times 4}{8 \times 4}$

$\qquad = \dfrac{1}{32}$

The numerator and denominator are multiplied by 4 to remove the fraction in the numerator. To keep the value of the fraction this also must be done to the denominator.

(c) $\dfrac{15}{1/2} = \dfrac{15 \times 2}{1/2 \times 2}$

$\qquad = 30$

The numerator and the denominator are multiplied by 2 to remove the fraction in the denominator. To keep the value of the fraction this also must be done to the numerator.

GLOSSARY OF TERMS

Cancellation of Numbers   when numbers are being multiplied and divided, there may be common terms in both the numerator and denominator that allow for cancellation. For example:

$$\frac{12 \times 7}{4 \times 7} = \frac{{}^{3}\cancel{12} \times \cancel{7}\, 3}{\cancel{4} \times \cancel{7}}$$

In this case, 4 divides evenly into 12, giving 3. 7 cancels with 7. The symbol used to note the cancellation of 7 is $\cancel{7}$.

Complex Fraction   see Fraction.

Dividend   see Quotient.

Divisor   see Quotient.

Fraction   a fraction is a way of expressing a portion of a number. Fractions have two parts, a numerator and a denominator. In the proper fraction $\dfrac{1}{4}$, 1 is the numerator and 4 is the denominator. A fraction may be written as $\dfrac{5}{2}$, called an improper fraction, which can be written as $2\dfrac{1}{2}$, a mixed number (mixed because it is a number with both a fraction [$\dfrac{1}{2}$] and a whole number [2]). Also, fractions can be complex if they look like $\dfrac{1/2}{3}$. Notice that the numerator is a fraction in a complex fraction.

Grouping   the process of bringing numbers together using brackets. The use of brackets gives rise to the order of operations, which is to perform all operations within the brackets first, before performing operations between the different groupings.

Improper Fraction   see Fraction.

Lowest Common Denominator   the lowest number into which all denominators can be divided evenly. Lowest common denominators are necessary for the addition and subtraction of fractions.

Minuend   the number from which one subtracts another number. For example, $5 - 3 = 2$, where 5 is the minuend and 2 is the difference or remainder.

Mixed Number   see Fraction.

Product   this is the result of the multiplication of two or more numbers. For example, $25 \times 50 = 1,250$, where 1,250 is the product, 25 and 50 are the factors in the multiplication.

Proper Fraction   see Fraction.

Quotient   the number of parts a number has been "broken" into as a result of division. For example, $8 \div 2 = 4$, where 4 is the quotient, 8 is the dividend, and 2 is the divisor. Since 2 divides evenly into 8 (i.e., there are exactly 4 twos in 8) the remainder is 0.

Remainder   see Quotient.

Sum   the result of the addition of two or more numbers.

Ratios, Decimals, and Percentages

Ratios are commonly used in finance and accounting. Decimals, on the other hand, are used in interest rate calculations for determining the cost of borrowing money. Percentages are used frequently in the retail business to set the selling price of a product over cost — called markup. Applications of each of these concepts will occur throughout later chapters and will require a firm foundation of the material in this chapter.

2.1 Ratios

A ratio is a comparison of one number to another. For example, a 5 to 1 ratio — expressed as 5:1 — means that the first number occurs 5 times for every 1 occurrence of the second number.

Carrying our example a little further, if we say that the number of workers in a factory who have grade 12 education is five times more than those who have not completed high school, then the ratio of grade 12 graduates to non-grade 12 graduates is 5 to 1.

In the stock market, if we say that the number of shares being traded in the resource industries on a particular day is 8 times more than any other grouping of industries, then we are saying that for every non-resource stock traded, 8 resource stocks were traded.

Often, ratios are not expressed in the 5 to 1 or 8 to 1 form. In some instances we may see a ratio such as 3 to 2 or 5 to 4. In the last two examples, the interpretation is the same as the 5 to 1 ratio, except when we say 3 to 2, which means that for every 3 of the first item we have 2 of the second item. If you listen to the stock market quotations, you may hear that the number of declines relative to increases were in an 8 to 5 ratio. In plain English this means that for every 8 stock price decreases there were 5 increases — sometimes stated as "declines led advances by an 8 to 5 margin".

In all cases we see that a ratio can be converted to a fraction. Consequently, the rules we apply to ratios are the same as the rules we use in fractions.

Consider Examples 2.1 and 2.2:

EXAMPLE 2.1

The provincial government offers a local community organization a grant based on the agreement that for every three dollars the community group can raise the government will give the organization one dollar. If the community organization has held a fund raising drive and raised $39,000, how much money can the group expect from the government?

Solution Since the condition for the government grant matches one dollar for every three raised, the ratio is 1 for every 3 raised. The community organization has raised $39,000, thus the government will provide $13,000. This answer was found by using the ratio of 1 to 3. Given that the community group raised $39,000, the government must provide:

$$\frac{1}{3} \times \$39{,}000 = \$13{,}000$$

EXAMPLE 2.2

A company that wishes to develop a piece of land for rental apartments is advised that in order to get the approval for the project it must allocate 2 square metres of space per 8 square metres of finished area for low cost housing accommodation. The company plans to build a 48,000 square metre building on twelve floors — 4,000 square metres per floor. How much space will be required for low cost accommodation? If the size of each suite is 100 square metres, how many low cost suites will be built?

Solution

STEP 1 The requirement of 2 square metres out of 8 square metres for low cost apartments can be expressed as an equivalent ratio of 1 square metre per 4 square metres of finished space. The manner in which we arrived at this was to divide each of the numbers of the ratio by a common term — 2 — just like we did when we were looking for a common denominator for fractions.

STEP 2 Since there is a requirement to have a ratio of 1 in 4 square metres for the low cost accommodation, we then express the ratio of 1 in 4 as a fraction, or $\frac{1}{4}$, and multiply this by the total size of the building, that is:

$$\frac{1}{4} \times 48{,}000 = 12{,}000$$

Thus, there will be 12,000 square metres for low cost housing suites.

STEP 3 The second part of the question was to determine how many low cost suites would be built. Since each suite has a size of 100 square metres, there would be $\frac{12{,}000}{(100)}$ or 120 low cost suites made available by the project.

Ratios can be simplified just as fractions can be simplified. In business they are often expressed in the most convenient form, which may not necessarily be the reduced form.

Another situation involving ratios occurs when something has to be allocated according to a ratio. For example, if the apartment problem in Example 2.2 had read, the ratio of low cost accommodation to regular housing space must be 2 to 8, then the solution would be quite different. That is, by stating that the ratio must be 2 to 8 it means that out of every 10 square metres, 2 must be for low cost accommodation and 8 for regular housing. In terms of a ratio, this would be a 1 to 5 ratio. What makes this problem so different is the wording of the ratio.

2.2 Decimals

Like fractions, decimals are a way of expressing parts of whole numbers. The sign used for a decimal is the period, and precedes the number. Decimals represent parts of a whole number and are expressed in tenths, hundredths, thousandths, etc., of the whole number. In everyday life and business, the most common use of decimals is representing cents in monetary quotations, for example, $99.95. In this case we read this as 99 dollars and 95 cents. **The decimal is used to tell us the fraction of a dollar,** in addition to the whole number of dollars — in this case, 99 dollars.

Since the calculations with money are so basic to business, it is important to have a solid understanding of how to use decimals and interpret their meaning.

A. Interpreting Decimals

Before we get into the operations of addition, subtraction, multiplication, and division with decimals, it is important to be able to interpret what a number with a decimal implies. Suppose a small business that purchases steel by the kilogram for a price of $3.50/kg were to purchase 5500.5 kg. How would one read these decimals? First, if we consider the price of $3.50, we would say they are paying 3 and one-half dollars per kilogram, or in the language of decimals, "three point five dollars". The same interpretation applies for the quantity of steel purchased. They have bought five thousand, five hundred point (decimal) five kilograms. **Note the word <u>point</u> being used interchangeably with the word decimal.** Depending on the units of measurement, the statement of what a decimal may measure will be different. To illustrate this, study Example 2.3.

EXAMPLE 2.3

Read each of the following numbers to yourself and write down the meaning of each, using the language of decimals:

(a) 0.50   (b) 0.545   (c) 0.115
(d) 20.135   (e) 0.005   (f) 2.3421

Solution (a) 0.50 = 50 hundredths, or one-half, or point five, or decimal five — all mean the same.

(b) 0.545 = 545 thousandths, or point five four five, or decimal five four five.

(c) 0.115 = 115 thousandths, or point one one five, or decimal one one five.

(d) 20.135 = twenty and 135 thousandths, or twenty point one three five, or twenty decimal one three five.

(e) 0.005 = five thousandths, or point zero zero five, or decimal zero zero five.

(f) 2.3421 = two and three tenths, four hundredths, two thousandths, and one ten-thousandth, or two point three four two one, or two decimal three four two one.

B. Rounding of Decimals

Often decimals are not expressed to the exact number of places. Rather, they are rounded or truncated (cut off) at a convenient point. For example, if a calculation in dollars and cents gave us $99.234, the final answer would be expressed to the nearest cent, or $99.23. The 0.004 would be dropped. However, if the answer that we calculated is $99.236, the answer would be expressed as $99.24. In the first case, we say we are rounding down. In the second case, we are said to be rounding up. The rules for rounding up or down are as follows:

Rounding Rules

If the first number to be dropped is 5 or more, increase the last number to be kept by 1. In the example above, $99.236 is to be rounded to two places, that is, the nearest cent. Since the number to be dropped is 6, we increased the last number to be kept, which was 3, to 4, giving us $99.24.

If the first number to be dropped is less than 5, the last number to be kept is not changed. In the example above, $99.234 is to be rounded to two places, and, since the number to be dropped is 4, we do not change the last number to be kept, which gives us $99.23.

EXAMPLE 2.4

Round the following numbers to the required number of decimal places.

(a) 0.50, round to nearest whole number (no decimal).

(b) 0.545, round to the nearest two decimal places.

(c) 0.115, round to the nearest one decimal place.

(d) 20.135, round to the nearest three decimal places.

(e) 0.005, round to no decimal place.

(f) 2.3421, round to two decimal places.

(g) 0.134568, round to three decimal places.

Solution (a) 1 Using the rounding rule, the number to be dropped is 5, so we will round <u>up</u> to a whole number. If increasing the last number to be left by 1 when rounding, using the rule above, 0 becomes a 1, and the final answer is 1.

Thus, 0.5 rounded to the nearest whole number is 1.

(b) 0.55 Using the rule of increasing the last digit by one when the number to be dropped is 5 or more.

(c) 0.1 Using the rule of decreasing the last digit by one when the number to be dropped is less than 5.

(d) 20.135 No change is required since this number is already expressed to three decimal places.

(e) 0 0.005 becomes 0.01 when rounded to two decimal places, 0.0 at one decimal place, and 0 with no decimal places.

(f) 2.34 Since the number to be dropped is less than 5.

(g) 0.135 Since the first number to be dropped is 5, we round up the last term from 4 to 5.

C. Addition, Subtraction, Multiplication, and Division of Numbers with Decimals

(i) Addition of Decimal Numbers

When we are adding decimal numbers, it is important that the decimals are all aligned. This will ensure that the tenths, hundredths, thousandths, etc., are in the right order, that is, in the same column. For example, if we had to add the following numbers, note the steps we go through before the addition.

$$3.146, 4.25, 24.987, 23.56, 108.3457$$

Step 1 First we align the numbers so that the decimals are in line.

$$
\begin{aligned}
&3.146\\
&4.25\\
&24.987\\
&23.56\\
&108.3457
\end{aligned}
$$

Step 2 This step is optional but it helps us in keeping things straight for addition. In this step, we set up the numbers with the same decimal places by adding zeros to each number so that each number has the number of decimal places equal to the number with the most decimal places. In our example it is 108.3457. This gives all numbers the same number of decimal places, without changing the value of each number. *Note*: 4.25 is the same as 4.2500.

$$
\begin{aligned}
&3.1460\\
&4.2500\\
&24.9870\\
&23.5600\\
&108.3457
\end{aligned}
$$

Step 3   Now undertake the addition.

$$
\begin{array}{r}
3.1460 \\
4.2500 \\
24.9870 \\
23.5600 \\
\underline{108.3457} \\
164.2887
\end{array}
$$

EXAMPLE 2.5

Add the following numbers and round your answer to the nearest tenth (one decimal place).

$$4.234 + 5.678 + 15.1 + 0.125$$

Solution   First we align the numbers so the place values are correct. Then add zeros as appropriate. This gives:

$$
\begin{array}{r}
4.234 \\
5.678 \\
15.100 \\
\underline{0.125}
\end{array}
$$

25.137, or 25.1, rounded to the nearest tenth.

(ii) Subtraction of Decimal Numbers

The process of subtraction with decimal numbers is similar to addition. First we align the numbers, fill in the zeros as required, and then perform the subtraction. Consider Example 2.6:

EXAMPLE 2.6

Subtract 34.5678 from 765.345 and round the answer to the nearest hundredth (two decimal places).

Solution   First align the numbers and add zeros as necessary.

$$
\begin{array}{r}
765.3450 \\
- \ \underline{34.5678}
\end{array}
$$

730.7772, or 730.78, rounded to the nearest hundredth (two decimal places).

(iii) Multiplication of Decimal Numbers

Multiplication of decimal numbers requires us to perform the multiplication and then place the decimal point based on the following rule:

Multiplication Rule for Decimals

When multiplying numbers with decimals, count the total number of decimal places in both numbers we are multiplying. Then, place the decimal point directly before the number <u>in the product</u>, which is the same number of places as the decimal count, counting from right to left.

EXAMPLE 2.7

Multiply 19.99×2.344 and round to the nearest thousandths (three places).

Solution

$$
\begin{array}{r}
19.99 \longleftarrow \text{Two decimal places.} \\
2.344 \longleftarrow \text{Three decimal places.} \\
7996 \\
79960 \\
599700 \\
3998000 \\
\hline
46.85656 \longleftarrow
\end{array}
$$

46.85656 ⟵ To five decimal places — counting, from the right, five numbers, since there are five decimal places in total from the original numbers.

Note that we counted the number of decimal places in each number being multiplied $(2 + 3)$, and then placed the decimal point in front of the number in our answer (product), which is 5 places to the left of the last number in the product. Rounding our answer to the nearest thousandths, we get the final answer of 46.857.

(iv) Division with Decimal Numbers

Division with decimal numbers requires us to move the decimal point in the divisor to the right as far as possible and move the decimal point in the dividend the same number of places. Once the decimal points have been moved in the divisor and dividend we can then perform the division. This is a little more complex than multiplication, so study Example 2.8:

EXAMPLE 2.8

Divide each of the following numbers:

(a) $34.5 \div 2.5$
(b) $15.3 \div 3.0$
(c) $45.5 \div 0.09$

Solution (a) $2.5\overline{)34.5}$ is written as $25\overline{)345.0}$.

Before the division, we move the decimal point in the divisor (2.5) to the right, giving us 25. Then we do the same to the dividend (34.5), which gives us 345. Now we can perform the division.

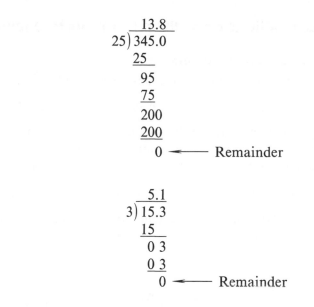

```
        13.8
   25) 345.0
       25
       95
       75
      200
      200
        0  ←——— Remainder
```

(b)

```
         5.1
    3) 15.3
       15
       0 3
       0 3
         0  ←——— Remainder
```

In this example, we did not need to move the decimal point since there was no decimal point in the divisor.

(c) $0.09\overline{)45.5}$ this is rewritten as $9\overline{)4550.0}$.

The difference in this example is that we moved the decimal point in the divisor by two places (from 0.09 to 9). Therefore, we had to do the same to the dividend (from 45.5 to 4,550). This was done by multiplying each number by 100. Moving the decimal point makes the division a little more direct. Now, performing the division we have:

```
        505.55      Note how the decimal point in the
   9) 4550.00       answer and the dividend are "lined up".
      45
       050
        45
        50
        45
        50
        45
         5  ←——— Remainder
```

As you can see, the answer will be a continual number of 5's after the decimal. This is called a **repeating decimal**. If we round the answer to two decimal places, the final answer would be 505.56.

D. Fractions and Mixed Numbers to Decimals

(i) Fractions to Decimals

Decimals are most commonly used in place of mixed numbers. For example, $2\frac{1}{2}$, a mixed number, can be written as 2.5 where the 0.5 is the $\frac{1}{2}$ unit. The problem we must solve is how to find the decimal equivalent for a fraction — that is, how do we convert the fraction into a decimal? The method we use to convert the fraction to a decimal is to perform the division indicated by the fraction. For example, to get the decimal equivalent of $2\frac{1}{2}$, $\frac{1}{2}$ must be converted to a decimal. To accomplish this we divide the numerator by the denominator as shown below:

$$
\begin{array}{r}
\text{Divisor} \longrightarrow 2\overline{)1.0} \\
\text{(denominator)} \quad \underline{1} \\
0
\end{array}
$$

Divisor ⟶ (denominator), Quotient ⟵ 0.5, Dividend (numerator) ⟵ 1.0, Remainder ⟵ 0

Therefore, the decimal equivalent to $2\frac{1}{2}$ is 2.5.

Often the division does not work out to be so simple. In fact, there are many cases where there is no final answer to the division. Consider the following examples of more difficult fractions:

EXAMPLE 2.9

Convert the following two mixed fractions to a number with three decimal places.

$$\text{(a) } 7\frac{2}{7} \qquad \text{(b) } 3\frac{2}{3}$$

Solution (a) $7\frac{2}{7}$ requires us to convert the $\frac{2}{7}$ into a decimal. The procedure is to divide the 2 by the 7 as follows:

$$
\begin{array}{r}
0.28571 \\
7\overline{)2.00000} \\
\underline{14} \\
60 \\
\underline{56} \\
40 \\
\underline{35} \\
50 \\
\underline{49} \\
10 \\
\underline{7} \\
3
\end{array}
$$

Divisor ⟶ 7)2.00000, Quotient ⟵ 0.28571, Dividend ⟵ 2.00000, Remainder ⟵ 3

In this problem it turns out that there is no solution. Rather, the decimal places will continue without any final answer — at least until we stop the division. This is one form of a repeating division. Each of the numbers repeat themselves in blocks of 6 numbers (0.285714285714, etc.,) whereas, in Example 2.10(c), the 5 repeated indefinitely after the decimal.
The final answer to three decimal places is 7.286.

(b) $3\frac{2}{3}$ requires us to convert the $\frac{2}{3}$ into a decimal. The procedure is to simply divide the 2 by the 3 as follows:

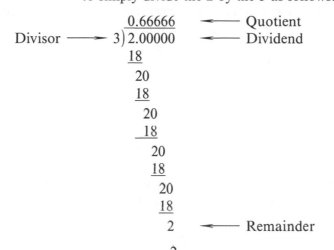

Thus, the mixed fraction $3\frac{2}{3}$ has a decimal equivalent of $3.6666\dot{6}$ — where the $0.6666\dot{6}$ is a repeating decimal (the · above the 6 means repeating decimal). Rounding to three places gives 3.667 as the answer.

(ii) Decimals to Fractions

When dealing with a fraction, the fraction is converted to a decimal equivalent by dividing the numerator by the denominator. The process is similar to that used with the fractional part of a mixed number. If you want to convert a decimal number to a fraction, it must be expressed in terms of a division. For example, if we wanted to express 0.375 as a fraction, we would write it as $\frac{375}{1,000}$ and, if possible, simplify it to its reduced form. In this case, $\frac{3}{8}$.
The thing to note is that the decimal is expressed as a fraction according to the number of places the decimal is carried, that is, tenths, hundredths, thousandths, etc. Let's consider an example that demonstrates three cases:

EXAMPLE 2.10

Express the following decimals as fractions and reduce to their lowest terms.
(a) 0.32
(b) 0.2456
(c) 0.68794

Solution   (a) 0.32 is a decimal to two places, or to the nearest hundredth. Therefore, to express this as a fraction we would rewrite it as $\dfrac{32}{100}$. Now finding the reduced form we have:

$$\frac{32}{100} = \frac{16}{50}$$

$$= \frac{8}{25}$$

(b) 0.2456 is a decimal to four places or to the nearest ten thousandth. Therefore the corresponding fraction is:

$$\frac{2,456}{10,000} = \frac{1,228}{5,000}$$

$$= \frac{614}{2,500}$$

$$= \frac{307}{1,250}$$

(c) 0.68794 is a decimal to five places or to the nearest hundred thousandth. Thus, the corresponding fraction is:

$$\frac{68,794}{100,000} = \frac{34,397}{50,000}$$

2.3 Percentages

As with decimals, percentages are common in business. All you need to do is to turn to a newspaper and there will be advertisements telling you about price reductions, often in percentage terms. Not only will you see percentages used in advertisements but also in articles discussing the percentage of people unemployed, the percentage increase in prices (a measure of inflation), or the interest rate (in percentage terms) being charged on consumer loans.

Percentages are simply another way of expressing fractions, decimal numbers, and, in some cases, mixed numbers. The term percentage refers to a measurement unit of hundredths, and the symbol used to indicate percentage is % — **the percentage sign**. Any number that is followed by the % sign refers to a number measured in hundredths. Since percentages are measured in hundredths we tend to think about the base of percentages as 100% — **a base means something we use as a reference point for comparison.** For example, if you are told that consumer prices have risen by 6.5%, you would interpret this as a relatively small increase. It is a "relatively" small amount because it is relative to the base of 100%. If you were told that prices had increased by 100%, you would say that prices had doubled. The way we arrive at this last statement is to think about the price of a litre of gasoline. If the price last year was $0.55 per litre and this year it is $1.10, we can see that the price has risen by its previous value. That is, the price has increased by $0.55, which is 100% of what it was a year ago. This would mean that the price has doubled over the past year.

Sometimes the word percentage is implied by the term **rate**. The use of the term rate is most common in the banking industry. Often when one discusses the rate of interest, it is quoted or expressed as a percentage.

A. Finding the Percentage

When we want to find the percentage it implies that two numbers are being compared, one relative to the other. Students are aware of percentages, since their grades on most exams and assignments are reported in percentages.

The computation of a percentage is done by division and then multiplication of the quotient (answer) by 100%, the base of percentage. For example, if 45,000 people in a community of 75,000 people want a certain project to occur, then we would say 60% of the people are in favour of the project. The way we arrived at this percentage was:

Step 1   Divide 45,000 by 75,000, which gives:

$$
\begin{array}{r}
0.6 \\
75{,}000\overline{)45{,}000.0} \\
\underline{45{,}000} \\
0
\end{array}
$$

Step 2   Multiply 0.6 by 100%, which gives 60%.

All percentages require these two steps.

Percentages do not always work out to be exact, since the decimal equivalent may have many decimal places or a repeating decimal.

B. Fractions, Decimals, and Percentages

As discussed in the previous section, a fraction can be readily expressed as a percentage by first transforming it to a decimal and then to a percentage. For example, $\frac{4}{5}$ can be expressed as the decimal 0.80, which is expressed as the percentage 80%. What is important to note is that the decimal is dropped and the % sign is inserted. The thing to understand is that the % term refers to hundredths, and if the fraction yields a decimal equivalent that has more than two decimal places, then there will be a decimal place in the percentage equivalent. For example, $\frac{3}{8}$ can be written as 0.375; the corresponding percentage is 37.5%. Note that the decimal comes after the hundredth term. The following example shows how we convert fractions and decimals to percentages.

EXAMPLE 2.11

Express the following fractions as percentages, and, where decimals are required, round to four places.

(a) $\dfrac{2}{3}$

(b) $\dfrac{7}{12}$

(c) $\dfrac{121}{200}$

(d) $\dfrac{25}{4,535}$

Solution (a) $\dfrac{2}{3}$ must first be written as a decimal equivalent, that is, 0.6667. Remember, to get the decimal we divided 2 by 3, which gives 0.666666 (a repeating decimal). Rounded to four places gives 0.6667. Now, as a percentage, 0.6667 is written as 66.67% — we moved the decimal two places to the right and added the % sign (i.e., we multiplied 0.6667 by 100%).

(b) $\dfrac{7}{12}$ as a decimal equivalent is $7 \div 12$, or $0.583\overset{.}{3}$ (repeating), and is rounded to four decimal places. The percentage equivalent is 58.33%.

(c) $\dfrac{121}{200} = 121 \div 200$

$= 0.605$, or 60.5%

(d) $\dfrac{25}{4,535} = 25 \div 4,535 = 0.00551268$

$= 0.55\%$ This has been rounded to four places, since 0.55% is 0.0055 rounded to four places in decimal notation.

(ii) Multiplication with Percentages

For multiplication and division with percentages, the most appropriate method to use will depend upon the type of problem you are solving. If you are simply multiplying a number times a percentage, for example, $3 \times 15\%$, the easiest way to find the solution is to leave the percentage as a percentage, giving a product of 45%.

If you are finding the percentage of a number — the most common business situation — then the method to use requires you to convert the percentage to a decimal equivalent and then perform the multiplication. For example, if

15% of 95 is required, then convert the percentage to 0.15 and then perform the multiplication, that is, 0.15×95, or 14.25.

Another example that often arises is multiplying two or more percentages. This is done by converting the percentages to decimal equivalents, then multiplying, and then converting the final answer back to a percentage.

The last type of calculation that needs further explanation is finding a percentage of a percentage. Consider Example 2.12:

EXAMPLE 2.12

A builder of new housing tells you that his labour cost for building a $200,000 house has risen by 10%. If labour costs are approximately 40% of the total cost of building a $200,000 house, by how much, in dollars, will the cost of this type of house rise because of the increase in labour costs?

Solution Your initial reaction may be simply to multiply $200,000 by 10%. However, if labour costs are only 40% of the $200,000, then the actual increase in the cost to build the house will be only 10% of 40%. To make this clear, let's first find out how much the labour costs are for a $200,000 house. Using our decimal equivalents, we know that 40% is the same as 0.4. Therefore, the labour portion of a $200,000 house is:

$$0.4 \times \$200,000 = \$80,000$$

Now, if labour costs have risen by 10%, this will apply only to the $80,000, the labour costs to build a new house. Therefore, the increase in labour costs are:

$$0.10 \times \$80,000 = \$8,000$$

Thus, labour costs have risen by $8,000. We should find that the new cost of building this type of house will be $200,000 + $8,000, or $208,000.

A more direct method for solving this problem is to find 10% of 40% and multiply this amount by $200,000. To determine 10% of 40% we can multiply the two percentages — after they have been converted to decimal equivalents. This would give:

$0.1 \times 0.4 = 0.04$, that is, a 10% increase in a cost that is 40% of all costs will cause the total to rise by 0.04, or 4%. Thus the increase in total cost caused by increasing labour costs will be:

$0.04 \times \$200,000 = \$8,000$ — the same as above.

Consequently, the new cost will be $200,000 + $8,000, or $208,000. (Note that labour costs are now more than 40% of total costs.)

Example 2.12 was designed to show how one can find the percentage of a percentage by multiplying the two percentages in their decimal equivalents. This is a useful calculation in business and will be used later in the chapters on financial mathematics.

(iv) Division with Percentages

The process of division with percentages relies on decimal equivalents. The steps involved are first, convert the percentage to a decimal equivalent and, second, perform the required division using the decimal equivalent as the divisor. Example 2.13 highlights the procedure:

EXAMPLE 2.13

Divide 250 by 12.5%.

Solution   First, convert the percentage to a decimal equivalent, or 0.125. Using the decimal equivalent, perform the division.

$$250 \div 0.125 = 2,000$$

Therefore, when 250 is divided by 12.5% it yields 2,000. Another way of thinking about this is to remember that 12.5% of 2,000 is 250.

GLOSSARY OF TERMS

Decimal   a way of expressing the parts of a whole number. Decimals are expressed in tenths, hundredths, thousandths, etc.

Percentage   another way of expressing parts of a whole number. A number is said to be 100% of itself. The parts that make up the number are expressed as a percentage and will be less than 100%. For example, 100% of 10 is 10; 20% of 10 is 2.

Ratio   a comparison of one number to another. For example, 5 to 1 means one number appears five times to one of another number.

CHAPTER 3

Basic Algebraic Concepts

Algebraic methods in business are used to solve problems in accounting, finance, economics, and marketing. Often solutions to business problems take only minutes using algebra, whereas without algebra the solution might be approached by trial and error. This can be costly and inefficient. Moreover, in some instances, without the assistance of algebra, solutions to quantitative business problems would be almost impossible to find.

Many situations arise where algebra may assist business. For instance, a small business needs to figure out the exact number of units of a product it must sell to cover all costs. Another business needs a quick and efficient way to provide quotations for work upon which it has been asked to bid. These are examples where a little algebra may assist a business enormously.

Clearly, algebra does not provide a solution to all quantitative problems of business. However, the fact that it can be used frequently is reason for students of business to have an understanding of the basic concepts and procedures of algebra.

The overall objective of this chapter and the following chapter is to provide information on the algebraic essentials for business. To achieve this objective, business examples are used where possible. Where possible, examples demonstrate a business situation. In some cases, the examples are quite long because they try to provide a realistic perspective on how algebraic methods are used in the "real world".

3.1 Algebraic Expressions

A. Algebraic Expressions — Basic Concepts

Algebra often conjures up ideas of complex formulas. In fact, this is not so for most business applications of algebra. Before we discuss how the basic rules of addition, subtraction, multiplication, and division apply to algebra, let's make sure we understand what the term algebra means.

With algebra, however, we are not limited to numbers. Algebra expands the use of the rules of arithmetic to letters, numbers, or both to express relationships. These relationships are given a variety of names including expressions and equations. **The relationships in algebra are formed between variables (letters) and numbers, or variables and variables. The term variable in algebra** is used to describe something that can change in an algebraic expression. In business the variable might be the number of units of a good produced.

An example of an algebraic expression is $x + y$, where x and y are called variables. The concept of variables will be explained in detail once we have reviewed how the operations of arithmetic apply to algebraic expressions. The key difference in algebra is that arithmetic operations are now applied to letters as well as numbers.

B. Arithmetic Rules and Algebraic Operations

The arithmetic rules apply to algebraic operations. If x, y, and z stand for three algebraic variables, the arithmetic rules apply to these algebraic variables as they would to numbers. The use of arithmetic rules for algebraic variables is summarized in Tables 3.1 and 3.2.

Table 3.1:   Basic Arithmetic Operations Applied to Algebraic Expressions

Arithmetic Rule Applied to Variables	Examples Using Numbers for the Variables Let $x = 14$, $y = 12$, and $z = 2$.
ADDITION Two variables x and y: $x + y = y + x$	$14 + 12 = 12 + 14$ $= 26$
Three variables x, y, and z: $(x + y + z) = (y + z) + x$	$(14 + 12 + 2) = (12 + 2) + 14$ $= 28$
MULTIPLICATION Two variables x and y: $xy = yx$	$14 \times 12 = 12 \times 14$ $= 168$
Three variables x, y, and z: $xyz = yzx = zyx$	$14 \times 12 \times 2 = 12 \times 2 \times 14$ $= 2 \times 12 \times 14$ $= 336$
DIVISION Two variables x and y: $x \div y = \dfrac{x}{y}$	$14 \div 12 = \dfrac{14}{12}$ $= \dfrac{7}{6}$
Three variables x, y, and z: $x \div y \div z = (x \div y) \div z$	$14 \div 12 \div 2 = (14 \div 12) \div 2$ $= 0.5833$
$(x \div y) \div z = \dfrac{x \div y}{z}$	$(14 \div 12) \div 2 = \dfrac{14 \div 12}{2}$ $= 0.5833$

The properties of 0 and 1 introduced in Chapter 1 have the same properties for algebraic terms as was found for numerical values. In Table 3.2, where x and y represent variables, a review of the properties of 0 and 1 is provided.

Table 3.2:   Properties of 0 and 1 When Used with Algebraic Variables

Properties of 0	Examples Let $x = 14$, $y = 12$, and $z = 2$
ADDITION A variable x, plus 0: $x + 0 = x$	$14 + 0 = 14$
SUBTRACTION When x is subtracted from zero, the result is: $0 - x = -x$	$0 - 14 = -14$
MULTIPLICATION A variable x, multiplied by 0: $x \times 0 = 0$ Two variables multiplied by 0: $xy \times 0 = 0$	$14 \times 0 = 0$ $14 \times 12 \times 0 = 0$
DIVISION Dividing a variable by 0: $x \div 0 -$ Undefined $= \infty$	$14 \div 0 =$ Undefined $= \infty$
Properties of 1	**Examples** Let $x - 14$, $y - 12$, and $z - 2$.
ADDITION A variable x, plus 1: $x + 1 = 1 + x$	$14 + 1 = 1 + 14$
MULTIPLICATION A variable x, multiplied by 1: $x \times 1 - x$ Two variables multiplied by 1: $xy \times 1 = xy$	$14 \times 1 = 14$ $14 \times 12 \times 1 = 14 \times 12$

C. Basic Terminology in Algebra

The best way to understand the meaning of the terms used in algebra, such as variables, equations, and expressions, is with an example. Suppose you are going to go into business for yourself and decide that business cards are necessary to leave with possible clients. A small printing company advises you that what you want in a business card will cost $500 as a set-up charge for the printing plate and, in addition, it will cost $0.05 per card for each card printed. Without algebra, if you had decided that you wanted 1,000 cards, you would find the cost for the 1,000 cards by using the following arithmetic method:

$$\$500 + \$0.05(1,000) = \$550$$

With algebra, it is possible to express the printing cost with an expression that can be used for any number of cards. This is done by introducing a variable. The introduction of a variable makes the expression an algebraic expression. To formulate an algebraic expression, we would introduce a letter for the variable, say y, and let y stand for the number of business cards to be printed. Using y in place of the number of cards, we can write an expression for the cost of y business cards as:

$$\$500 + \$0.05y$$

To make this expression into an equation we introduce the equal sign and make the expression equal to the total cost of y business cards.

$$\$500 + \$0.05y = \text{total cost of } y \text{ business cards}$$

This equation will give the total cost for any number of business cards you want to order. In the example above, y could be 1,000, 2,000, or any other number of cards. Because the value of y can change, it is called a variable.

From this simple example there are some terms that we should understand:

Variable

If y is a variable, then the value of y will <u>change</u> depending upon the number of business cards you want printed. Note that y is a letter that stands for the number of cards you purchase. This letter could have been any letter. The fact that there is now a letter in our cost formulation, as opposed to the number (1,000), makes the expression an algebraic expression.

Expression

An expression refers to a statement that defines a relation between variables. For example, the expression that describes the cost of business cards is $\$500 + 0.05y$.

Equation

An equation defines a relation between numbers and variables, or variables and variables. An algebraic expression becomes an equation if an equal sign (=) is used to express the specific relationship. For example:

$$\$500 + 0.05y = \text{Total Cost}$$

is an equation because of the equal sign. It equates the number of cards and set-up costs to the total cost. Once the equal sign is applied we have an equation. Equations are sometimes called formulas if they are used to find an unknown when given a value for a variable.

Coefficient

This refers to the number in front of the variable and means that this number multiplies the value of the variable. In our example, $500 + \$0.05y$, 0.05 is the numerical coefficient and multiplies the variable y. In algebra, any number in front of a variable is called a coefficient and can be a fraction, a decimal number, or a whole number. The y in $0.05y$ is called a literal coefficient. If the expression has a letter in front of another letter, say $3ax$, where a and x are variables, then ax is called a **literal coefficient** and 3 is the **numerical coefficient**. If a term is simply x or another variable, the numerical coefficient is 1 although it is never stated, e.g., $1x = x$.

Term

A term refers to the parts of the expression. In the example, Total Cost = \$500 + \$0.05y, \$500 and 0.05y are the terms of the cost equation.

Factor

If two or more numbers are multiplied, each number, or the product of the numbers, is called a factor. Consider 0.05y: 0.05, 0.05y, and y are each called a factor.

Substitution

Substitution means assigning a number or another algebraic term in place of a variable. For example, in \$500 + \$0.05y, if we want $y = 1,000$, then we substitute 1,000 for y in the expression to get \$500 + \$0.05(1,000).

The examples that follow are designed to show how the information from a business problem can be stated in algebraic terms, and then produce a result that has a business application. Generally, the most difficult part of the problem is translating the written information into a concise algebraic statement.

EXAMPLE 3.1

Sharon has a window washing business and often has to provide quotations to people for doing their windows. Sharon has found that a price of \$8.00 per window will cover her costs and provide a small profit. The price of \$8.00 is for each window of a house with a basement and a main floor. If the house has two floors (main floor and upstairs) plus a basement, the average price to clean each window for the second story is \$15.00, which covers costs and makes a small profit. Sharon will not do homes with more than two floors and a basement.

Make up an equation that would allow Sharon to count the number of windows on any house and work out a price for a potential customer. Let the variable w stand for the number of windows for the basement and the first floor. Let u be variable for the number of windows on the second floor.

Solution The first thing Sharon would do is to set up an expression for the number of windows in the basement and on the main floor. This would be \$8w.

Where applicable, houses with a second floor will have a cost of \$15 per window. Using u as the term for the number of windows on the second floor would give an expression of \$15u.

Thus, if a house had a basement and a main floor and had ten windows ($w = 10$) the quotation for window cleaning would be \$8(10), or \$80. Similarly, if a house had a second floor with 15 windows on the second floor ($u = 15$), the quotation for the second floor would be \$15(15), or \$225.

Bringing the two expressions together, the **equation** Sharon could use for quoting would be:

$$\$8w + \$15u = \text{quoted price to do the windows on all jobs.}$$

In this case, the equation could be called a **formula,** since Sharon will use it repeatedly, just substituting different values for w and u.

EXAMPLE 3.2

Sharon has been asked to give a quotation for washing the windows for an old house that has two floors and a basement. The number of windows in the basement and on the main floor is 12. On the second floor there are 16 windows. Using the expression you set up in Example 3.1, 8w$ + 15u$, find the price Sharon should quote for this window washing job.

Solution The formula we will use is

$$\$8w + \$15u = \text{Quotation},$$

where the values for w and u will be 12 and 16, respectively. Substituting the numbers for w and u gives:

$\$8(12) + \$15(16) = \$336$, the price she should quote using the formula.

3.2 Rules of Exponents

Most often the algebraic expressions we use are more complex than the ones discussed so far. For example, we often work with expressions that have different exponents and look like:

$$4x^3y + 5x^2$$

The numbers 3 and 2, which appear "raised" above x, are called exponents of x. The term exponent is sometimes referred to as the power of a number. **A positive integer exponent or power refers to how many times a number, variable, or algebraic expression is multiplied by itself.** For example, $4 \times 4 \times 4$ can be written as 4^3. The 3 is referred to as an exponent or power and tells us how often the number is to be multiplied by itself.

In business and economics, there is a need to use **exponents or powers** in many problems where algebraic expressions are used. The use of exponents or powers is of particular importance in finance, since the formulas used for compound interest on money, mortgages, loans, and retirement plans require the use of exponents.

In algebra we often write what is called the general form of an exponent as:

x^n: where x is the variable and n is the exponent. For example, with x^3 the 3 would be the value of n in the general form. (Although x is a variable, when exponents are involved some refer to x as a base.)

In order to understand exponents and the laws that govern the use of exponents, there are some basic definitions that must be understood. These are summarized in Table 3.3.

When an exponent is negative it implies division. More complicated forms of exponents are fractional exponents, such as $x^{\frac{1}{n}}$ or $x^{\frac{m}{n}}$, which means finding the *n*th root of a number, before the number has been raised to the *m*th power. These types of exponents are defined in Sections 5 to 7 in Table 3.3. The root of a number is the opposite of raising a number to an exponent. For example, $4^{\frac{1}{2}}$ is referred to as taking the root of a number or in this case, finding the second root of 4 (also called the square root). The concept of finding a root can best be shown by the following examples:

$8^{\frac{1}{3}} = 2$ The third root of 8. Finding the third root means finding a number that, when raised to the third power, gives 8. If we raise 2 to the third power, $2 \times 2 \times 2 = 8$.

$16^{\frac{1}{4}} = 2$ When 2 is raised to the fourth power it gives 16. Thus, 2 is called the fourth root of 16, since $2 \times 2 \times 2 \times 2 = 16$, and therefore $16^{\frac{1}{4}} = 2$.

The symbol $\sqrt[n]{x}$ is called a radical and refers to the *n*th root of *x*, where $\sqrt[n]{x} = x^{\frac{1}{n}}$ and $\sqrt[n]{x^m} = (x^{\frac{1}{n}})^m$, where *m* and *n* represent positive numbers.

Table 3.3:   Definitions for Exponents

Definitions of x^n for *x* greater than 0	Example
1. If *n* is a positive integer: $x^n = x \times x \times x \times x \times \ldots$	If $x = 3$, and $n = 4$, then $3^4 = 3 \times 3 \times 3 \times 3 = 81$
2. If *n* is equal to zero, then $x^0 = 1$	If $x = 3$, and $n = 0$, then $3^0 = 1$
3. If *n* is equal to one, then $x^1 = x$	If $x = 3$, and $n = 1$, then $3^1 = 3$
4. If *n* is positive, then $x^{-n} = \dfrac{1}{x^n}$	If $x = 3$, and $n = 2$, then $3^{-2} = \dfrac{1}{3^2} = \dfrac{1}{9}$
FRACTIONAL EXPONENTS	
5. If *n* is a positive integer, then $x^{\frac{1}{n}} = \sqrt[n]{x}$ (called a radical). $\sqrt[n]{x}$ is also referred to as the *n*th root of *x*.	If $x = 4$ and $n = 2$, then $4^{\frac{1}{2}} = \sqrt[2]{4} = 2$
6. If *m* and *n* are positive integers, then $x^{\frac{m}{n}} = (\sqrt[n]{x})^m$	If $x = 8$, $m = 2$, and $n = 3$, $8^{\frac{2}{3}} = (\sqrt[3]{8})^2 = 4$
7. If *m* and *n* are positive integers, then $x^{\frac{-m}{n}} = \dfrac{1}{x^{\frac{m}{n}}}$	If $x = 8$, $m = 2$, and $n = 3$, $8^{\frac{-2}{3}} = \dfrac{1}{8^{\frac{2}{3}}} = \dfrac{1}{4}$

The laws that govern how exponents are to be applied to numbers are summarized in Table 3.4. Work through the examples in the table to make sure each law is understood. The examples that follow show how each of the laws and definitions can be used.

Table 3.4: Laws of Exponents

Law	Examples: $n = 3$, $m = 4$
1. $x^n \times x^m = x^{n+m}$	$x^3 \times x^4 = x^{3+4} = x^7$
2. $(x \times y)^n = x^n y^n$	$(x \times y)^3 = x^3 y^3$
3. $(x^n)^m = x^{n \times m}$	$(x^3)^4 = x^{3 \times 4} = x^{12}$
4. $\dfrac{x^n}{x^m} = x^n \times x^{-m} = x^{n-m}$	$\dfrac{x^3}{x^4} = x^3 \times x^{-4} = x^{-1} = \dfrac{1}{x}$
5. $\dfrac{x^n}{y^n} = \left[\dfrac{x}{y}\right]^n$	$\dfrac{x^3}{y^3} = \left[\dfrac{x}{y}\right]^3$

Examples 3.3 through 3.8 use the definitions and laws of exponents in Tables 3.3 and 3.4. Read the examples carefully to ensure you understand the operations of exponents.

EXAMPLE 3.3

Complete the computations for the following exponent questions.

(a) $4^2 \times 4^3$
(b) $(5 \times 2)^4$
(c) $(12^2)^3$
(d) Using Law 4, show that $3^0 = 1$.

Solution (a) $4^2 \times 4^3$ This is an example of Law 1.

$$4^2 4^3 = 4^{2+3}$$
$$= 4^5$$
$$4 \times 4 \times 4 \times 4 \times 4 = 1{,}024$$

(b) $(5 \times 2)^4$ This example uses Law 2.

$$(5 \times 2)^4 = 5^4 2^4$$

   or

$$(5 \times 2)^4 = 10^4$$
$$(10)^4 = 10 \times 10 \times 10 \times 10 = 10{,}000$$

(c) $(12^2)^3$ This is Law 3.

$$(12^2)^3 = 12^{2 \times 3}$$
$$= 12^6$$
$$= 2{,}985{,}984$$

(d) The final example, showing that $3^0 = 1$, requires the use of Law 4:

$$\frac{3}{3} = \frac{3^1}{3^1}$$

$$= 3^{1-1}$$

$$= 3^0$$

$$= 1$$

EXAMPLE 3.4

Complete the computations for the following exponent questions.

(a) $x^4 \times x^6$ (b) $(y \times x)^8$ (c) $(a^2)^7$

Solution   (a) This is an example of Law 1. Therefore:

$$x^4 \times x^6 = x^{4+6}$$
$$= x^{10}$$

(b) $(y \times x)^8 = y^8 x^8$ Applying Law 2.

(c) This example uses Law 3, and can be solved as follows:

$$(a^2)^7 = a^{2 \times 7}$$
$$= a^{14}$$

EXAMPLE 3.5

Perform the following divisions.

(a) $4^3 : 4^2$
(b) $4^4 \div 4^4$
(c) $6^3 \div 2^2$
(d) $x^4 \div x^2$
(e) $x^4 \div x^6$

Solution   (a) $4^3 \div 4^2 = \dfrac{4^3}{4^2}$

$$= \frac{4 \times 4 \times 4}{4 \times 4}$$

$$= 4^{3-2}$$

$$= 4^1$$

$$= 4$$

(b) $4^4 \div 4^4 = \dfrac{4^4}{4^4}$

$$= \dfrac{4 \times 4 \times 4 \times 4}{4 \times 4 \times 4 \times 4}$$

$$= 4^{4-4}$$

$$= 4^0$$

$$= 1$$

(c) $6^3 \div 2^2 = \dfrac{6^3}{2^2}$

$$= \dfrac{6 \times 6 \times 6}{2 \times 2}$$

$$= \dfrac{216}{4}$$

$$= 54$$

(d) $x^4 \div x^2 = \dfrac{x^4}{x^2}$

$$= \dfrac{x \times x \times x \times x}{x \times x}$$

$$= x^2$$

(e) $x^4 \div x^6 = \dfrac{x^4}{x^6}$

$$= \dfrac{x \times x \times x \times x}{x \times x \times x \times x \times x \times x}$$

$$= \dfrac{1}{x^2}$$

$$= x^{-2}$$

In part (e), above, it should be noted that the final answer uses a negative exponent. Remember, a negative exponent implies division, which in this case is $\dfrac{1}{x^2}$, or x^{-2}.

EXAMPLE 3.6

Using Law 5, find $12^4 \div 3^4$.

Solution $12^4 \div 3^4 = \dfrac{12^4}{3^4}$

$$= \dfrac{12 \times 12 \times 12 \times 12}{3 \times 3 \times 3 \times 3}$$

$$= \left[\frac{12}{3}\right]^4$$

and

$$\left[\frac{12}{3}\right]^4 = [4]^4$$
$$= 4 \times 4 \times 4 \times 4$$
$$= 256$$

EXAMPLE 3.7

The following radicals can be expressed using both fractional exponents and decimal equivalent forms. Study each example.

(a) $\sqrt[4]{6^2} = 6^{\frac{2}{4}}$
$$= 6^{\frac{1}{2}}$$
$$= 6^{0.5}$$

(b) $\sqrt[4]{x^2} = x^{\frac{2}{4}}$
$$= x^{\frac{1}{2}}$$
$$= x^{0.5}$$

(c) $\sqrt[8]{y^5} = y^{\frac{5}{8}}$
$$= y^{0.625}$$

(d) $\sqrt[3]{3^2} = 3^{\frac{2}{3}}$
$$= 3^{0.66667} \quad \text{Rounded to 5 places.}$$

(e) $\dfrac{1}{\sqrt[3]{3^2}} = \dfrac{1}{3^{\frac{2}{3}}}$
$$= 3^{-0.66667}$$

(f) $\dfrac{1}{\sqrt[3]{x^2}} = \dfrac{1}{x^{\frac{2}{3}}}$
$$= x^{-\frac{2}{3}}$$
$$= x^{-0.66667}$$

In the next example, the results have been found by using the power or exponent function on an electronic calculator. All numbers have been rounded to three decimal places.

EXAMPLE 3.8

Using an electronic calculator, confirm the following answers.

(a) $\sqrt[4]{8^3} = 8^{\frac{3}{4}}$

$= 8^{0.75}$

$= 4.757$

(b) $\sqrt[4]{7^2} = 7^{\frac{1}{2}}$

$= 7^{0.5}$

$= 2.646$

(c) $\sqrt[8]{12^5} = 12^{\frac{5}{8}}$

$= 12^{0.625}$

$= 4.726$

(d) $\sqrt[3]{9^2} = 9^{\frac{2}{3}}$

$= 9^{0.667}$

$= 4.330$ If $\dfrac{2}{3}$ is used on the calculator, the

answer is 4.327.

(e) $\dfrac{1}{\sqrt[3]{8^2}} = \dfrac{1}{8^{\frac{2}{3}}}$

$= 8^{-0.667}$

$= 0.25$

(f) $\dfrac{1}{\sqrt[3]{16^2}} = \dfrac{1}{16^{\frac{2}{3}}}$

$= 16^{-0.667}$

$= 0.157$

The root of an expression using the radical sign, $\sqrt{}$, is understood to be a positive root. If a negative root is required, then the negative sign would precede the $\sqrt{}$ term, e.g., $-\sqrt{}$).

3.3 Types of Algebraic Expressions

Algebraic expressions can be classified as either **monomials** or **polynomials**. **Monomials** are expressions that have only one term. An example of a monomial is:

$$\text{Monomial} \qquad 4x \text{ or } 4z$$

Polynomials are expressions that have two or more terms in the expression, for example:

$$\text{Polynomials} \qquad \text{A: } 3x + 5$$
$$\text{B: } 3xy + 3x + 4$$

The name **binomial** means the expression has two terms — e.g., A above. **Trinomial**, B above, refers to an expression with three terms. It is common to use the term polynomial to describe expressions that have two or more terms.

EXAMPLE 3.9

Identify whether each of the following is a monomial or a polynomial. If there are any polynomials, where appropriate, identify whether the expression is a binomial or trinomial.

(a) $5x$
(b) $4x - 6y + 7$
(c) $12c + 0.5y$
(d) $13a + 14c + (56t + 23)$

Solution   (a) $5x$ ◄——

> This is a monomial since there is only one term.

(b) $4x - 6y + 7$ ◄——

> This is a polynomial, and, since it has three terms, it is a trinomial.

(c) $12c + 0.5y$ ◄——

> This is a polynomial, and, because there are only two terms, it is a binomial.

(d) $13a + 14c + 56t + 23$ ◄——

> This expression is a polynomial. Because there are four different terms, it is neither a trinomial nor a binomial.

3.4 Algebraic Operations

A. Addition and Subtraction of Monomials and Polynomials

(i) Monomials: Addition and Subtraction

In Table 3.1 we demonstrated how the arithmetic operations could be applied to algebraic expressions. Now we need to understand how these operations apply to more complex expressions.

When adding or subtracting algebraic expressions, the operation can only be done if the literal terms are the same, that is, if they have the same letters with the same exponents. This is called adding and subtracting **like terms**. The procedure of finding like and unlike terms is called **collecting terms**. Thus, the sum or difference will be done by adding or subtracting the numerical coefficients after the terms have been collected. The following examples show the use of like terms:

EXAMPLE 3.10

Add the following monomials: $6xy$, $3xy$, and xy.

Solution Each term has the same literal terms (xy). Therefore, the sum of these three terms is simply the sum of their numerical coefficients. Namely:

$$6 + 3 + 1 = 10. \text{ Therefore: } 6xy + 3xy + xy = 10xy$$

The addition could have been written as:

$$(6 + 3 + 1)xy = 10xy \quad \text{Remember, the term } xy \text{ has a coefficient 1.}$$

If any of the terms have unlike terms, for example, $6y$ and $3x$, these terms cannot be combined since they are unlike terms.

EXAMPLE 3.11

Add the following monomials: $2bx^2$, $(-3bx^2)$, $5x$, and $(-6x)$.

Solution Collecting like terms and adding gives:

$$2bx^2 + (-3bx^2) + 5x + (-6x) = -bx^2 - x$$

The procedure of subtraction of monomials requires that the numerical coefficients of the like terms be subtracted.

EXAMPLE 3.12

Subtract the following monomials: $15bx$ from $26bx$.

Solution $26bx - 15bx = (26 - 15)bx$

$26bx - 15bx = 11bx$

EXAMPLE 3.13

Subtract the following monomials: $(-3ax^2)$ from $15ax^2$.

Solution $15ax^2 - (-3ax^2) = ax^2(15 + 3)$

$\qquad\qquad\qquad = 18ax^2$

> Note sign change from $-(-)$ to $+$.

(ii) Polynomials: Addition and Subtraction

When polynomials are added together, the basic principle of adding and subtracting like terms is applied. In doing this we group the like terms and do the addition or subtraction and then bring the terms together.

EXAMPLE 3.14

Add the following polynomials:
$(12xy + 2ax + 8)$ and $(15xy + ax + 5)$.

Solution   Set the expression up as an addition, with columns of like terms:

$$12xy + 2ax + 8$$
$$\underline{15xy + ax + 5}$$
$$27xy + 3ax + 13 \longleftarrow \text{ Final sum of the polynomials.}$$

EXAMPLE 3.15

Subtract the following polynomials:

$(2y^2 - 4a + 3c)$, from $(5y^2 - 2a - 6c)$.

Solution   Set the expression up as a subtraction with columns of like terms:

$$5y^2 - 2a - 6c$$
$$\underline{-(2y^2 - 4a + 3c)} \longleftarrow$$
$$3y^2 + 2a - 9c$$

> Change the signs of the terms inside the brackets.

B. Multiplication and Division of Monomials and Polynomials

(i) Multiplication: Monomials and Polynomials

Multiplication of monomials and polynomials is undertaken by multiplying the numerical coefficients and multiplying the literal coefficients. If there are similar literal coefficients in both the monomial and polynomial, we can use exponents to summarize these like terms. The use of exponents is very common in the multiplication and addition of polynomials.

EXAMPLE 3.16

Multiply the two monomials $3xy$ and $4a$.

Solution

$$(3xy)(4a) = (3)(4)(xya)$$
$$= 12xya$$

EXAMPLE 3.17

Using the laws of exponents in Table 3.4, multiply the four monomials $4a$, $4ax$, $6a^2$, and $2x^2$.

Solution

$$(4a)(4ax)(6a^2)(2x^2) = (4 \times 4 \times 6 \times 2)(a^{1+1+2})(x^{1+2})$$
$$= 192a^4x^3$$

Multiplying a polynomial by a monomial requires that each term of the polynomial be multiplied by the monomial. The final answer for the multiplication will be the sum of the separate products for each term. Read Example 3.18, which demonstrates this point.

EXAMPLE 3.18

Using the laws of exponents in Table 3.4, multiply $(3x + 2y - 3a)$ by $3x$.

Solution

$$(3x + 2y - 3a)(3x) = (3x3x + 3x2y - 3x3a)$$
$$= 9x^{1+1} + 6xy - 9xa$$
$$= 9x^2 + 6xy - 9xa$$

Sometimes the problem is more complex and may involve the multiplication of several algebraic expressions involving terms with different exponents. When we have many terms, each must be handled separately and then brought together for a solution. The procedure used when we have multiple terms is shown in Examples 3.19 and 3.20.

EXAMPLE 3.19

Multiply $(4x^2a^3 + 6x^2y)$ by $5x$.

Solution
STEP 1

$$(4x^2a^3 + 6x^2y)(5x) = (5x4x^2a^3 + 5x6x^2y)$$
$$= 20x^{2+1}a^3 + 30x^{2+1}y$$
$$= 20a^3x^3 + 30x^3y$$

It is important to note that we generally express the answer to a problem, such as Example 3.19, in a more simplified form using the process of factoring. Factoring will be reviewed a little later in this chapter.

The last type of multiplication for algebraic expressions is the multiplication of a polynomial by a polynomial. The method used to perform the operation requires the multiplication of **each term of one polynomial by each term of the other polynomial**. Then, the separate multiplications are brought together by addition.

EXAMPLE 3.20

Multiply the two polynomials $(3x^2 + 4xy)$ and $(5x + 3y^4)$.

Solution

STEP 1 $(3x^2 + 4xy)(5x) = 15x^3 + 20x^2y$ Multiply each term of the first polynomial by the first term of the second polynomial.

STEP 2 $(3x^2 + 4xy)(3y^4) = 9x^2y^4 + 12xy^5$ Multiply each term of the first polynomial by the second term of the second polynomial.

STEP 3 $15x^3 + 20x^2y + 9x^2y^4 + 12xy^5$ Bring the terms together by addition.

The order in which the multiplication of terms is done is not critical. Another approach that could have been used is to take the first and second terms and multiply these by the second expression; the resulting product is the same.

(ii) Division: Monomials and Polynomials

When we divide algebraic expressions, the process is to divide the numerical and literal coefficients to find the quotient.

EXAMPLE 3.21

Divide $40x$ by $2x$.

Solution

$$\frac{40x}{2x} = \frac{20\cancel{x}}{\cancel{x}}$$
$$= 20$$

If there had been two different variables, the division could have been undertaken on only the numerical coefficients. Example 3.22 demonstrates this point.

EXAMPLE 3.22

Divide $40x$ by $5y$.

Solution $\dfrac{40x}{5y} = \dfrac{8x}{y}$

The division of a monomial by a monomial can be dealt with by using Law 4 of exponents.

EXAMPLE 3.23

Perform the division of $65x^4 \div 13x$.

Solution

$$65x^4 \div 13x = \frac{65x^4}{13x}$$

$$= \frac{5x^4}{x}$$

$$= (5x^4)(x^{-1})$$

$$= 5x^{4-1}$$

$$= 5x^3$$

Dividing a polynomial by a monomial is a similar type of problem, but here <u>each</u> term of the polynomial must be divided by the monomial. The next example shows two possibilities. In each case, note how the process requires each term of the polynomial to be handled separately:

EXAMPLE 3.24

Perform a division on each of the following:

(a) Divide $6ax^4 + 9a^2x^6$ by $3ax$.
(b) Divide $12a^3x^2 - 16a^2x^3$ by $4a^2x$.

Solution

(a) $6ax^4 + 9a^2x^6 \div 3ax$

$$\frac{(6ax^4 + 9a^2x^6)}{3ax} = \frac{6ax^4}{3ax} + \frac{9a^2x^6}{3ax}$$

Performing a division on each term of the expression is done as follows:

$$\frac{6ax^4}{3ax} = \left(\frac{6}{3}\right)\left(\frac{a}{a}\right)\left(\frac{x^4}{x}\right)$$

$$= 2x^3 \qquad\qquad \text{First term}$$

$$\frac{9a^2x^6}{3ax} = \left(\frac{9}{3}\right)\left(\frac{a^2}{a}\right)\left(\frac{x^6}{x}\right)$$

$$= 3ax^5 \qquad\qquad \text{Second term}$$

Bringing the two terms together, the final answer to the division is:

$$2x^3 + 3ax^5$$

(b) $(12a^3x^2 - 16a^2x^3) \div 4a^2x$

$$= \frac{12a^3x^2}{4a^2x} - \frac{16a^2x^3}{4a^2x}$$

Now, performing the division on each term we have:

$$\frac{12a^3x^2}{4a^2x} = \left(\frac{12}{4}\right)\left(\frac{a^3}{a^2}\right)\left(\frac{x^2}{x}\right)$$

$$= 3ax \qquad\qquad \text{First term}$$

$$\frac{-16a^2x^3}{4a^2x} = \left(\frac{-16}{4}\right)\left(\frac{a^2}{a^2}\right)\left(\frac{x^3}{x}\right)$$

$$= -4x^2 \qquad\qquad \text{Second term}$$

Bringing the terms together, the quotient of the division is:

$$3ax - 4x^2$$

Another division that may arise is the division of a polynomial by a polynomial. This is a slightly more difficult division, but uses the same principle of dividing each term of one polynomial by the other polynomial. Since this type of division is not required for the later topics for the mathematics of finance, it will not be discussed in this book.

3.5 Factoring of Algebraic Expressions

Factoring of expressions is a process designed to make the computations with algebraic expressions more manageable and less complex. The process of factoring requires one to look for what is called a **common factor** to each term of the expression.

A. Finding a Monomial Factor

Factoring an expression requires one to scan an expression and look for a factor that is common to each term.

For example, $xy + xz$ can be rewritten using the process of factoring by identifying the common factor, in this case x. The key to factoring is the use of brackets: (), [], and {}, discussed in Chapter 1. Thus, $xy + xz$ can be written as:

$$xy + xz = x(y + z)$$

We can see by the expression that we have a multiplication of a polynomial by a monomial as a result of factoring x from each term of the expression. The method by which the factor $(y + z)$ is obtained is to divide $xy + xz$ by x. This would yield $(y + z)$.

The expression $xy + xz$ is called the expanded form of the factored form, $x(y + z)$.

Factoring can be applied to both numerical and literal factors. Consider the following examples, which take single polynomial expressions and turn the factored form of the expression into a product of a more simple polynomial and monomial:

EXAMPLE 3.25

Factor $3x + 9y$.

Solution $3x + 9y = 3(x + 3y)$

If the final expression of Example 3.25, $3(x + 3y)$, is examined, it shows that if the terms inside the brackets are multiplied by 3, the original expression will be obtained, i.e., $3x + 9y$. In the next example, study how the division is made to arrive at the factored expression.

EXAMPLE 3.26

Factor the following.

(a) $3x + 4x^2$
(b) $2x^2 + 3x^2 + 4x^3y^2$
(c) $P + Prt$
(d) $A + 500A^2$

Solution (a) Find the common term. In this example it is x. Factoring out the x from both expressions by dividing the original expression by x yields:

$$3x + 4x^2 = x(3 + 4x)$$

A check can be made by multiplying the terms inside the brackets by x to arrive at the original expression.

(b) In this problem, there are three terms that have x^2, so factoring out this common term yields:

$$2x^2 + 3x^2 + 4x^3y^2 = x^2(2 + 3 + 4xy^2)$$
$$= x^2(5 + 4xy^2)$$

A check can be made by multiplying the terms inside the brackets by x^2 to arrive at the original expression.

(c) Factoring out the common term, P, gives:

$$P + Prt = P(1 + rt)$$

(d) Factoring the common term, A, yields:

$$A + 500A^2 = A(1 + 500A)$$

B. Binomial Factors

Often the terms that are factored are more complex than those considered so far. The most common example occurs when there are a series of algebraic terms, and the term that is factored is a binomial, not simply a monomial. To illustrate this point, consider the following example:

$$(1 + x) + (1 + x)^2 + (1 + x)^3 + (1 + x)^4$$

Fortunately, the logic involved in factoring the above expression is the same used in the earlier examples. What must be found is a term or terms common to each term or collection of terms in the expression.

In this example, the common term is $(1 + x)$, which is a binomial. Factoring this term from the expression gives:

$$(1 + x)[1 + (1 + x) + (1 + x)^2 + (1 + x)^3]$$

It is important to note the use of the [] besides the () brackets. The use of brackets is of particular importance in this type of factoring. Make sure you understand how they have been used to separate the expressions.

EXAMPLE 3.27

Factor $6yz - 2xz + 12ay - 4ax$.

Solution The easiest way is to factor the obvious terms:

$$6yz - 2xz + 12ay - 4ax = 2z(3y - x) + 4a(3y - x)$$

Looking to see if there are any other factors, it can be seen that $(3y - x)$ is common to both terms of the factored expression. Factoring this expression gives:

$$2z(3y - x) + 4a(3y - x) = (2z + 4a)(3y - x)$$

3.6 Finding a Solution to an Algebraic Equation

The term equation was used earlier when the concept of an algebraic expression was introduced. In earlier examples, the procedures for operations on algebraic expressions were reviewed. In this section, you will be shown how to formulate an algebraic expression and then solve the expression for an unknown term.

Before proceeding, the concept of an equation must be clearly understood. From our earlier discussion, remember that an equation is a statement of equality between two algebraic expressions or between an algebraic expression and a number. Two examples are:

$$3x + 5x = x + 4 \quad \text{Two algebraic expressions.}$$
$$3x + 5x = 4 \quad \text{Algebraic expression and a number.}$$

Our objective is to find a method to determine a numerical value for x that allows the equality sign to be satisfied. This value of x is called **the solution to the equation**. The next section focuses on the methods one can use to find a value for an unknown variable, and consequently a solution to the equation.

A. Solving Equations with One Variable

Solving equations with only one variable means finding a numerical value for the variable that will satisfy the equality sign of the equation. For example:

$$3x + 4 = 5x$$

If $x = 2$, the equation is satisfied since the left and right sides are 10. That is:

$$3(2) + 4 = 5(2)$$

and:

$$10 = 10$$

Although the expression $3x + 4 = 5x$ has x on both sides of the equation, it still is a one-variable equation. If an equation has an x and y term then it is referred to as a two-variable equation (e.g., $3x + 4y = 17$). **If all the variables have an exponent of 1, the equation is said to be a linear equation.** The terms that must be understood in working with equations are:

Members of the Equation

The expressions on each side of the equal sign (=) are called members of the equation. Often people refer to the members as the right and left hand sides of the equation. For instance,

$$3x + 18 = 6x - 9$$

$3x + 18$ is the left member, or left side, of the equation.
$6x - 9$ is the right member, or right side, of the equation.

Solving the Equation

Solving an equation means finding a number that, when used in place of the variable, satisfies the equation. In the example, $3x + 18 = 6x - 9$, the solution would be $x = 9$. What was done to find the solution was to replace x with numbers until we found a number for x that made both sides of the equation equal. In our case:

$$3(9) + 18 = 45 \text{ and } 6(9) - 9 = 45$$

We can say that a solution of $x = 9$ satisfies the equation. The technical term for 9 is the **root of the equation**.

(i) Solving Equations Using Addition and Subtraction Rules

When finding a solution to a linear equation, the objective is to find a numerical value for the variable that satisfies the equation. To illustrate this point, a solution to $x - 7 = 5$ can be found by adding 7 to each side of the equation. If this is done, we would have:

$$x - 7 + 7 = 5 + 7, \text{ or } x = 12$$

The 7 was selected because when it is added to the left side of the equation it has the effect of eliminating the -7. However, to satisfy the equality sign the addition of 7 must occur to both sides of the equation.

This principle — adding the same term to both sides of the equation — is fundamental and must be clearly understood. Consider the following example:

EXAMPLE 3.28

Find the solution to the following equations using the addition principle.

(a) $x - 9 = 15$

(b) $3x - 5 = 2x + 20$

(c) $4 + x = 16$

Solution   (a) $x - 9 = 15$

To find a value for x, isolate x on the left side of the equation. Adding 9 to the left hand side leaves only x. To maintain the balance of the equal sign, also add 9 to the right hand side. This would give:

$$x - 9 + 9 = 15 + 9$$
$$x - \cancel{9} + \cancel{9} = 15 + 9$$

$$x + 0 = 24$$

Therefore, $x - 24$ is the value of x that satisfies the equation.

(b) $3x - 5 = 2x + 20$

This expression requires two additions to be done to isolate x. First, add 5 to both sides of the equation:

$$3x - 5 + 5 = 2x + 20 + 5$$
$$3x = 2x + 25$$

Now, isolate x by adding $-2x$ to both sides of the equation. *Note*: this operation involves adding a negative number to both sides of the equation.

$$3x + (-2x) = 2x + 25 + (-2x)$$
$$x = 25$$

(c) $4 + x = 16$

As with part (b), add (-4) to both sides of the equation, giving us:

$$4 + (-4) + x = 16 + (-4)$$
$$x = 12$$

(ii) Solving Equations Using Multiplication and Division

Often we find that algebraic expressions cannot be solved with only the addition or subtraction of terms. Many solutions to algebraic expressions require multiplication and division, as well as addition and subtraction. Consider the following expression:

$$3x = 15$$

It is obvious that the value of x must be 5 if the equality is to be satisfied.

However, to find the solution for x we can either multiply both sides of the equation by $\frac{1}{3}$ or divide each side by 3, since these are equivalent operations. If we multiply each side by $\frac{1}{3}$ we have:

$$\left(\frac{1}{3}\right)(3x) = \left(\frac{1}{3}\right)(15)$$ This permits us to cancel the 3's.

$$\left(\frac{1}{\cancel{3}}\right)(\cancel{3}x) = \frac{15}{3}$$

$$x = 5$$

The principle of using multiplication and division is most helpful in more complicated linear equations. An example of a more complicated situation is:

$$3(x + 4) + 2x = 4(x + 6) - 5x$$

In this type of problem the most direct way to solve for x is to treat each part of the expression separately: do the indicated operation, and then solve for x. For this example, the steps one might take are:

STEP 1   Left side:

$$3(x + 4) + 2x = 3x + 12 + 2x$$ Eliminate the brackets on both sides of the equation by performing the necessary operations.

Right side:

$$4(x + 6) - 5x = 4x + 24 - 5x$$

STEP 2 $$3x + 12 + 2x = 4x + 24 - 5x$$ Place the completed operations from Step 1 into the original equation.

STEP 3 $$5x + 12 = 24 - x$$ Reduce the number of terms by adding the similar terms giving $5x + 12$ on the left hand side of the expression, and $24 - x$ on the right hand side.

STEP 4 $$5x + 12 - 12 + x = 24 - 12 - x + x$$ Subtract 12 from both sides of the equation, and add x to both sides, giving us:

$$6x = 12$$

STEP 5 $$\frac{6x}{6} = \frac{12}{6}$$ The final step is to divide each side by 6, which will give us our solution for equation.

$$x = 2$$

After we have found a solution to an equation, we often check the solution by substituting the solution value of the variable back into the original equation. This assures us that our solution does satisfy the equation. In the last example, the checking would be done by substituting $x = 2$ into the original equation, that is:

$$3(x + 4) + 2x = 4(x + 6) - 5x$$

Now substituting 2 for each x gives:

$$3(2 + 4) + 2(2) = 4(2 + 6) - 5(2)$$
$$3(6) + 2(2) = 4(8) - 5(2)$$
$$18 + 4 = 32 - 10$$
$$22 = 22$$

Thus, the solution $x = 2$ is correct and satisfies the equation.

EXAMPLE 3.29

Find a solution for the following equations and check the answer.

(a) $4x + 3(x + 3) = 15 + 2(x + 4)$
(b) $3x - 7(0.5x + 13) = -37 + 7(x - 2x)$
(c) $3x + 2x + x - 15 = 27$

Solution (a) $4x + 3(x + 3) = 15 + 2(x + 4)$

STEP 1 Left side: $4x + 3(x + 3) - 4x + 3x + 9$ Remove the brackets on both sides of the equation by performing the necessary operations.

Right side: $15 + 2(x + 4) = 15 + 2x + 8$

STEP 2 $4x + 3x + 9 = 15 + 2x + 8$ Set the right hand side equal to the left hand side.

STEP 3 $7x + 9 = 2x + 23$ Reduce the number of terms by adding the similar terms.

STEP 4 $7x + 9 - 9 - 2x = 2x + 23 - 9 - 2x$ Subtract 9 and $2x$ from both sides of the equation, giving us:

$5x = 14$

STEP 5 $\dfrac{5x}{5} = \dfrac{14}{5}$ The final step is to divide each side by 5, which will give us our solution for x.

$x = \dfrac{14}{5}$

$= 2.8$

STEP 6 $4(2.8) + 3(2.8 + 3) = 15 + 2(2.8 + 4)$ Checking the answer by sub-
$4(2.8) + 3(5.8) = 15 + 2(6.8)$ stituting $x = 2.8$ into the origi-
$11.2 + 17.4 = 15 + 13.6$ nal expression:
$28.6 = 28.6$

(b) $3x - 7(0.5x + 13) = -37 + 7(x - 2x)$

$3x - 3.5x - 91 = -37 + 7x - 14x$ Working out the terms with brackets and rewriting the equation gives:

$-0.5x - 91 = -37 - 7x$

$-0.5x + 7x = -37 + 91$ Bringing the terms together we add 91 and $7x$ to both sides, which gives:

$6.5x = 54$ Dividing both sides by 6.5:

$$x = \frac{54}{6.5}$$

$x = 8.30769$

$3x - 7(0.5x + 13) = -37 + 7(x - 2x)$ Checking the solution, remove the brackets by multiplying.

$-0.5x - 91 = -37 - 7x$ After combining terms, we substitute 8.30769 for x.

$-0.5(8.30769) - 91 = -37 - 7(8.30769)$

$-95.153846 = -95.153846$ The solution works!

(c) $3x + 2x + x - 15 = 27$

$6x - 15 = 27$ Adding the similar terms.

$6x = 42$ Adding 15 to each side of the expression.

$$\frac{6x}{6} = \frac{42}{6}$$ Dividing each side of the expression by 6.

$x = 7$ $x = 7$ is the solution for x.

$3(7) + 2(7) + 7 - 15 = 27$ Checking the solution by substituting 7 for x.

$27 = 27$ Our solution for x is verified.

(iii) The Solution of an Equation with Two Variables

Equations also may involve a solution for a variable that has as its solution an unknown variable. For example:

$$4x + 3y = 10$$

$$4x + 3y - 3y = 10 - 3y$$ To solve for x, we would first subtract $3y$ from each side of the
expression.

$$4x = 10 - 3y$$

$$x = \frac{10 - 3y}{4}$$ Solving for x, we divide each side
of the equation by 4.

What makes the difference in this solution is that there is not a unique solution for x, at least in a numerical sense, since the value of x will change for different values substituted for y.

Finding a solution for a two-variable equation is a common application in business and should be well understood. Consider Example 3.30, which shows the solution of equations with more than one variable.

EXAMPLE 3.30

Solve the following equations for x.

(a) $2x - y = 15$

(b) $0.5x - 2y + s = 10$

(c) $x(1 + i) = 3s$

Solution   (a) $2x - y = 15$

Add y to each side of the
equation.

$$2x - y + y = 15 + y$$
$$2x = 15 + y$$

Dividing each side by 2 to find a
solution for x yields:

$$x = \frac{15 + y}{2}$$

(b) $0.5x - 2y + s = 10$

In this expression there
are three variables. The
procedure for finding x is
the same as in part (a),
that is, isolate x on one
side of the equation. To
do this, add $2y$ and subtract s from both sides of
the equation which gives:

$$0.5 - 2y + s + 2y - s = 10 + 2y - s$$

$$0.5x = 10 + 2y - s$$

$$x = \frac{10 + 2y - s}{0.5}$$
Dividing each term by 0.5.

$$x = \frac{10}{0.5} + \frac{2y}{0.5} - \frac{s}{0.5}$$

$$x = 20 + 4y - 2s$$
Solving for x.

(c)
$$x(1 + i) = 3s$$

$$\frac{x(1 + i)}{(1 + i)} = \frac{3s}{(1 + i)}$$
Dividing each side of the equation by $(1 + i)$ yields the solution for x as:

$$x = \frac{3s}{(1 + i)}$$

B. Algebraic Equations Involving Fractions and Decimals

Algebraic expressions that have fractional or decimal equivalent numerical coefficients require us to use the rules of fractions or the rules of decimal equivalents discussed in Chapter 1.

At one time, it was the practice to look for common denominators in an algebraic expression with fractions and then solve the equation for the unknown variable. However, this is not the most common method any more — at least in a business context. With the wide use of the electronic calculator and the computer, expressions with fractions generally have the fractions converted to decimal equivalents. After the conversion, the solution to the algebraic expression is found — this is particularly true in business. The only problem is that sometimes there may be a difference in the solution for a variable, depending upon whether one uses fractions or decimal equivalents in one's method of solution.

Example 3.31 shows a situation where a difference occurs in the solution because of rounding of the number of decimal places. As will be seen in Example 3.31, the two methods — one using fractions and one using decimal equivalents — produce solutions that are marginally different because of the rounding error. This rounding error sometimes occurs with decimal equivalents.

EXAMPLE 3.31

Find the solution to $\frac{1}{6}x - 10 = 5$

Solution 1 Using fractions.

$$6\left[\frac{1}{6}x\right] - 6(10) = 6(5)$$
Multiplying both sides of the equation by 6, the lowest common denominator.

$$x - 60 = 30 \qquad \text{Add 60 to both sides to find } x.$$
$$x = 90$$

Solution 2 Using decimals.

Rewrite the equation using decimal equivalents

$$0.1667x - 10 = 5 \qquad \text{Rewrite the equation using decimal equivalents in place of the fraction } \frac{1}{6}.$$

$$0.1667x = 15 \qquad \text{Isolate } x \text{ by adding 10 to each side of the equation.}$$

$$\frac{0.1667x}{0.1667} = \frac{15}{0.1667} \qquad \text{Divide each side by 0.1667.}$$

$$x = 89.9820$$

As shown in Example 3.31, the solution obtained when using fractions produced a result that was marginally different from the solution with the decimal equivalents. If the number of decimal places had been carried further, the answers would have been the same. Sometimes the solution for the variable will be the same regardless of the method used. Example 3.32 demonstrates such an example:

EXAMPLE 3.32

Find a solution for x in the following equation using the rules of fractions and then solve the problem using decimal equivalents in place of the fractions.

$$\frac{1}{3}x + 15 = -\frac{2}{3}x + 45$$

Solution 1 Using fractions.

$$\frac{1}{3}x + 15 = -\frac{2}{3}x + 45$$

$$3\left[\frac{1}{3}x\right] + 3(15) = 3\left[-\frac{2}{3}x\right] + 3(45) \qquad \text{First, multiply both sides by the lowest common denominator, 3. Note that each term is multiplied by 3.}$$

$$x + 45 = -2x + 135 \qquad \text{Add } 2x \text{ and subtract } -45 \text{ from both sides of the equation.}$$

$$3x = 90$$

$$x = 30$$

Solution 2   Using decimal equivalents.

$$\frac{1}{3}x + 15 = -\frac{2}{3}x + 45$$ Convert the fractional coefficients to decimal equivalents.

$$0.3333x + 15 = -0.6667x + 45$$ Add $0.6667x$ and subtract 15 from both sides of the equation; then add similar terms.

$$0.3333x + 15 + 0.6667x - 15 = -0.6667x + 45 + 0.6667x - 15$$
$$x = 30$$

The question that may come to mind is, which method should be used? The answer is, it depends on the problem. Very complex expressions with fractions are more easily solved for the variable using decimal equivalents with the assistance of an electronic calculator. Other problems, like Example 3.32, are better handled using the rules of fractions. As a consequence, it will be up to the person solving the problem to decide whether decimals or fractions are used. The only thing that must be recognized is that the two methods may produce slightly different answers. Using a calculator with six or more decimal places will produce answers that are very close to each other.

3.7 Break-Even Analysis: A Business Application of an Algebraic Solution

In business, algebraic equations can be used to determine how much of a product or service must be sold to cover all the costs as well as make a profit. Finding the point where sales revenue is exactly equal to costs is called the **break-even point**. This point, **where costs and revenue are identical,** can be found by using an algebraic solution to an equation.

Another example of where algebra can be used in business is in the establishment of a formula to help a business in preparing cost estimates for contracts. The business card example in the first section of this chapter was a simple example of how a formula could be developed and used to provide a measure of cost.

In this section, you will learn how to develop expressions from the information given in a word problem. This is often the most difficult part, translating words and numerical information into equations or algebraic expressions.

For example, suppose that you were the owner of a small furniture manufacturing shop. How much would your sales need to be in order to cover paying the rent, wages to yourself and employees, utilities, insurance, and any equipment that you have leased or purchased? The answer to this question would be to find the break-even point. That is, the point where total dollar sales or total business revenue is sufficient to generate enough money to cover all your direct costs. The term direct cost is used because these are costs that can be recorded and are also acceptable to your accountant or bookkeeper. There are other indirect costs such as the interest forgone on any money that you have invested in the business, or all the time you spend organizing the operations of the business, which is not reflected in your wages. Indirect costs will not be considered in our discussion of break-even analysis because they require us to make certain assumptions. However, in the real world of business they must be recognized since they represent a cost of "doing" business and are sometimes forgotten in cost analysis by business people.

To see how we can use algebra for business problems, let us continue with our furniture business to define the terms **cost** and **revenue**. Once these are clear then we can apply the rules of algebra to help us solve a business problem.

Definition of Costs and Revenue

Total Variable Cost

Total variable costs are those costs that occur as a result of producing a good or service. For example, if you produce maple or oak furniture, your variable costs would be the materials and labour. If you produce nothing, your variable cost is zero. As soon as you start to produce, you incur a variable cost.

Total Fixed Cost

Fixed costs are costs that must be paid regardless of whether you are producing anything or not. Continuing with the furniture operation, examples of fixed costs would be the rent on your shop, insurance, tools, and any other costs you must incur whether you produce a piece of furniture or not.

Total Cost

Total cost refers to all costs, variable and fixed. Therefore, if you want to find total cost you must add variable and fixed costs together.

Total Revenue

Total revenue is the total amount of money brought in by the operation of a business. Often it is found by multiplying price per unit (sometimes called revenue per unit or average revenue) by the number of units sold.

It is important to understand that when variable and fixed costs are considered there are two ways they can be viewed: in total or so much per unit. In the furniture example, if the furniture shop produces 100 fine oak tables, there is a total variable cost for 100 tables, but there is a variable cost per table. That is, a variable cost per unit produced. As for fixed cost per unit, we tend to think about dividing the total fixed cost over all the units produced, which would give us a fixed cost per unit. That is, divide the fixed cost by the number of furniture units produced.

The most difficult part of using algebra to solve a break-even problem is translating the information into an algebraic statement. Example 3.33 demonstrates how the information in a business situation can be translated into an algebraic problem and then, using the rules of algebra, produce the desired information.

EXAMPLE 3.33

Nancy and Sharon are planning to open a small furniture shop where they will make fine oak reproductions of turn-of-the-century chairs and tables. After working out all their expected costs, they have estimated that a chair will take 4 board feet of oak that costs $10 per board foot, plus another $25 for finishing materials, including varnish, sand paper, and miscellaneous items. The labour time per chair is estimated to be 9 hours for construction and finishing work. Nancy and Sharon plan to pay themselves $25 per hour for their time.

Tables are expected to take 30 board feet of oak. The finishing materials are estimated at $75 per table and the construction time is expected to take 30 labour hours. Each table is sold with four chairs.

The fixed costs for the operation are rent for a work shop at $28,000 per year, which includes utilities. Other required costs are insurance at $2,500 per year and the purchase of $3,000 worth of tools.

Nancy and Sharon plan to sell their table and chairs at the same price other firms in the business charge: $3,500 for a table and four chairs. What is the number of chairs and table sets that must be sold to break even?

Solution The reading of the problem is the difficult part of the question. First let's define the costs:

Variable Costs

	Chairs:		Variable cost per chair.
Oak cost per chair:		$40	$10 per board foot times 4 board feet per chair (4 × $10 = $40).
Material cost per chair:		$25	Given in the problem.
Labour cost per chair:		$225	$25 per hour times 9 hours per chair (9 × $25 = $225).
Variable cost per chair:		$290	The sum of the above, i.e., $40 + $25 + $225.
	Tables:		Variable cost per table.
Oak cost per table:		$300	$10 per board foot times 30 board feet per table (30 × $10 = $300).
Material cost per table:		$75	Given in the problem.

Labour cost per table:	$750	$25 per hour times 30 hours per table (30 × $25 = $750).
Variable cost per table:	$1,125	The sum of the above, i.e., $300 + $75 + $750.

Bringing the variable costs for chairs and tables together, the variable cost of four chairs and one table (a set) will be:

4 chairs at $290 per chair:	$1,160
1 table at $1,150:	1,125
Variable Cost per set	**$2,285**

Fixed Costs

In the problem, the costs that are fixed are rent, equipment, and insurance. These costs will be the same whether any chairs and tables are made. That is, once the money is spent on the fixed costs these costs will not change with the number of chairs and tables produced. The fixed costs are:

1. Rent and utilities:	$28,000
2. Insurance:	2,500
3. Tools:	3,000
Total Fixed Costs	**$33,500**

Finding the Break-Even Point

If we let x stand for the number of units (1 table and 4 chairs), then the equation that will describe our total cost is:

Total Cost = Total Fixed Cost + Total Variable Costs

Total Cost = $33,500 + $2,285$x$ The term $2,285$x$ says that whatever number of sets they sell, this number when multiplied by $2,285 will tell us the total variable costs. For example, if two sets are sold, the total cost is $33,500 + $2,285(2), or $38,070.

Total Revenue:

The other side to this problem is the revenue from the sale of the table and chair sets. Since x stands for the number of units sold, and we know from the problem that the price is going to be $3,500 per set, then we know that the expression for total revenue will be $3,500$x$. Therefore, the revenue expression is stated as:

Total Revenue = $3,500$x$ For example, if only two sets are sold, the revenue is $3,500(2), or $7,000.

Bringing revenue and cost together, we know that at the break-even point, the firm is just covering their costs and making no profit. Thus, if we set the revenue equation equal to the cost equation, we can look for a value of x that makes the revenue and cost equations the same. Therefore:

The above expression is now a one-variable equation, just like the ones we solved earlier. To find the solution for x, we first subtract $2,285x from both sides of the equation:

$$\$3,500x - \$2,285x = \$33,500 + \$2,285x - \$2,285x$$
$$\$1,215x = \$33,500$$

$$\frac{\$1,215x}{\$1,215} = \frac{\$33,500}{\$1,215} \qquad \text{Dividing both sides of the equation by } \$1,215 \text{ to find } x.$$

$$x = 27.572 \qquad \text{This tells us that they must sell approximately 28 sets to break even. The reason the answer is rounded up to 28 is that at 27 units they would be just "short" of breaking even.}$$

Checking our solution: using the exact value of x we substitute 27.572 into our cost and revenue equation. If our break-even solution is correct, the revenue and the cost should be the same. Checking this by substitution gives:

Total Cost of 27.572 units:

$$\$33,500 + \$2,285\,(27.572) = \$96,502.02$$
$$\text{Total Cost} = \$96,502.02$$

Total Revenue at 27.572 units:

$$\$3,500(27.572) = \$96,502.00$$
$$\text{Total Revenue} = \$96,502.00$$

Note: The number of decimal places used for x was to reduce the size of the rounding error ($0.02 in this case). If the value $x = 28$ had been used there would have been a difference in the dollar value for cost and revenue.

EXAMPLE 3.34

The High Tech computer shop assembles and sells computers. After reviewing their accounting data, the following was determined:

Fixed costs: $100,000 per year
Variable costs: $1,450 per computer
Sales capacity per year: 1,000 computers
Selling price per computer: $2,450

(a) What is the break-even point?

(b) What number of computers would need to be sold to make a $25,000 profit? Profit refers to how much money is remaining from revenue after all costs (fixed and variable) have been covered.

(c) At what percent of capacity is the break-even point?

Solution   Let the number of computers sold be x. Then the expression that describes costs will be:

Total Costs = $100,000 + $1,450$x$

The revenue is calculated as:

Total Revenue = $2,450$x$

(a) The break-even point will be where costs and revenue are the same, or:

$$\$2,450x = \$100,000 + \$1,450x$$ Solving for x, first subtract $1,450$x$ from both sides of the expression.

$$\$2,450x - \$1,450x = \$100,000 + \$1,450x - \$1,450x$$

$$\$1,000x = \$100,000$$ Dividing each side by $1,000 gives:

$$\frac{\$1,000x}{\$1,000} = \frac{\$100,000}{\$1,000}$$

$$x = 100$$ This means High Tech must sell 100 computers to break even.

Checking, substitute $x = 100$ into our revenue and cost expressions to ensure that the solution is correct. This yields:

Total Costs: $100,000 + $1,450(100) = $245,000

Total Revenue: $2,450(100) = $245,000

Therefore, if High Tech sells 100 computers it will break even, just covering all costs.

(b) To find out how many computers High Tech would need to sell to make a profit of $25,000, simply take the expression for cost and add $25,000. This would now read:

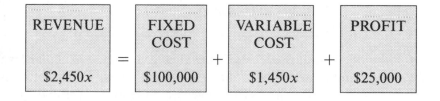

Isolating x, we subtract $1,450 from both sides of the expression and add the common terms:

$$\$2,450 - \$1,450 = \$125,000 + \$1,450 - \$1,450$$

$$\frac{\$1,000x}{\$1,000} = \frac{\$125,000}{\$1,000} \qquad \text{Dividing each side by } \$1,000 \text{ gives:}$$

$$x = 125$$

Therefore, if High Tech sells 125 computers it will cover all costs and make a profit of $25,000.

(c) Determining the percent of capacity at the break-even point:

Capacity = 1,000 computers per year
Break-even point = 100

Therefore, the break-even point is 10% of capacity. This was found as follows:

$$\frac{100}{1,000} = 0.1, \text{ or } 10\% \text{ of capacity.}$$

It is worth noting that the last two examples could be solved through other approaches. One such approach is to use the concept of **contribution**. Contribution refers to the difference between price and variable cost per unit. For example, if a company has a fixed cost of $10,000, a variable cost per unit of $6, and sells its product for $10, then the contribution would be $10 – $6 or $4 per unit.

The notion of contribution is that the price (revenue per unit) goes toward covering variable and fixed cost per unit. Thus, the amount left over, after the variable cost has been covered, contributes toward covering fixed cost. If one knows the contribution per unit, one can determine how much in total must be sold so that the total contribution covers total fixed costs. Moreover, contribution is also the source of profit. That is, once the total fixed costs are covered, the contribution per unit begins to add to profit. In our example, the break-even point using contribution would be:

$$\frac{\$10,000}{\$4/\text{unit}} = 2,500 \text{ units would need to be sold to break-even.}$$

From this we can say that the break-even point using the contribution approach is:

$$\boxed{\text{Break-even point (in units)} = \frac{\text{Total Fixed Costs}}{\text{Price/unit} - \text{Variable Cost/unit}}}$$

To find the level of output to generate a particular level of profit, one would simply add this profit to the fixed costs. Then, determine what level of sales (in units) is necessary to generate the profit, using the contribution approach. That is:

$$\frac{\text{Fixed Costs} + \text{Required profit}}{\text{Price/unit} - \text{variable cost/unit}} = \text{Required unit sales}$$

In our example, if the company was seeking a profit of $22,000, then the required level of sales (in units) would be:

$$\frac{\$10,000 + \$22,000}{\$10 - \$6} = 8,000 \text{ units}$$

Another procedure for solving break-even problems is to use a graphic approach. This will be shown in Chapter 4 after the concept of a graph has been explained.

GLOSSARY OF TERMS

Binomial   an expression with two terms.

Break-Even Point   the point at which a business's revenue is exactly the same as its costs. The break-even point is the output or service level necessary to make revenue and costs the same.

Coefficient   there are two types of coefficients: numerical and literal. Numerical coefficients are numbers in front of a variable, e.g., $4x$, 4 is a numerical coefficient and x is the literal coefficient.

Contribution   the difference between revenue and variable costs. Contribution per unit is found by subtracting variable cost per unit from the price per unit. Contribution goes toward covering the fixed cost and once these are covered contribution adds to profit.

Equation   a relation between variables and numbers that use an equality sign to express the relation.

Exponent   refers to the number of times a number or variable is multiplied by itself. The term power is also used to describe an exponent.

Expression   an expression defines a relationship between variables or numbers.

Factoring   the procedure of simplifying an expression by collecting like terms in the expression.

Fixed Costs   costs that do not change with the volume of output. Fixed costs are costs that are incurred even if no product is produced. Examples are taxes, insurance, and depreciation on equipment.

Monomial   an expression with only one term.

Polynomial   an expression with two or more terms.

Term   a term is one of the parts of an expression or equation. For example, in $3x + 5y = k$, $3x$ and $5y$ are terms.

Variable   a term or part of a term in an algebraic expression that may take on different values. A variable is normally represented by a letter.

Variable Costs   costs that change with the volume of output.

Additional Topics in Algebra

Algebra is used to help solve many business problems. For example, a manufacturing problem may require the solution of equations with more than one variable. On other occasions, a business may need to present information in a graphic form. Information is translated from an algebraic expression into the visual form of a graph. In finance we may need to determine precisely the value of money at different points in time, or, determine how long it will take for a sum of money to accumulate to a desired amount. These are all important applications of algebra to business problems. These examples are useful applications for the topics of this chapter.

4.1 Systems of Linear Equations

The term **system of linear equations** means working with two or more linear equations at the same time. The importance of a system of linear equations in business is that we occasionally need to express a series of statements (e.g., costs, revenue, production, etc.), each by an equation. In most circumstances, we not only have to express the equations, but also we want to find a value for each variable in the system that **simultaneously will satisfy all the equations**. An example of a system of equations with two equations and two variables would be:

$$3x + 7y = 15$$
$$4x + 15y = 10$$

These two equations are called independent simultaneous equations (or just independent equations). They are called independent because each equation is not another form of the other. To understand this point consider the following two equations:

$$2x + 5y = 10 \qquad ①$$
$$4x + 10y = 20 \qquad ②$$

If both sides of equation ① were multiplied by 2, equation ① would be:

$$2(2x) + 2(5y) = 2(10)$$

$$4x + 10y = 20$$

As can be seen, $4x + 10y = 20$ is the same as equation ②, above. When this happens we say the equations of the system are dependent equations. When this dependence occurs it is not possible to find a *unique* value for x and y that satisfies both equations simultaneously.

In Chapter 3, we found that when an equation had one variable, a unique solution for the variable could be found; that is, the value of x was equal to a specific number that satisfied the equation. However, a single linear equation with two variables has an unlimited number of possible solutions that can satisfy the equation. For example:

$$x + y = 8$$

This equation can be satisfied with $x = 0$, $y = 8$; $x = 1$, $y = 7$; $x = 2$, $y = 6$; as well as an infinite number of other combinations of values of x and y, which sum to 8. However, if we have two independent equations with x and y it may be possible to find unique values for x and y that satisfy the two equations simultaneously (assuming there is such a solution, since sometimes there are none). This is what we want to learn: how to solve a linear system of equations to find a specific value of x and a specific value of y that will satisfy the equation system.

In the previous chapter, break-even analysis had two equations: one for cost and one for revenue. In each of these equations, there was only one variable — the output x. The difference with linear systems is that we may have two or more equations, each of which will have at least one variable. If there are two equations, then there must be one independent variable per equation to find a solution (and sometimes there may be no solution). In general, the conditions that must be satisfied in a linear system of equations if we are to find a solution for the variables are: **the number of equations and the number of variables must be the same and that the equations are independent**.

In this book we will only deal with the solution for systems that have two equations. However, the methods we use for two equations can be extended to a linear system of equations with n equations and n variables.

There are three methods that can be used to solve systems of equations with two variables. The first is the method of elimination using the rules of subtraction and/or addition. The second method uses elimination by substitution. The third procedure, the graphic approach, will be discussed in a later section of this chapter, once the topic of graphs has been fully explained.

A. Solving of a Linear System of Equations Using Elimination Through Subtraction and/or Addition

The most direct way to solve a system of two linear independent equations is to eliminate one of the variables (unknowns), and solve the resulting equation for the remaining variable. The first method we will use to find a solution for the variables in the system of equations is **by eliminating a term** and applying addition or subtraction to the equations. Consider Example 4.1, which finds a simultaneous solution for a linear system of equations with 2 equations. Remember, the word **simultaneous solution** means finding a value for each variable that satisfies both equations at the same time.

EXAMPLE 4.1	Solution of a linear system of equations by elimination using the addition/subtraction method

Find the solution to the following system equations by using the addition/subtraction method of elimination.

$$4x + 3y = 8 \qquad ①$$
$$2x + 9y = 4 \qquad ②$$

Solution

STEP 1   First, we must be able to eliminate either the x or y variable. The most direct way is to select one variable, say y, and decide what numbers we would need to multiply each equation by to get the numerical coefficients for y to be the same in each equation. Looking at equation ①, we see that if $3y$ was multiplied by 3 we would get $9y$, which is the same as the y term in equation ②. We cannot simply multiply one term of an equation by another term without doing the same to the entire equation. Why? Because to maintain the equality, what is done to one side of an equation must be done to the other side. Thus, we must multiply both sides of equation ① by 3.

$$3(4x + 3y) = 3(8)$$
$$12x + 9y = 24$$

The system of equations now looks like:

$12x + 9y = 24$ ① — After multiplication by 3.

$2x + 9y = 4$ ②

STEP 2   Next eliminate the y term by subtracting one equation from the other. Subtracting equation ② from equation ① gives:

$$\begin{array}{r} 12x + 9y = 24 \\ -(2x + 9y = 4) \\ \hline 10x + 0y = 20 \\ 10x = 20 \end{array}$$

Subtracting equation ② from equation ①, to eliminate the y variable.

STEP 3   Find a solution for x by dividing each side by 10:

$$\frac{10x}{10} = \frac{20}{10}$$
$$x = 2$$

STEP 4   To find a value for y, substitute $x = 2$ into either of the equations. This yields a value of y that will satisfy both of the equations *when* $x = 2$. Substituting $x = 2$ for x in equation ② (we could have selected equation ①):

$$2x + 9y = 4$$
$$2(2) + 9y = 4$$
$$4 + 9y = 4$$
$$9y = 0$$
$$y = 0$$

Therefore, the values of x and y that simultaneously satisfy both equations are $x = 2$ and $y = 0$.

To check if the values of x and y satisfy both equations, substitute $x = 2$ and $y = 0$ into both equations:

$$4x + 3y = 8 \qquad ①$$
$$4(2) + 3(0) = 8$$
$$8 = 8$$

$$2x + 9y = 4 \qquad ②$$
$$2(2) + 9(0) = 4$$
$$4 = 4$$

As we can see, both equations are satisfied and thus the simultaneous solution for this system is $x = 2$ and $y = 0$.

In Example 4.1 we decided to multiply equation ① by 3, and subtract equation ② from equation ①. Another method, <u>which is equivalent</u>, is to multiply equation ① by –3 and then add the two equations. This alternate method would also permit us to eliminate the y term.

B. Solving of a Linear System of Equations Using Elimination Through Substitution

The second method that will eliminate one of the terms in a system of linear equations is called the **substitution method**. This method requires us to substitute one equation for one of the variables of the other equation. The key to this method is that we must find a solution for either x or y in one equation and then use this solution in the other equation. You should study Example 4.2 carefully before proceeding.

EXAMPLE 4.2   Solution of a linear system of equations using the substitution method

Find a value of z and c that satisfies the following two equations simultaneously.

$$5z - 3c = 3 \qquad ①$$
$$z + 4c = 4 \qquad ②$$

Solution

STEP 1   Select the equation that can most readily be solved in terms of one of the variables. Equation ② can be directly solved for z by subtracting $4c$ from each side of the equation, which would give:

$$z + 4c - 4c = 4 - 4c \qquad ②$$
$$z = 4 - 4c$$

STEP 2   Substitute equation ②'s solution for z into z in equation ①:

$$5z - 3c = 3 \qquad ①$$

$$5(4 - 4c) - 3c = 3 \qquad \text{Substitute } z = 4 - 4c.$$

$$20 - 20c - 3c = 3$$

$$20 - 23c = 3 \qquad \text{Subtract 20 from both sides of the equation.}$$

$$-23c = -17 \qquad \text{Divide each side by } -23 \text{ to find } c.$$

$$c = \frac{17}{23}$$

$$c = 0.73913$$

STEP 3   Substitute $c = 0.73913$ into one of the equations and solve for z. Using equation ② we have:

$$z + 4c = 4 \qquad ②$$

$$z + 4(0.73913) = 4 \qquad \text{Substituting } c = 0.73913.$$

$$z = 4 - 4(0.73913) \quad \text{Solving for } z.$$

$$z = 1.04348$$

Therefore, the simultaneous solution for the system is $z = 1.04348$ and $c = 0.73913$.

Checking this, we substitute the values for z and c into our original equations and get:

Substituting $z = 1.04348$ and $c = 0.73913$.

$$5z - 3c = 3 \qquad ①$$

$$5(1.04348) - 3(0.73913) = 3$$

$$5.21740 - 2.21739 = 3$$

$$3.00001 = 3 \qquad \text{(It's close enough!)}$$

$$3 = 3$$

$$z + 4c = 4 \qquad ②$$

$$1(1.04348) + 4(0.73913) = 4$$

$$1.04348 + 2.95652 = 4$$

$$4 = 4$$

A business example that requires the solution of simultaneous equations is shown in Example 4.3. As with our earlier problems, the most difficult part of the problem is translating the information into an equation form to solve for the variables.

EXAMPLE 4.3

A small computer company has two types of computers (Computer A and Computer B), each performing a very specific operation. In checking its accounting records, the company finds that it has sold $27,500 worth of computer time, which amounts to 150 hours. The computer company charges $200 per hour for Computer A and $150 per hour for Computer B. How many hours of computer time has been sold for each computer?

Solution   Let the variables be A and B, where A stands for the number of hours sold on Computer A, and B the number of hours sold on Computer B. In the problem, we have two pieces of information. First, we know that between the two computers 150 hours of time has been sold. This can be expressed as:

$$A + B = 150 \qquad ①$$

Second, and on the revenue side, we know that each hour on Computer A generates $200 in revenue, while each hour on Computer B produces $150 in revenue. We also know that the total time sold for Computers A and B is worth $27,500. This can be expressed by the following relationship:

$$\$200A + \$150B = \$27,500 \qquad ②$$

From the above, we can formulate the system of equations:

$$A + B = 150 \qquad ①$$

$$\$200A + \$150B = \$27,500 \qquad ②$$

Remember, A and B represent the number of hours sold on each computer.

Using the method of substitution, solve for A in equation ①, and substitute this expression for A in equation ②.

$$A + B = 150 \qquad ①$$

$$A = 150 - B \qquad \text{Solved for } A.$$

Substituting $A = 150 - B$ into equation ② gives:

$$\$200A + \$150B = \$27,500 \qquad ②$$

$$\$200(150 - B) + \$150B = \$27,500 \qquad \text{Substituting for } A.$$

$$\$30,000 - \$200B + \$150B = \$27,500$$

$$-\$50B = -\$2,500 \qquad \text{Divide both sides by } -\$50.$$

$$B = 50$$

To find a value for the number of hours for Computer A, substitute $B = 50$ into either equation and solve for A. Use equation ① since it is easier to solve for A when $B = 50$. This gives:

$$A + B = 150 \qquad ①$$
$$A + 50 = 150 \qquad \text{Substituting } B = 50$$
$$A = 100$$

Therefore, the number of hours sold on each computer that produces exactly $27,500 and uses 150 hours of computer time is 100 hours on Computer A and 50 hours on Computer B.

Checking:
$$A + B = 150 \qquad ①$$
$$100 + 50 = 150 \qquad \text{It checks.}$$

$$\$200A + \$150B = \$27,500 \qquad ②$$
$$\$200(100) + \$150(50) = \$27,500 \qquad \text{It also checks.}$$

4.2 Constructing Graphs of Algebraic Equations

Graphic analysis is very common in business. If you pick up a copy of a business newspaper you will find graphs used throughout the paper. Some examples are graphs of stock prices, graphs of interest rates over time, or graphs of the value of the Canadian dollar with respect to the U.S. dollar. Another common use of graphs is in economics, where they are used to portray supply and demand equations. One reason graphs are used so frequently is because they portray information in a visual form that is easy to read and understand. However, behind most graphs are equations and, therefore, we must understand how to translate equations to a graphical form.

A. Terminology of Graphs

Graphs are constructed on a system that is called the **Rectangular Coordinate System**. This system uses the principle of referencing everything to two perpendicular lines that intersect at right angles. Two such lines are shown in Figure 4.1. The vertical line, the y line, is called the **y-axis**. The horizontal line, the x line, is called the **x-axis**. The point where the two lines intersect is called the **origin** and is the reference point for both the y- and x-axis.

The numbers on each axis in Figure 4.1 represent a position relative to the origin, point 0. By convention, the numbers on the x-axis and to the right of the origin, 0, are positive numbers, and numbers to the left of the origin on the x-axis are negative. Similarly, for the vertical scale, numbers above the origin are positive and numbers below the origin are negative. The key element to the axes is that it is possible to find the precise location of any point by using the number scale on each axis. The values for a point on each of the axes are called the **coordinates of the point**.

Figure 4.1

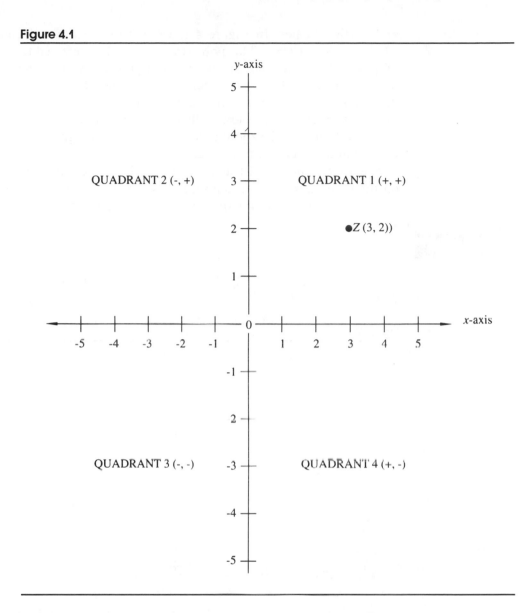

A rectangular coordinate system has four **quadrants**, each numbered in a counterclockwise manner. Quadrant 1 (see Figure 4.1) is the region where values of x and y will be 0 or positive. Coordinates that have negative values of x and y have very limited use in business. In most business and economic problems Quadrant 1 is the portion of the coordinate system that is used.

Graphs include units of measurement on the axis. In business, the unit of measurement on the vertical and horizontal axes will depend upon the problem being considered. A common unit on the vertical axis is dollars. The horizontal scale has a variety of possible units. The most common measurements are quantity (produced, demanded, or supplied) and time. The choice of the units for each axis will depend upon the variables being analyzed.

B. Location of a Point

To describe the location of point Z (see Figure 4.1) relative to the x- and y-axis, we would define the position of Z by using the units of the horizontal and vertical scales. In Figure 4.1, we can see that Z is located at the point where $x = 3$ and $y = 2$. This point, ($x = 3$, $y = 2$), is referred to as the coordinates of point Z. By convention, when specifying each coordinate, the first value in the brackets refers to the location of the point on the x-axis and is called the x coordinate. The second value in the brackets refers to the location of the point on the y-axis and is called the y coordinate.

The notation for the coordinates of a point, (x, y), gives us the precise location of the point — relative to each axis.

The first step in constructing a graph is to identify the position of points on the coordinate system; the second step is to plot these points on the graph. Study how the positioning of coordinates is done in Example 4.4:

EXAMPLE 4.4

On the following graph, find the coordinates (ordered pairs) of the points A, B, C, D, E, and F.

Figure 4.2

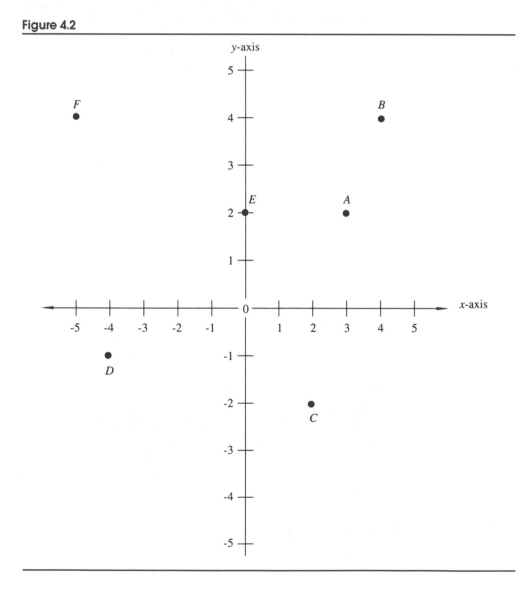

Solution

	Coordinates
Point *A*	(3,2)
Point *B*	(4,4)
Point *C*	(2,–2)
Point *D*	(–4,–1)
Point *E*	(0,2)
Point *F*	(–5,4)

If we draw a straight line — at right angles to each axis — to a specific point you will note that a rectangular box is formed. This is true for any two lines drawn at right angles to each axis and intersecting at a specific point. If you can imagine drawing many vertical lines through each value of x on the x-axis and many horizontal lines through each value of y on the y-axis, you will see a series of little boxes develop. Consider Figure 4.3 and observe the boxes that develop at the points A (3,3), B(–4,2), C(2,1), and D(4,–4) when the points are connected with perpendicular lines from each axis. These little boxes are the basis for the name <u>rectangular</u> coordinate system.

Figure 4.3

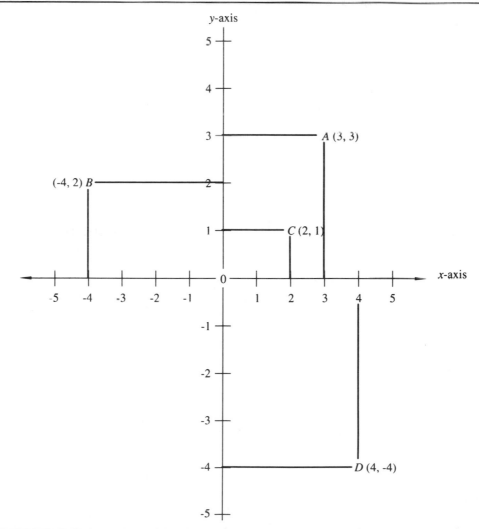

C. Graphs of a Linear Equation

A linear equation when plotted on a graph will be a straight line — the term linear means just that, a straight line. To graph a linear equation, just identify sets of coordinates that satisfy the equation, locate these on the graph, and then join the coordinates with a line. To understand this approach study Example 4.5, which requires you to plot a series of coordinates and connect them with a line.

EXAMPLE 4.5

Plot the following coordinates on the graph.

$$A\,(5, 5)\ [\text{i.e.,}\ (x = 5,\ y = 5)]$$
$$B\,(1, 1)$$
$$C\,(4, 4)$$

Solution

Figure 4.4

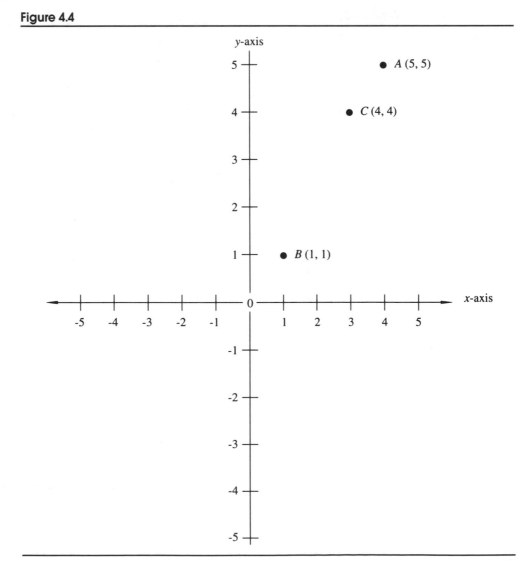

Although drawing a line graph requires one to identify only two points, it is recommended that a third point be identified to ensure that the points do form a straight line. For example, if we were drawing the graph of the equation $y = 3 + 5x$, it would be necessary to find a set of coordinates, which could then be joined by a line. Since any point on a straight line will have coordinates that satisfy the linear equation, we need to plot at least three points to construct the graph of a straight line. To demonstrate this principle, consider Example 4.6. In this example, we will determine a set of coordinates that satisfy the equation and then place these coordinates on the graph. What is evident is that the points can be connected with a continuous line.

EXAMPLE 4.6

Find four sets of coordinates for the linear equation:

$$y = 1 + 2x$$

Locate these coordinates on the graph and then join them with a continuous line.

Figure 4.5

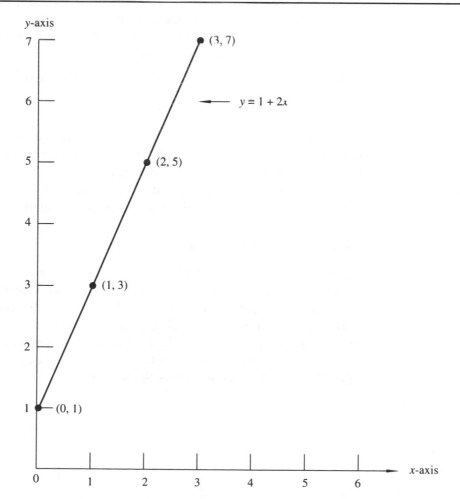

Solution The most direct way to find four sets of coordinates is to assign values to x and determine the corresponding values for y. The values that were selected for x (0, 1, 2, 3) were chosen only because they were convenient to use. Other values could have been selected.

x values	y values for each x $y = 1 + 2x$	Coordinates (x, y)
0	$y = 1 + 2(0) = 1$	(0, 1)
1	$y = 1 + 2(1) = 3$	(1, 3)
2	$y = 1 + 2(2) = 5$	(2, 5)
3	$y = 1 + 2(3) = 7$	(3, 7)

Plotting the points on the graph in Quadrant 1, the upper right hand portion of our rectangular coordinate system, we have:

From Example 4.6 we can summarize the steps to plotting a linear equation (a straight line). These steps are:

1. Construct a table of coordinates by substituting values of x and determining the corresponding values of y. (*Note:* one could have an equation like $x = 3y + 2$. Here you would substitute y values and determine the x values to find the coordinates.)

2. Plot the coordinates from the table on the graph.

3. Join the coordinates with a straight line.

It is worth noting that the plotting of a linear equation requires only three coordinates. This is most helpful since it reduces the need to compute many coordinates. You should choose two coordinates that are sufficiently far apart so that the line drawn will accurately represent the equation. The third coordinate is often found just to check the accuracy of the line.

D. Intercepts and Linear Equations

One approach to selecting two coordinates is to select the two coordinates where the line crosses the x- and y-axis. **A point where the line crosses an axis is called an intercept.** Where the line crosses the y-axis is called the y-intercept; it is found by replacing x in the equation with 0 and determining the corresponding value of y. To determine the x-intercept we find the value of x when y is replaced by 0, i.e., set $y = 0$. Example 4.7 shows how one might plot a linear equation using the intercepts:

EXAMPLE 4.7

Graph the following equations using the *x*- and *y*-intercepts as the coordinates.

(a) $x - y = 3$
(b) $2x + y = 6$

Solution (a) First we find the *x*- and *y*-intercepts.

For $x - y = 3$

when $y = 0$ $x = 3$

and

when $x = 0$ $y = -3$

Therefore, the two coordinates for the *x*- and *y*-intercepts are:

x-intercept   (3, 0)
y-intercept   (0, –3)

Figure 4.6

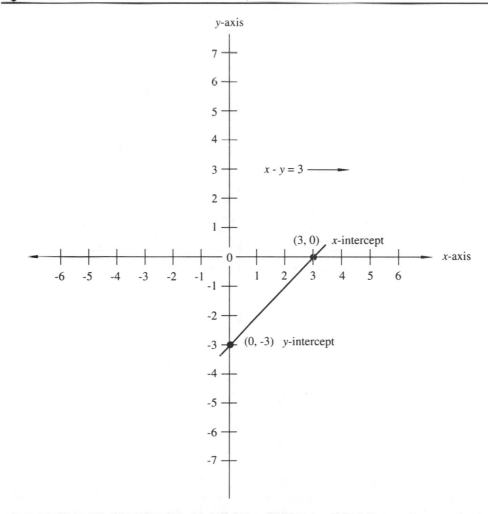

(b) Using the same approach as in (a), we find the *x*- and *y*-intercepts. These are:

For $2x + y = 6$

      when $y = 0$ $x = 3$

   and

      when $x = 0$ $y = 6$

Therefore the intercepts are:

     x-intercept   (3, 0)

     y-intercept   (0, 6)

Plotting the intercept coordinates and drawing the line gives:

Figure 4.7

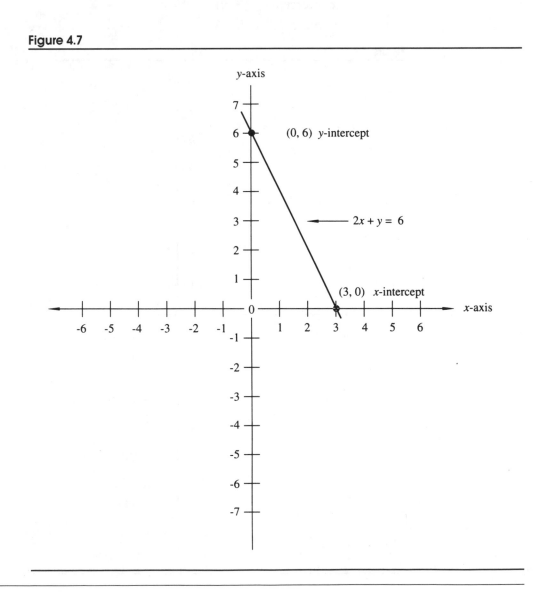

E. Slope of a Linear Equation

In the graph of a line, the steepness, or the angle of inclination of the line relative to the *x*-axis, is referred to as the **slope**. What the slope tells us is how a change in *x* will change y. For example, for the linear equation:

$$y = 4 + 5x$$

it can be seen that as *x* changes, *y* changes by 5 times the change in *x*. In this equation, the coefficient of *x*, namely 5, tells us that if *x* changes by 1, then *y* will change by $5x$. This coefficient, 5, is called the slope of the line. Consider the value of *y* if *x* = 1 and if *x* = 2. This would give:

x = 1:	y = 4 + 5(1) = 9	The difference
x = 2:	y = 4 + 5(2) = 14	or change in y is 5.

In the above equation, we can see that for the one unit change in *x*, from 1 to 2, *y* changes by 5. This change in *y* for each unit change in *x* is what the slope measures.

The slope describes the exact nature of the relationship between the *y* variable and the *x* variable. In mathematics, the term **dependent variable** is often used to describe the *y* variable, since its value depends upon the *x* variable. The *x* variable is called the **independent variable**. For the equation:

$$y = 4 + 5x$$

it can be seen that *y* depends upon the value assigned to *x*, since both 4 and 5 are constants, that is, 4 and 5 remain fixed regardless of the value of *x*.

Another valuable piece of information from the equation $y = 4 + 5x$, is that the *y*-intercept is 4. This follows from our knowledge that the *y*-intercept is the value of *y* when *x* = 0. In this equation we see that when *x* = 0, *y* = 4, which is the *y*-intercept. In mathematics, there is a general equation for a straight line, called the **slope-intercept form,** which is written as:

$$y = b + mx$$

⟵ Slope-Intercept Form

In the slope-intercept form, *b* represents the *y*-intercept and *m* is the slope of the line.

An application of the slope-intercept form in business would be the total cost equation, where *y* stands for total cost and *x* represents the number of units produced. From our examples in Chapter 3, you will recall that total costs were described by the relation:

$$\text{Total Cost} = \text{Total Fixed Cost} + \text{Total Variable Cost}$$

If the cost equation was:

$$y = \$5,000 + \$10x$$

it is possible to give a business interpretation to values $5,000 and $10. The $5,000 does not change with *x*; if *x* = 0, the point of no output, then the total costs, *y*, are $5,000. This value would be the fixed costs. As output is increased by one unit, the total cost, *y*, goes up by $10. Thus $10, the slope of the line, would be the variable cost per unit.

The importance of knowing the slope is that it gives us an idea of the direction of the line. If a line has a positive slope — a positive coefficient for x — then the line is said to slope upward to the right. If the slope is negative — a negative coefficient for x — then we know the line slopes downward to the right. To show both cases consider the equations:

$y = 3 + 2x$ The slope is $+2$ and thus the line slopes upward to the right.

$y = 4 - 4x$ The slope is -4 and thus the line slopes downward to the right.

The graph of these two equations is shown in Figure 4.8.

Figure 4.8

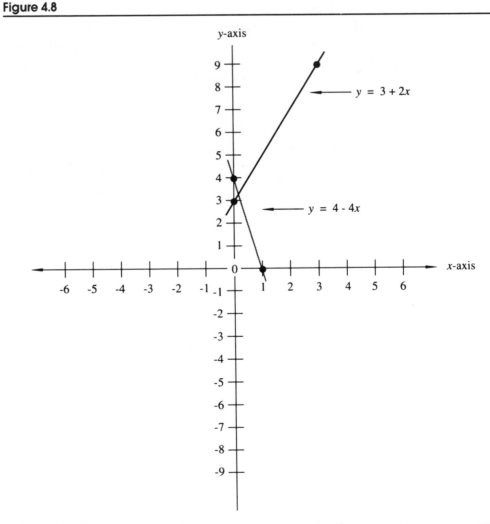

To see the importance of the slope-intercept form in understanding the relation between x and y, study Example 4.8:

EXAMPLE 4.8

Express $3y + x = 12$ in the slope-intercept form and find the value of the slope and the intercept. What direction does the line slope?

Solution

$$3y + x = 12$$ Rearrange the equation to isolate y on the left side.

$$3y = 12 - x$$ Divide each side by 3.

$$y = \frac{12}{3} - \frac{x}{3}$$

$$y = 4 - \frac{1}{3}x$$

Since we know from the slope-intercept form,

$$y = b + mx,$$ where b is the intercept and m is the slope, for our example we can say:

$$b = 4, \text{ and } m = -\frac{1}{3}$$

Thus, the point where the line crosses the y-axis is 4, and the line slopes downward to the right with a slope of $-\frac{1}{3}$.

F. Finding the Slope

The slope of a line, m, can be found by measuring the change in y relative to a change in x. We can find m by constructing a ratio of the relative change in y for a given change in x as:

$$m = \frac{\text{Change in } y}{\text{Change in } x}$$

To compute the slope using the relation for m requires us to measure the changes in y and x using two coordinates. Let the first coordinate be (x_1, y_1). The 1 for x and y is a way of defining the first value of x and y — it is called a subscript. The second coordinate will be defined by using the subscript 2; thus the second coordinate would be (x_2, y_2).

To understand how we interpret these two coordinates with their respective subscripts, think about each as:

$$\text{when } x = x_1, y = y_1, \text{ and}$$
$$\text{when } x = x_2, y = y_2.$$

Therefore, by measuring the relative change in y, from y_1 to y_2, as a result of changing x from x_1 to x_2, a ratio of the changes would be constructed. This ratio would be:

$$m = \frac{\text{Change in } y}{\text{Change in } x} = \frac{y_2 - y_1}{x_2 - x_1} \qquad \textbf{Formula 4.1}$$

Thus, if you know two coordinates of a line, then the slope of the line can be found by comparing the coordinates in the slope formula. In terms of a business example, consider Example 4.9:

EXAMPLE 4.9

An accountant of a small manufacturing company is checking the production and cost records. She discovers that when production was at 1,000 units, total cost was $6,000. She also found that when production was 1,500 units, the total cost was $7,500. If she knows that total cost and production are related in a linear manner, using y for total cost and x for the number of units, help her do the following:

(a) Find the slope of the total cost equation.
(b) Using the slope-intercept form, find the total cost equation from the information provided.
(c) Interpret the business meaning of the slope and intercept for this problem.

Solution (a) The information in the problem gives two coordinates, (1,000, $6,000) and (1,500, $7,500). In addition, we are told to let y represent total cost and x the number of units. Defining the coordinates in terms of x and y for Formula 4.1 gives:

$x_1 = 1,000, y_1 = \$6,000$ and
$x_2 = 1,500, y_2 = \$7,500$

Substituting these coordinates into Formula 4.1 gives:

$$\frac{y_2 - y_1}{x_2 - x_1} = \frac{\$7,500 - \$6,000}{1,500 - 1,000}$$

$$\frac{y_2 - y_1}{x_2 - x_1} = \frac{\$1,500}{500}$$

$$\frac{y_2 - y_1}{x_2 - x_1} = \$3$$

$$m = \$3$$

Therefore, $3 is the slope of the line.

(b) To find the cost equation we turn to the slope-intercept form, $y = b + mx$. Since we know $m = \$3$, we can solve for b by substituting values for x and y, from either one of the coordinates given. That is, we can substitute a pair of values for x and y that satisfies the equation. Therefore:

$$y = b + mx \qquad \text{Substituting } m = \$3$$

$$y = b + \$3x \qquad \text{Select one of the given coordinates,}$$
say (1,000, $6,000). Substitute
(1,000, $6,000) for x and y.

$$\$6,000 = b + \$3(1,000)$$
$$\$6,000 - \$3,000 = b$$
$$\$3,000 = b \qquad \text{Rearrange.}$$
$$b = \$3,000$$

Now we substitute $m = 3$ and $b = \$3,000$ into the slope-intercept form:

$$y = b + mx \qquad \text{Substitute } m = \$3 \text{ and } b = \$3,000.$$
$$y = \$3,000 + \$3x$$

This is the total cost equation and tells us that for every unit produced the cost goes up by $3. In addition, it tells us that if output is zero, cost will be $3,000. *Note*: the coordinate for y_2 and x_2 ($7,500, 1,500) could have been used to determine b.

(c) The interpretation is that for every unit of output costs rise by $3. Thus, we would say that, in this example, $3 must be the variable cost per unit. Since the term $3,000 remains constant for all values of x, then this must be the fixed cost portion of total costs.

A check of the solution for the equation could be found by substituting values for x and determining whether the values for y are as expected.

G. The Slope of Horizontal and Vertical Lines

The slope of horizontal and vertical lines are special cases. First, let's consider a horizontal line.

When one places a horizontal line on a graph it means that y is constant for all values of x. That is, no matter what the value of x, the value of y remains constant. In terms of the slope-intercept form of the line, $y = b + mx$, this would mean that $m = 0$, since x values have no influence on y. If $m = 0$, then,

$$y = b$$

In terms of the slope-intercept form, the expression would be:

$$y = b + 0x$$
$$y = b$$

Example 4.10 shows the situation where the slope is zero:

EXAMPLE 4.10

Graph the equation $y = 5$, and find the values of the slope and y-intercept.

Solution Using our slope-intercept equation $y = b + mx$, it can be seen that:

$$y = 5 + 0x$$
$$y = 5$$

In terms of the slope formula, the change in y is 0 for any change in x, or:

$$\frac{\text{Change in } y}{\text{Change in } x} = \frac{0}{\text{Change in } x}$$

$$= 0$$

Thus, b must be 5 and $m = 0$.

The graph of the equation $y = 5$ is:

Figure 4.9

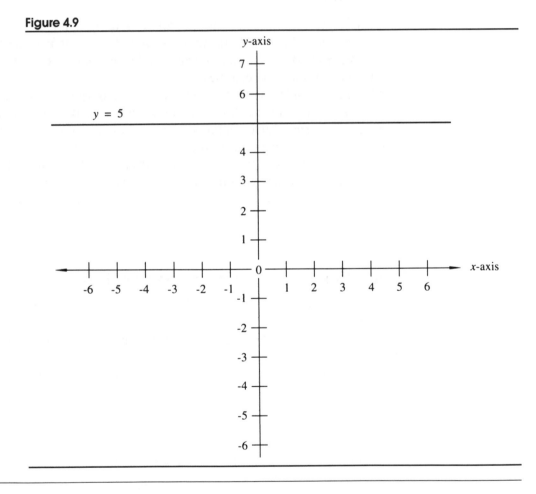

It is important to remember that the slope of a horizontal line is zero. This tells us that there is no change in y as a result of a change in x. In terms of a business example, if you were to plot fixed costs on a graph, where the horizontal scale was units of output and the vertical scale was dollars, then the fixed cost line would be horizontal, telling us that fixed costs are constant for all levels of output, x.

A vertical line is another special case and is more difficult to comprehend. What a vertical line implies is that the value of x remains constant for all values of y. In terms of the slope-intercept form of the linear equation, the value of b will be zero, since the line never intersects the y axis. In fact, x is constant for all values of y — that's right, all values. In terms of the slope formula, because x is constant for all values of y, this means that the change in x is zero. This would give:

$$\frac{\text{Change in } y}{\text{Change in } x} = \frac{y_2 - y_1}{x_2 - x_1}$$

$$= \frac{y_2 - y_1}{0}$$

$$= \text{Undefined}$$

The problem is that division by zero is undefined, and thus the slope of a vertical line is undefined. The best way to think about a vertical line is to refer to it as the steepest slope of all lines.

4.3 Graphic Solution to a Linear System of Equations

In our discussion of linear systems of equations, it was stressed that our objective was to find values for x and y that simultaneously satisfied a system of two linear equations. Another way of looking at a simultaneous solution is to think of the rectangular coordinate system, and look for a coordinate that is common to both equations. This coordinate can be found by plotting the two equations on a graph. At the point where the lines of the equations intersect will be a coordinate where the value of x and y is the same for both equations. This common coordinate is the simultaneous solution to the system of equations. Consider Example 4.11:

EXAMPLE 4.11

Find the simultaneous solution to the following equation system using a graphic approach.

$$2x + y = 100 \quad ①$$
$$x - 2y = -50 \quad ②$$

Solution

STEP 1 Find the intercepts for each equation:

Intercepts for equation ①:

Setting $x = 0$,
$$2x + y = 100 \quad ①$$
$$2(0) + y = 100$$
$$y = 100$$

Setting $y = 0$,
$$2x + y = 100$$
$$2x + (0) = 100$$
$$x = 50$$

Thus, for equation ① we have (0, 100) and (50, 0) as the y- and x-intercept coordinates.

Finding the intercepts for equation ②:

Setting $x = 0$,
$$x - 2y = -50 \quad ②$$
$$(0) - 2y = -50$$
$$y = 25$$

Setting $y = 0$,
$$x - 2y = -50 \quad ②$$
$$x - 2(0) = -50$$
$$x = -50$$

For equation ② we have (0, 25) and (–50, 0) as the y- and x-intercept coordinates.

STEP 2   Plotting these points on our graph and drawing the lines gives:

Figure 4.10

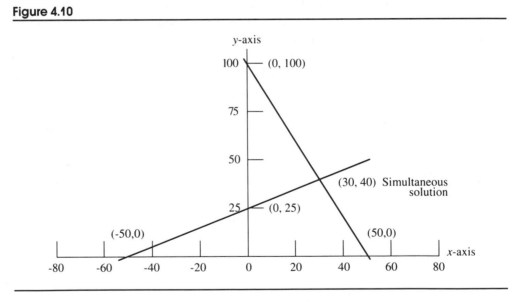

From the graph it is possible to determine that the lines of the two equations intersect at the point when $x = 30$ and $y = 40$.

To check the intersection, we can solve the two equations using the substitution approach. From equation ①, we solve for y:

$$2x + y = 100 \qquad ①$$
$$y = 100 - 2x \qquad ① \qquad \text{Solve for } y.$$

Substituting $y = 100 - 2x$ into equation ② gives:

$$x - 2y = -50 \qquad ②$$
$$x - 2(100 - 2x) = -50$$
$$x - 200 + 4x = -50$$
$$5x = 150$$
$$x = 30$$

To get y we substitute $x = 30$ into equation ①:

$$2(30) + y = 100$$
$$60 + y = 100$$
$$y = 40$$

Thus, we see that the graphic solution to the system of equations and the algebraic method give identical simultaneous solutions: $x = 30$ and $y = 40$.

4.4 Graphical Approach to Break-Even Analysis

The use of graphs in break-even analysis allows one to observe how costs and revenue change with changes in output. In general, the vertical axis (y-axis) is defined in terms of dollars, with costs or revenues placed on this axis. The volume of output, in units, is usually placed on the x-axis. To see how the axes are set up, consider the following example:

EXAMPLE 4.12

A company produces plastic coffee filters and has the following costs:

> Variable cost per unit: $0.50
> Total Fixed Costs: $6,000
> Selling price per filter: $4.50

What is the break-even point? Graph the total cost equation, the total revenue equation, the fixed cost equation, and show the break-even point on the graph.

Solution The most direct way to solve the problem is to define a cost and a revenue equation. Letting x represent output in units, and using the information from the problem in addition to the cost relationship:

$$\text{Total Costs} = \text{Total Fixed Costs} + \text{Total Variable Costs}$$

Substituting we get:

$$\text{Total Cost} = \$6{,}000 + \$0.50x$$
$$\text{Total Revenue} = \$4.5x$$
$$\text{Fixed Cost} = \$6{,}000$$

At the break-even point cost and revenue are equal, therefore:

Total Revenue = Total Fixed Cost + Total Variable Cost
$4.5x = $6,000 + $0.50x

$$\$4x = \$6,000$$
$$x = 1,500 \text{ units}$$

Therefore, the break-even point is at 1,500 units.

To show the revenue and cost equations on the graph, we first must find coordinates for each equation. Choosing easy-to-use values of x and y, we use $x = 1,000$ and $x = 2,000$ (*Note:* any other values could have been used). Now, find the value of y for the assumed x-values. The coordinates are listed below for each equation.

Find total cost for $x = 1,000$ and $x = 2,000$.

Total Cost $y = \$6,000 + \$0.50x$

	Coordinates
Substituting $x = 1,000$	
Total Cost = $6,000 + $0.50 (1,000)	
Total Cost = $6,500	(1,000, $6,500)
Substituting $x = 2,000$	
Total Cost = $6,000 + $0.50 (2,000)	
Total Cost = $7,000	(2,000, $7,000)
Find total revenue for $x = 1,000$ and $x = 2,000$.	
Total Revenue = $4.5x	
Substituting $x = 1,000$	
Total Revenue = $4.5 (1,000)	
Total Revenue = $4,500	(1,000, $4,500)
Substituting $x = 2,000$	
Total Revenue = $4.5 (2,000)	
Total Revenue = $9,000	(2,000, $9,000)

Total Fixed Cost = $6,000 constant for all x.

Plotting the cost and revenue equations gives Figure 4.11:

In Example 4.12, output larger than the break-even point allows the firm to make a profit. This profit can be measured by the vertical distance between the total cost and revenue equations, to the right of the break-even point; a loss would be the vertical distance to the left of the break-even point. Figure 4.12 shows the profit and loss areas.

Figure 4.11

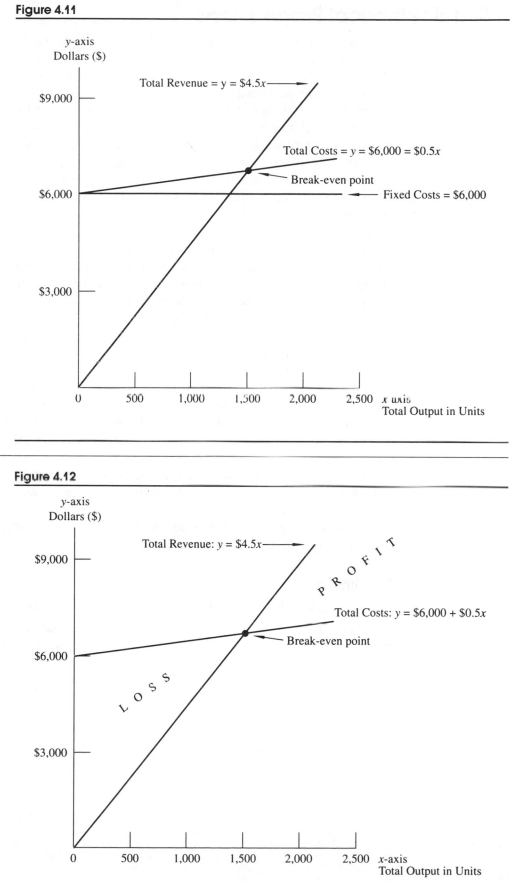

Figure 4.12

4.5 Mathematical Progressions

In later sections of this book, it will be necessary to find the sum of values of money over time. The formulas that we will be using will give us the sum of money over time, where this sum is based on the addition of a series of terms (different numbers).

The addition of these terms can be quickly determined by knowing the type of pattern that has been used to generate the numbers — that is, the mathematical relationship between each term. There are two common types of sequences used to generate numbers in a particular pattern. These two types of sequences are called arithmetic and geometric progressions. Each generate numbers in a precise order. However, the choice of which progression — arithmetic or geometric — will depend upon how the differences between successive values of the terms in the series are related.

Our objective in learning about arithmetic and geometric progressions (also called series) is to be able to find one or more terms of the sequence without having to work out all the terms in the sequence. The value of finding the terms of the sequence will be of great assistance when it is necessary to find the value of money at different points in time.

For example, if you have a loan and the loan is charged interest, you may want to determine how much you will owe in two years. If you do not make any payments toward the loan, then you would only be interested in finding the value of the original amount borrowed plus all the accumulated interest. The amount you would owe at the end of the loan is the sum of a sequence of numbers — the interest over time and the amount you borrowed. The most important part of this example is our need to find only the dollar value at the end of the two years. The exact amount you owe in six months would not be of particular importance if the loan is not to be repaid for two years.

To avoid having to work out all the intermediate terms or numbers in the series, we use the properties of a series to help us. One of these properties allows us to compute the value for any term in the sequence, without having to evaluate other terms in the sequence.

A. Arithmetic Progressions

(i) Finding the Value of the *n*th Term of an Arithmetic Progression

An arithmetic progression is a sequence of numbers that are in a definite order or pattern. Each number in the sequence is dependent upon the previous number in the sequence, in a precise manner. The manner in which the terms of the sequence are determined results from the **addition of a constant to the previous term in the series**. For example:

$$1, 5, 9, \_\_\_, \_\_\_, \_\_\_$$

What are the next three terms? As can be seen, the second and third terms, 5 and 9, result from adding 4 to the first term and 4 to the second term in the sequence. Each new term is the result of adding 4 to the preceding term of the sequence. Thus the blanks for the next three terms should be 13, 17, and 21. For each term, we see there is a **common difference of 4. The common difference can be found by subtracting the first term from the second term**.

EXAMPLE 4.13

Find the common difference and the missing terms in the following sequences.

(a) 3, 5, 7, ___, ___, ___, ___
(b) –3, 0, 3, ___, ___, ___, ___
(c) –4, –2, 0, ___, ___, ___, ___
(d) 7, 15, 23, ___, ___, ___, ___

Solution (a) 3, 5, 7, ___, ___, ___, ___

First we find the common difference:

5 – 3 = 2, and 7 – 5 = 2. Therefore, the missing terms must be:

9 (7 + 2), 11 (9 + 2), 13 (11 + 2), and 15 (13 + 2)

or

3, 5, 7, _9_, _11_, _13_, _15_

(b) –3, 0, 3, ___, ___, ___, ___

Find the common difference by subtracting the terms 0 – (–3) = 3, and 3 – 0 = 3. Therefore, adding this common difference to the last term in the sequence gives us:

–3, 0, 3, _6_, _9_, _12_, _15_

(c) –4, –2, 0, ___, ___, ___, ___

Finding the common difference we have:

–2 – (–4) = 2. Thus, the remaining terms must be:

–4, –2, 0, _2_, _4_, _6_, _8_

(d) 7, 15, 23, ___, ___, ___, ___

The common difference is 15 – 7 = 8. Thus, the missing terms are:

7, 15, 23, _31_, _39_, _47_, _55_

What we must do is find an expression for an arithmetic progression so that we can find the *n*th term of the sequence, without having to work out all the terms of the sequence. For example, in part (a) above, how could we determine the 100th term of the sequence? To be able to do this directly, without having to find each term of the sequence, requires us to find a formula that will permit us to find the term directly. To derive a formula we must define the terms of an arithmetic progression using letters, then we will assign numbers to the letters when we know which term of the progression we are seeking. The definitions we require are:

a— the value of the first term in the sequence;

d— the common difference between each term of the sequence;

n— the number of terms in the sequence;

t_n— the *n*th term in the sequence;

S_n— S is the sum of the terms in the sequence, and in the general case, the sum of *n* terms.

Now using the symbols we have defined it is possible to say:

$t_1 = a$ = first term of the sequence;

$t_2 = a + d$ = the second term in the sequence;

$t_3 = a + 2d$ = the third term in the sequence, which is simply $a + d + d$;

$t_4 = a + 3d$ = the fourth term in the sequence and is found by adding $a + d + d + d$.

The thing to note is that the coefficient for *d* is always one less than the term being found. Therefore, $a + 3d$ would be the fourth term of an arithmetic sequence. Suppose the first term in the sequence was 100 ($a = 100$) and the difference between each term was 50 ($d = 50$), then the fourth term in the sequence would be $100 + 3(50)$, or 250. From this, we can say that the value of the *n*th term in the sequence is:

$$t_n = a + (n - 1)d \qquad \text{Formula 4.2}$$

To see how this expression works, consider Example 4.14, which uses the examples worked out in Example 4.13:

EXAMPLE 4.14

Find the last term (the last blank) for the four sequences in Example 4.14, by using Formula 4.2:

$t_n = a + (n - 1)d$

Solution (a) From Example 4.13, (a): 3, 5, 7, ___, ___, ___, ___

$a = 3$ The first term in the sequence.

$d = 2$ The common difference.

$n = 7$ The last blank is the 7th term in the sequence.

Substituting all the numbers for the letters in the expression for t_n, the 7th term of the sequence is:

$t_n = a + (n - 1)d$

$t_7 = 3 + (7 - 1)2$

$t_7 = 15$ The same as we found in Example 4.13 (a).

(b) From Example 4.13, (b): –3, 0, 3, ___, ___, ___, ___

$a = -3$ The first term in the sequence.

$d = 3$ The common difference.

$n = 7$ The last blank is the 7th term in the sequence.

Substituting all the numbers for the letters in the expression for t_n, the 7th term of the sequence is:

$t_n = a + (n - 1)d$

$t_7 = -3 + (7 - 1)3$

$t_7 = 15$ The same as we found in Example 4.13 (b).

(c) From Example 4.13, (c): –4, –2, 0, ___, ___, ___, ___

$a = -4$ The first term in the sequence.

$d = 2$ The common difference.

$n = 7$ The last blank is the 7th term in the sequence.

Substituting numbers for the letters in the expression for t_n, the 7th term of the sequence is:

$t_n = a + (n - 1)d$

$t_7 = -4 + (7 - 1)2$

$t_7 = 8$ The same as we found in Example 4.13 (c).

(d) From Example 4.13 (d): 7, 15, 23, ___, ___, ___, ___

$a = 7$ The first term in the sequence.

$d = 8$ The common difference.

$n = 7$ The last blank is the 7th term in the sequence.

Substituting the numbers for letters in the expression for t_n, yields:

$t_n = a + (n - 1)d$

$t_7 = 7 + (7 - 1)8$

$t_7 = 55$ The same as we found in Example 4.13 (d).

(ii) The Sum of an Arithmetic Progression

The most often used property of arithmetic progressions in business is finding the sum of a specific number of terms where each term represents a period of time.

To illustrate how to find the sum of an arithmetic progression, the following example is presented. Find the sum of the arithmetic series:

$$5, 7, 9, 11, 13$$

There are two ways we can find the sum. One way is:

$$45 = 5 + 7 + 9 + 11 + 13 \longleftarrow \text{Adding from the first term to the last term and;}$$

$$45 = 13 + 11 + 9 + 7 + 5 \longleftarrow \text{Adding from the last term to the first term.}$$

Now, if you add each term, that is, first term + last term, second term + second last term, etc., you see the sum of the two terms is constant at 18. That is,

$$
\begin{array}{llllll}
45 = & 5 + & 7 + 9 + 11 + 13 & & \text{Sum from first term to last term.} \\
45 = & \underline{13 + 11 + 9 + 7 + 5} & & & \text{Sum from last term to first term.} \\
90 & 18 & 18 \quad 18 \quad 18 \quad 18 & & \text{Sum of terms.}
\end{array}
$$

To find the sum of the series of these 5 numbers:

$$\frac{18 \times 5}{2} = \frac{90}{2}$$

We divide by 2 since the series has been added twice — once from each end of the series.

$$= 45$$

However, if you look closely you will see that the sum could have been found by doing the following:

$$\frac{[\text{first term} + \text{last term}][\text{number of terms}]}{2} = \frac{[5 + 13] \, 5}{2}$$

$$= 45$$

Finding an expression for the sum of an arithmetic progression can be formulated by using the earlier definitions:

> a— the value of the first term in the sequence;
> d— the common difference;
> n— the number of terms in the sequence;
> t_n— the nth term in the sequence;
> S_n— the sum of the terms in the sequence.

Therefore, since we know the sum of an arithmetic series can be found by:

$$\frac{[\text{first term} + \text{last term}][\text{number of terms}]}{2} = \frac{[a + t_n] \, n}{2}$$

$$= S_n$$

we can say that the sum of an arithmetic series can be found by the following formula:

$$S_n = \frac{n}{2}(a + t_n)$$ **Formula 4.3**

To see how Formula 4.3 works, let us return to Example 4.14. In part (a), the problem was to find the last four terms. Instead of finding four separate terms, suppose we had wanted to find the sum of all seven terms, that is, the sum of 3, 5, 7, 9, 11, 13, and 15. Using our formula for S_n, we have:

$a = 3$, the first term in the sequence;
$t_n = 15$, the 7th or last term of the sequence;
$n = 7$, the number of terms.

Placing these values in our formula for S_n gives:

$$S_n = \frac{n}{2}(a + t_n)$$

$$S_n = \frac{7}{2}(3 + 15)$$

$$S_n = 63$$

Checking to see if this sum is correct, add each term of the original sequence:

$$3 + 5 + 7 + 9 + 11 + 13 + 15 = 63$$

EXAMPLE 4.15

Find the sum of the terms for part b from Example 4.13. Check your answer.

Solution (b) −3, 0, 3, 6, 9, 12, 15

$a = -3$ The first term in the sequence.
$t_7 = 15$ The 7th or last term of the sequence.
$n = 7$ The number of terms.

Placing these values in Formula 4.3 to find S_n gives:

$$S_n = \frac{n}{2}(a + t_n)$$

$$S_n = \frac{7}{2}(-3 + 15)$$

$$S_n = 42$$

Checking this sum:

$$-3 + 0 + 3 + 6 + 9 + 12 + 15 = 42$$

B. Geometric Progressions

(i) Finding the nth Term of a Geometric Progression

A geometric progression is a sequence of numbers in which each term is found by multiplying the preceding term by a constant. For example, 2, 4, 8, 16, ... is a geometric progression since each term is a result of multiplying the previous term by a constant. In this situation, 2 is the constant. This constant is called the **common ratio** and can be either a positive or negative number. For example, if the first term of a geometric progression is 4 and the common ratio (the constant in the multiplication) is 3, the first four terms of the progression would be:

$$\begin{aligned}
\text{First Term} &= 4 \\
\text{Second Term} &= 4(3) &= 12 \\
\text{Third Term} &= 4(3)(3) &= 4(3^2) = 36 \\
\text{Fourth Term} &= 4(3)(3)(3) = 4(3^3) = 108
\end{aligned}$$

If you examine one of the terms, say the third term, 36, you can see that it is found by multiplying the first term, 4, by the constant ratio, 3, squared. Further, the fourth term is found by multiplying the first term by the constant ratio raised to the third power. Consequently, we can say that the nth term of the series will be the first term multiplied by the constant ratio raised to the power $n - 1$. This would be stated as:

Given a first term of 4, with a common ratio of 3, the nth term of the series is:

$$t_n = 4(3^{n-1})$$

For example, if we wanted to find the 6th term of the series it would be found as:

$$\begin{aligned}
t_6 &= 4(3^{6-1}) \\
&= 4(3^5) \\
&= 972
\end{aligned}$$

Defining the parts of a geometric series as:

a = the value of the first term;
r = the value of the common ratio;
t_n = the value of the last term of the sequence;
n = the number of terms in the sequence;

the value of the nth term, t_n, can be found by using the formula:

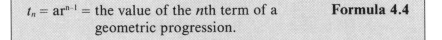

$t_n = ar^{n-1}$ = the value of the nth term of a geometric progression.   **Formula 4.4**

EXAMPLE 4.16

Find the value of the term required for the following geometric sequences.

(a) 2, 6, 18; find the 6th term of the sequence.
(b) 1, 4, 16; find the 7th term of the sequence.

Solution (a) 2, 6, 18; finding the value of the 6th term of the sequence:

Define the values for a, n, and r:

$$a = 2 \qquad \text{First term of the series.}$$
$$n = 6 \qquad \text{The number of terms.}$$
$$r = \left(\frac{6}{2}\right)$$
$$= 3 \qquad \text{Common ratio.}$$

Substitute these values into Formula 4.4:

$$t_n = ar^{n-1}$$
$$t_6 = 2(3^{6-1})$$
$$t_6 = 486$$

(b) 1, 4, 16; finding the value of the 7th term of the sequence:

Define the values for a, n, and r:

$$a = 1 \qquad \text{First term of the series.}$$
$$n = 7 \qquad \text{The number of terms.}$$
$$r = \left(\frac{4}{1}\right) \qquad \text{Common ratio.}$$
$$= 4$$

Substitute these values into Formula 4.4:

$$t_n = ar^{n-1}$$
$$t_7 = 1(4^{7-1})$$
$$t_7 = 4,096$$

Note that in the formula for t_n, the nth term can be used to find any term of a sequence simply by treating the term you are seeking as the last term. This concept is used later when we want to find the future value of money (the original amount plus interest).

(ii) Finding the Sum of a Geometric Progression

As with finding the sum of an arithmetic progression, the sum of the terms of a geometric progression will be denoted by S_n. To find a formula for the sum of a geometric progression, we use a procedure similar to that used when we developed an expression for the sum of an arithmetic progression.

First we define the sum as:

$$S_n = a + ar + ar^2 + ar^3 + ar^4 + \ldots + ar^{n-1} \quad ①$$

If we multiply both sides of the expression for S_n by r we get:

$$rS_n = ar + ar^2 + ar^3 + ar^4 + ar^5 + \ldots + ar^n \quad ②$$

If we subtract expression ② (rS_n) from expression ① (S_n) we get:

$$S_n - rS_n = [a + ar + ar^2 + \ldots + ar^{n-1}] - [ar + ar^2 + \ldots + ar^{n-1} + a^n]$$

$$S_n - rS_n = a - ar^n$$

In the last expression, $a - ar^n$ comes from the subtraction of rS_n from S_n. In each expression, the terms are the same except for the first term in S_n, namely a, and the last term in rS_n, namely ar^n.

Factoring out common terms and solving for S_n yields:

$$S_n - rS_n = a - ar^n$$

$$S_n(1 - r) = a(1 - r^n)$$

Rearranging to find S_n, the sum of a geometric progression, gives:

$$S_n = \frac{a(1 - r^n)}{(1 - r)} \ldots \qquad \textbf{Formula 4.5}$$

To see how Formula 4.5 works, try Example 4.17, which uses the series from Example 4.16:

EXAMPLE 4.17

Find the sum of the following sequences.

(a) Find the sum of the first 6 terms of the sequence 2, 6, 18.
(b) Find the sum of the first 7 terms of the sequence 1, 4, 16.

Solution (a) The sum of 2, 6, 18, up to the 6th term of the sequence.

Define the values for a, n, and r:

$a = 2$ \qquad First term of the series.

$n = 6$ \qquad The number of terms.

$r = \left(\dfrac{6}{2}\right)$ \qquad Common ratio.

$\quad = 3$

Substituting these values into Formula 4.5 gives:

$$S_n = \frac{a(1 - r^n)}{(1 - r)}$$

$$S_n = \frac{2(1 - 3^6)}{(1 - 3)}$$

$$S_n = \frac{2(1 - 729)}{(1 - 3)}$$

$$S_n = 728$$

(b) The sum of 1, 4, 16, up to the 7th term of the sequence:

Define the values for a, n, and r:

$a = 1$ First term of the series.

$n = 7$ The number of terms.

$r = \left(\frac{4}{1}\right)$ Common ratio.

$= 4$

Substitute these values into Formula 4.5:

$$S_n = \frac{a(1 - r^n)}{(1 - r)}$$

$$S_n = \frac{1(1 - 4^7)}{(1 - 4)}$$

$$S_n = \frac{1(1 \quad 16,384)}{(1 - 4)}$$

$$S_n = 5,461$$

4.6 Logarithms

Before 1970, one of the basic tools used in the physical sciences and business for evaluating complex multiplications, operations with exponents, and certain divisions was the logarithm. Logarithms were used extensively in finance, engineering, and navigation before the introduction of the electronic calculator and the personal computer. Now with the new electronic technology, the need to use logarithms has been reduced significantly, or so it seems. In reality, many computations the computer and calculator perform use logarithms, though it is not apparent to the user.

Logarithms are still used as a tool in business, especially in statistics and finance. Our interest in logarithms is with their application to finance problems where it is often necessary to find an unknown exponent. It is the application of logarithms that permits us to find an unknown exponent. Before using logarithms, it is helpful to gain an understanding of exactly what is meant by a logarithm.

A. What Is a Logarithm?

To understand the concept of a logarithm, consider the following expressions:

$$2^4 = 16$$
$$3^6 = 729$$
$$5^3 = 125$$
$$10^2 = 100$$

Using the notation of exponents, called **exponential form**, the equivalent statement for logarithms can be stated as:

$b^x = N$ ◂——— The exponential form, and using the language of logarithms, x is the logarithm of N.

Taking our previous examples, we can now write each exponential expression using logarithms as:

Exponential Form	Logarithmic Form
$b^x = N$	$\log_b N = x$
$2^4 = 16$	$\log_2 16 = 4$
$3^6 = 729$	$\log_3 729 = 6$
$5^3 = 125$	$\log_5 125 = 3$
$10^2 = 100$	$\log_{10} 100 = 2$

In each example, a number has been raised to an exponent to produce another number. Thus **we see that a logarithm is an exponent**. For example, in the first expression, 2 has been raised to the power of 4 to produce 16. In the language of logarithms, 4 is a logarithm of 16 when the base is 2. To state this in another way, if N is a positive number (in our case 16), and if x is an exponent (in this case 4) of a number b, called a base (2 in this example), then x is the logarithm of N. The logarithm of a number is expressed using the following notation:

$\log_b N = x$ ◂——— Read as: the logarithm of N to the base b, is x.

Using some more examples, we can see the relationship among b, x, and N:

Exponential Form	Logarithmic Form	Base b	Number N	(Logarithm) Exponent x
$3^4 = 81$	$\log_3 81 = 4$	3	81	4
$5^2 = 25$	$\log_5 25 = 2$	5	25	2
$10^4 = 10,000$	$\log_{10} 10,000 = 4$	10	10,000	4

In each case we see the logarithm is simply the exponent to which the base must be raised to give the original number N.

EXAMPLE 4.18

Write the following expressions in logarithmic notation. For each, specify the exponential form, the logarithmic form, the base, and the logarithm.

(a) $2^5 = 32$ (b) $25^{\frac{1}{2}} = 5$ (c) $13^3 = 2,197$

Solution Using the general form, $\log_b N = x$, we have:

	Exponential Form	Logarithmic Form	Base b	Number N	Logarithm x
(a)	$2^5 = 32$	$\log_2 32 = 5$	2	32	5
(b)	$25^{\frac{1}{2}} = 5$	$\log_{25} 5 = \dfrac{1}{2}$	25	5	$\dfrac{1}{2}$
(c)	$13^3 = 2{,}197$	$\log_{13} 2{,}197 = 3$	13	2,197	3

In business and the physical sciences there are two logarithms that are used with considerable frequency. The first is called a **common logarithm**, and has a base of 10. The second is called a **natural logarithm** and has as its base e, where $e = 2.718282 \ldots$; there is no end to the number of decimal places.

(i) Common Logarithms

Common logarithms always have a base of 10 and are written as $\log y = x$, where the base 10 is understood. For example:

$\log 100 = 2$ ⟵   Here the base 10 is understood. If this expression was to be written in exponential form it would be 10^2 or 100.

Remember, when you see the expression **$\log y = x$**, without a subscript, the base of the logarithm is 10. Base 10 logarithms are often used because 10 is the basis of our number system. To see the usefulness of base 10 logarithms read the following:

Logarithmic Form	Exponential Form
$\log 1 = 0$	$10^0 = 1$
$\log 10 = 1$	$10^1 = 10$
$\log 100 = 2$	$10^2 = 100$
$\log 1{,}000 = 3$	$10^3 = 1{,}000$
$\log 10{,}000 = 4$	$10^4 = 10{,}000$
$\log 100{,}000 = 5$	$10^5 = 100{,}000$
$\log 1{,}000{,}000 = 6$	$10^6 = 1{,}000{,}000$

From the above we should take note of two things. First, it is possible to estimate a common logarithm before using the calculator to find the logarithm of a number. For example, if one was looking for the log of 50, it must be a number greater than 1 but less than 2. Further, for a number like 15,000, we know the logarithm of the number must be between 4 and 5, and in particular, it will be closer to 4 than 5.

The second thing that can be seen is that although logarithms (or logs) increase by unit values (1, 2, 3, etc.), the numbers for which we are finding the logarithm increase in magnitude of 10 times the previous number (10, 100, 1,000, etc.). It is this last property that made logarithms so useful in computations involving large numbers.

(ii) Natural Logarithms

As mentioned, natural logarithms refer to logarithms with a base of e, where $e = 2.718282 \ldots$. The value of e results from the expression:

$$\left[1 + \frac{1}{n}\right]^n$$

In this expression, we find that as n becomes a very large number the value of this expression "tends" toward the value e.

The last point can be shown by evaluating $\left[1 + \dfrac{1}{n}\right]^n$ for $n = 100$, $n = 1,000$, and $n = 1,000,000$. Using an electronic calculator:

for $n = 100$:

$$\left[1 + \frac{1}{n}\right]^n = \left[1 + \frac{1}{100}\right]^{100} = 2.704814$$

for $n = 1,000$:

$$\left[1 + \frac{1}{n}\right]^n = \left[1 + \frac{1}{1,000}\right]^{1,000} = 2.716924$$

for $n = 1,000,000$:

$$\left[1 + \frac{1}{n}\right]^n = \left[1 + \frac{1}{1,000,000}\right]^{1,000,000} = 2.718281$$

As can be seen, as n gets larger the value of the expression tends toward 2.718282.

Natural logarithms tend to be the most common logarithm, on the electronic calculators used in business and can be computed by depressing the **ln** key. If you take your calculator and depress the ln key for the following numbers you should get these results:

Logarithmic Form	Exponential Form
$\ln 1 = 0$	$e^0 = 1$
$\ln e = 1$	$e^1 = 2.718282$
$\ln 10 \doteq 2.302585$	$e^{2.302585} \doteq 10$
$\ln 100 \doteq 4.605170$	$e^{4.605170} \doteq 100$
$\ln 1,000 \doteq 6.907755$	$e^{6.907755} \doteq 1,000$

If you look at each value, you will note that ln 100 is twice ln 10, ln 1,000 is three times ln 10, and so forth. This relationship can be used to approximate natural logarithms as a check when using a calculator, since it is easy to input the wrong number.

EXAMPLE 4.19

Specify the following logarithms in exponential form and then evaluate the logarithm using an electronic calculator (round to four decimal places).

(a) ln 30 (b) ln 50 (c) ln 450 (d) ln 2.718

Solution:

Logarithmic Form	Logarithm	Exponential Form
(a) $\ln 30 =$	3.4012	$e^{3.4012} = 30$
(b) $\ln 50 =$	3.9120	$e^{3.9120} = 50$
(c) $\ln 450 =$	6.1092	$e^{6.1092} = 450$
(d) $\ln 2.718 =$	0.9999	$e^{0.9999} = 2.718$

B. Rules of Logarithms

Once we have a basic understanding of logarithms for base 10 and base e, we can understand how some basic arithmetic calculations are done using logarithms.

If we let A and B be two positive numbers, then we can state the basic rules of logarithms as follows:

Table 4.1

Rules for Logarithms	Examples Let $A = 10$, $B = 1,000$, and $n = 3$.
RULE 1 Base 10 $\log(AB) = \log A + \log B$	$(A = 10$ and $B = 1,000)$ $\log(10 \times 1,000) = \log 10 + \log 1,000$ $\log(10 \times 1,000) = 1 + 3$ $\log(10 \times 1,000) = 4$ $\qquad 10^4 = 10,000$
Base e $\ln(AB) = \ln A + \ln B$	$\ln(10 \times 1,000) = \ln 10 + \ln 1,000$ $\ln(10 \times 1,000) = 2.302585093 + 6.907755279$ $\ln(10 \times 1,000) = 9.210340372$ $\qquad e^{9.210340372} = 10,000$
RULE 2 Base 10 $\log\left[\dfrac{A}{B}\right] = \log A + \log B$	$(A = 10$ and $B = 1,000)$ $\log\left(\dfrac{10}{1,000}\right) = \log 10 - \log 1,000$ $\log\left(\dfrac{10}{1,000}\right) = 1 - 3$ $\log\left(\dfrac{10}{1,000}\right) = -2$ $\qquad 10^{-2} = 0.01$
Base e $\ln\left[\dfrac{A}{B}\right] = \ln A - \ln B$	$\ln\left(\dfrac{10}{1,000}\right) = \ln 10 - \ln 1,000$ $\ln\left(\dfrac{10}{1,000}\right) = 2.302585093 - 6.907755279$ $\ln\left(\dfrac{10}{1,000}\right) = -4.605170186$ $\qquad e^{-4.605170186} = 0.01$
RULE 3 Base 10 $\log(A^n) = n(\log A)$	$(n = 3$ and $A = 10)$ $\log 10^3 = 3\log 10$ $3\log 10 = (3)(1)$ $3\log 10 = 3$ $\log 10^3 = 1,000$
Base e $\ln(A)^n = n(\ln A)$	$\ln 10^3 = 3\ln 10$ $3\ln 10 = 3(2.302585093)$ $3\ln 10 = 6.907755279$ $\qquad e^{6.907755279} = 1,000$

The rules in Table 4.1 should be understood. Rule 3 is very important to the financial computations that follow in later chapters. The solutions for the following examples require the use of an electronic calculator. If you only have

a ⊡ log key on your calculator, use it in the exact steps noted. But remember, your intermediate answers will be different. However, your final answer will be the same — regardless of the base you select for logarithms.

It is important to understand that numerical differences may arise from rounding of decimal places. Also, differences also may arise if two people are working side-by-side with the same numbers, but <u>using different</u> calculators. Because the electronics in each calculator can differ, each calculator may give slightly different numbers in rounding of decimals when there are many decimal places. This is not a serious problem. The differences normally arise after five decimal places.

The following example uses Rule 3 throughout since it is the operation you must be able to perform in the finance sections of later chapters. The use of logarithms for multiplication and division is not often required because of the availability of electronic calculators.

EXAMPLE 4.20

Use logarithms to evaluate the following expressions:

(a) $(50)(75)^n = 500$

(b) $5{,}000 = 1{,}000(1 + 0.01)^n$

(c) $10{,}000 = 500 \left[\dfrac{1 - (1 + 0.005)^{-n}}{0.005} \right]$

(d) $18{,}000 = 600 \left[\dfrac{(1 + 0.125)^n - 1}{0.125} \right]$

Solution (a) $(50)(75)^n = 500$

STEP 1 Divide both sides by 50:

$$(75)^n = \frac{500}{50}$$

$$(75)^n = 10$$

STEP 2 Taking logarithms of both sides:

$$\ln 75^n = \ln 10$$
$$n(\ln 75) = \ln 10$$

STEP 3 Solve for n:

$$n = \left[\frac{\ln 10}{\ln 75} \right]$$

$$n = 0.533315907$$

Solution   (b) $5,000 = 1,000(1 + 0.01)^n$

STEP 1   Rearrange the expression and divide each side by 1,000:

$$(1 + 0.01)^n = \frac{5,000}{1,000}$$

$$(1.01)^n = 5$$

STEP 2   Take logarithms of both sides:

$$\ln(1.01)^n = \ln 5$$
$$n\ln(1.01) = \ln 5$$

STEP 3   Solving for n:

$$n = \left[\frac{\ln 5}{\ln (1.01)}\right]$$

$$n = \frac{1.609437912}{0.00995033}$$

$$n = 161.7471757$$

Solution   (c) $10,000 = 500 \left[\dfrac{1 - (1 + 0.005)^{-n}}{0.005}\right]$

STEP 1   Divide both sides by 500:

$$\frac{10,000}{500} = \left[\frac{1 - (1.005)^{-n}}{0.005}\right]$$

$$20 = \left[\frac{1 - (1.005)^{-n}}{0.005}\right]$$

STEP 2   Multiply both sides by 0.005:

$$(20)(0.005) = 1 - (1.005)^{-n}$$

STEP 3   Remove brackets and subtract 1 from both sides:

$$0.1 - 1 - (1.005)^{-n}$$
$$0.1 - 1 = -1.005^{-n}$$
$$-0.9 = - 1.005^{-n}$$

STEP 4   Rearranging the sides of the equation:

$$- (1.005)^{-n} = -0.9$$

STEP 5   Multiply both sides by -1 to eliminate the negative sign:

$$(1.005)^{-n} = 0.9$$

STEP 6   Taking logarithms of both sides:

$$-n\ln 1.005 = \ln 0.9$$

STEP 7   Solving for n:

$$-n = \left[\frac{\ln 0.9}{\ln[1.005]}\right]$$

$$-n = -21.1247396$$

$$n = 21.1247396 \qquad \text{After multiplying each side by } -1.$$

Solution   (d) $18{,}000 = 600\left[\frac{(1 + 0.125)^n - 1}{0.125}\right]$

STEP 1   Divide each side by 600:

$$\frac{18{,}000}{600} = \left[\frac{(1.125)^n - 1}{0.125}\right]$$

$$30 = \left[\frac{(1.125)^n - 1}{0.125}\right]$$

STEP 2   Multiply each side by 0.125:

$$(30)(0.125) = (1.125)^n - 1$$
$$3.75 = (1.125)^n - 1$$

STEP 3   Rearranging and adding 1 to both sides:

$$(1.125)^n = 4.75$$

STEP 4   Taking logarithms gives:

$$n\ln(1.125) = \ln 4.75$$

STEP 5   Solving for n:

$$n = \left[\frac{\ln 4.75}{\ln(1.125)}\right]$$

$$n = 13.2289392$$

SUMMARY OF FORMULAS

Formula 4.1 $m = \dfrac{\text{Change in } y}{\text{Change in } x} = \dfrac{y_2 - y_1}{x_2 - x_1}$ The formula to find the slope for a straight line.

Formula 4.2 $t_n = a + (n - 1)d$ The formula to find the nth term of an arithmetic series.

Formula 4.3 $S_n = \dfrac{n}{2}(a + t_n)$ The formula to find the sum of an arithmetic series with n terms.

Formula 4.4 $t_n = ar^{n-1}$ The formula to find the value of the nth term of a geometric progression.

Formula 4.5 $S_n = \dfrac{a(1 - r^n)}{(1 - r)}$ This formula finds the sum for a geometric series with n terms.

GLOSSARY OF TERMS

Arithmetic Progression a series of numbers that are in a pattern where each number in the pattern is based on the previous number. The difference between each number is the common difference, d. This difference is constant for the series.

Geometric Series a series of numbers such that each term is found by multiplying the preceding term by a constant. This constant is the common ratio, r.

Intercept the point at which a line crosses one of the axes. The point where a line crosses the y-axis is called the y-intercept. The point at which the line crosses the x-axis is called the x-intercept.

Logarithm a logarithm is the exponent to which a base must be raised to achieve a particular number. Two logarithms commonly used are those with a base of 10 (called common logarithms); the other type uses a base of e (called natural logarithms).

Quadrant The rectangular coordinate system is made up of four quadrants. In business, the quadrant that is most relevant is quadrant 1, which has positive values for both x and y.

Rectangular Coordinate System the name given to the system used to graphically depict equations.

Slope the measure of how steep a line is. The slope tells us how much y will change for a given change in x.

Slope Intercept Form $y = b + mx$, where b is the intercept and m is the slope. If m is positive, the line slopes upward to the right. If m is negative, the line is downward sloping.

Solution for a Simultaneous System of Equations a value for each variable in the equation system that satisfies all the equations simultaneously.

CHAPTER 5

Invoicing and Commercial Discounts: Merchandise Pricing — Markup and Markdown

The use of simple arithmetic computations in business goes on every working day, in every business, regardless of size. The topics of this chapter — invoicing, trade discounts, cash discounts, markup, and markdown — are normally considered part of the merchandising function: things that are not visible to the consumer.

Each of these aspects of merchandising requires the use of the basic tools of arithmetic and algebra discussed in the previous chapters.

5.1 Invoicing Goods

When a buyer purchases goods, there is a need to have a record of the transaction. This record will show the goods purchased, the quantity of each good purchased, the price per unit, the terms of payment, and other important information. Such a record is called an **invoice**. Sometimes the invoice acts as a record of a sale and is referred to as a sales invoice. The best way to understand an invoice is to examine a typical invoice. Figure 5.1, opposite, is a sample of what an invoice might look like.

All the numbers in the circles correspond to the components of the invoice and are explained below. In examining Figure 5.1, you must keep in mind that this invoice is only a sample. Since each business has unique needs, there are many different types of invoices used to record the sale of merchandise.

1. **Invoice number:** This is a reference for the seller and used for accounting references.
2. **Name of the Seller and Buyer:** Venture Sporting Supplies is the seller and Hightest Sports is the buyer.
3. **Customer Number:** This refers to the number the seller has given to the purchaser for the accounting and billing records. Within this

Figure 5.1   Sample Invoice

Invoice Number	C 435689

Venture Sporting Supplies
145 Bay Street
Toronto, Ontario
M3X 3Y9

Date of Purchase	09-07-92
Customer Number	HS-4356

Sold to

Hightest Sports
3775 Duke Road
Victoria, B.C.
V8X 3W9

Shipped to

Hightest Sports
3775 Duke Road
Victoria, B.C.
V8X 3W9

Salesperson	Shipped Via	Terms
Judy Copps	Loomis Courier Service	3/10, 1/20, n/30

Quantity Ordered	Quantity Shipped	Unit Type	Item Number	Product Description	Unit Price	EXTENSION TOTAL
50	50	pr.	12695	Track Shoes — Lts.	55.50	2,775.00
12	10[1]	ea.	R-342T	Tennis Racq. — Md.4	89.46	894.60
12	11[1]	ea.	J-12tl	Ski Jackets — Md.13	159.23	1,751.53
20	20	doz.	B-34Jl	Tennis Balls — Md.9	22.49	449.80

1. Items on back order, will be shipped when available.

Invoice Total	$5,870.93
Less Trade Discount (35%)	–2,054.82
Net Price	3,816.11
Sales Tax	NA
GST @ 7% (7% of Net Price)	NA
Shipping Charges	125.25
Invoice Amount	$3,941.36

number, there may be a code that identifies the size of discount offered to the buyer.

4. **Date of Purchase:** The invoice date is 09-07-92. This is the date the invoice was prepared.

5. **Shipped Via:** This refers to the company that is the carrier. In this example, the carrier is Loomis.

6. **Quantity Ordered:** The actual amount ordered by the customer.

7. **Quantity Shipped:** This is the amount shipped. What is actually shipped may be different than the amount ordered, since occasionally a supplier may be out of a product. The supplier will ship later once they have received or produced the item. When an item is out of stock and to be shipped later it is referred to as a **back order**.

8. **Unit Type:** The unit type refers to how the good is sold. In the example, we see the goods are sold by pairs (pr.), single units (ea.), and by the dozen (doz.).

9. **Item Number:** This is an identification code for the goods for inventory and warehousing needs.

10. **Product Description:** This is a clear statement of the type of good sold, i.e., shoes, gloves, etc.

11. **Unit Price:** The unit price is the price per unit of the good sold. In this example, the unit prices are quoted per pair, per unit, or per dozen.

12. **Extension Total:** The extension total is the unit price multiplied by the quantity shipped. This multiplication gives the total cost for each type of product. The extension column determines the basis for the invoice amount.

13. **Trade Discounts:** These refer to the discount that is applicable to the buyer. Trade discounts vary depending upon the volume of business the buyer does with the seller and the type of good. A trade discount is a method used to find the wholesale price of a product. Trade discounts will be discussed in detail in the next section of this chapter.

14. **Terms of Payment:** Terms of payment refer to how soon the invoice must be paid. Often, to encourage early payment, a supplier will allow a cash discount for early payment. In our example, the 3/10, 1/20, n/30 in the "Terms of Payment" section of the invoice mean that if the invoice is paid within 10 days of the invoice date, the buyer may deduct 3% of the **net price** of the invoice. This discount does not apply to taxes or to transportation costs, since they are costs external to the supplier of the good. If the invoice is paid after 10 days, but within 20 days of the invoice date, there is a 1% cash discount; and, if the invoice is paid after 20 days, the total balance is due 30 days from the invoice date (that is, net in 30 days, n/30).

15. **Salesperson:** This is a record of the person who made the sale or contacted the buyer. This information is important if any inquiries result after delivery. In addition, if the salesperson is paid a commission, this may be the only record of the salesperson who made the sale.

EXAMPLE 5.1

The invoice in Figure 5.2 was issued by Ronic Mills for an order of floor covering for a new housing project. The quoted price for Ansel IV was $75.50/m² and the price for Armstrong Kitchen flooring was $36.46/m². The carpet is sold to Unitex Carpets. Based on the invoice below, find the invoice entries for the boxes with the question marks.

Solution The unit prices for each floor covering are:

Ansel IV carpet:
— The unit price is $75.50/m².
Armstrong Kitchen Floor:
— The unit price is $36.46/m².

Figure 5.2   Sample Invoice

				Invoice Number	**B 138921**

Ronic Mills
1345 William Head
Metchosin, B.C.

Date of Purchase 10-15-92
Customer Number UCL-189

Sold to

Unitex Carpets
1553 1st Avenue
Winnipeg, Manitoba

Shipped to

Unitex Carpets
1553 1st Avenue
Winnipeg, Manitoba

Salesperson	Shipped Via	Terms
J. Anderson	Volke Transport Services	1/20, n/30

Quantity Ordered	Quantity Shipped	Unit Type	Product Type	Product Description	Unit Price	EXTENSION TOTAL
150	150	Sq.m.	12-957	Ansel IV carpet	?	?
300	300	Sq.m.	12-345	Armstrong Kit. Floor	?	?

Invoice Total	$?
Less Trade Discount (25% of invoice total)	?
Net Price	?
Shipping Charges	152.50
Tax (7% GST on net price)	?
Sales Tax (provincial tax 6% of sub-total)	?
Invoice Amount	$

The appropriate entries for the extension column are:

Ansel IV:

— Extension total: $75.50 × 150, or $11,325

Armstrong Kitchen Floor:

— Extension total: $36.46 × 300, or $10,938

The invoice total is the total before any trade discounts, taxes, or transportation costs are applied. This total would be the addition of the extension entries in the extension column. These were found above. Therefore, the invoice total and the remaining entries will be:

Invoice Total = $11,325 + $10,938, or $22,263

Invoice Total	$22,263.00

Trade Discount = 0.25 × 22,263

Less Trade Discount (25% of invoice total)	5,565.75

Net Price = $22,263 – $5,565.75

Net Price	16,697.25

Shipping is given

Shipping Charges	152.50

$$\text{GST} = 0.07(16,697.25 + 152.50)$$

Tax (7% GST; applied to net price)	1,168.81

$$\text{Sales Tax} = 0.06(16,697.25)$$

Sales Tax (provincial tax 6% applied to net price)	1,001.84
Invoice Amount	$19,020.40

5.2 Trade Discounts

A. Single Trade Discounts

When a retail business (retail means where the final sale to the consumer occurs, e.g., Eaton's), or wholesale business (wholesalers are sometimes called distributors, e.g., Acklands) purchases its goods from a supplier (a manufacturer) there is a discount offered. This discount is called a **trade discount**. In general, trade discounts are applied to a catalogue price or a list price. The list prices often appear in a published price list to businesses — sometimes a catalogue, sometimes a computer print-out of products and prices. Frequently the list price or the catalogue price is also the suggested retail price when the good is sold to a retail consumer. An example is a tradesman, such as a plumber, who must purchase necessary materials for each job. Usually, the plumber purchases the materials from a wholesaler. The wholesaler sells the materials to the plumber at a "list price" (from a catalogue or published list price), less a trade discount on the list price. In the end, the plumber charges his/her customer the list price. By charging the list price the plumber earns a revenue to cover profit plus the time taken to pick up the materials.

The size of a trade discount will vary from firm to firm. Normally, the larger the buyer and/or the larger the order, the larger the trade discount provided. Since trade discounts are applied as a percentage of the list price, a wholesaler can adjust for price increases by changing the size of the trade discount without having to change the list price. That is, dropping the size of the trade discount raises the price of the goods, and the supplier does not have to republish its catalogue or price list.

When the trade discount is subtracted from the list or catalogue price, what remains is called the **net price**. The net price is what must be paid for the goods. Thus we can say:

> Net Price = List Price (Catalogue Price) – Trade Discount   **Formula 5.1**

EXAMPLE 5.2

A plumber is plumbing a new house with materials having a list price of $3,550.60. A trade discount of 25% is offered to the plumber. How much would the net amount of the invoice be? (Forget taxes and transportation.)

Solution To find the trade discount, we multiply the list price (catalogue price) by the discount rate (25%), thus:

Since 25% = 0.25, the trade discount is

0.25 × $3,550.60 = $887.65

Applying Formula 5.1:

Net Price = List Price (Catalogue Price) – Trade Discount
Net Price = $3,550.60 – $887.65
Net Price = $2,662.95

When a retailer purchases goods for resale they are purchased from a wholesaler or wholesale agent. The wholesaler purchases the goods from the manufacturer. Sometimes, if the retailer is extremely large, the retailer may be able to purchase directly from the manufacturer. Consequently, there is no strict rule about where a retailer might purchase goods for resale.

In Example 5.2, it was shown that a trade discount is a percentage discount that is applied to the list or catalogue price. The size of the trade discount will depend largely on the volume of business done by the buyer with the supplier. In general, the larger the amount purchased — on a regular basis — the larger the trade discount offered. To find the **dollar amount of the trade discount** we simply apply the relation:

> Dollar Amount of Trade Discount = Rate of Trade Discount × List Price

EXAMPLE 5.3

Ace Printing Services purchases coloured stencils from a wholesaler at a list price of $135.00 per box. If Ace gets a 30% trade discount find:

(a) the amount of the discount;
(b) the net price of the good.

Solution (a)

$$\text{Amount of Trade Discount} = \text{Rate of Trade Discount} \times \text{List Price}$$

Rate of Trade Discount = 30%, or 0.30
List Price = $135.00

Amount of Trade Discount = 0.30 × $135.00
= $40.50

(b) The net price of the stencils is:

Net Price = List Price – Trade Discount
Net Price = $135.00 – $40.50
= $94.50

Another way of finding the net price is to use what is called the **Net Cost Factor** approach, or simply the *NCF* approach. The net cost factor allows one to calculate the net price directly by determining what percent of the list price is to be paid by a buyer. In Example 5.3, since the trade discount was 30%, we can conclude that the net price must be 70% of the list price. To see if this works, take the list price and multiply it by 70%. This gives:

$$\$135.00 \times 0.7 = \$94.50 \qquad \text{The same net price as}$$
$$\text{determined in Example 5.3.}$$

From the above there are two relations we can state. The first defines the net cost factor as:

$$\text{Net Cost Factor } (NCF) = 100\% - \% \text{ Discount}$$

We can also state the net price as:

$$\text{Net Price} = NCF \times \text{List Price}$$

To make things a little more simple, the previous expressions can be rewritten using the following definitions:

LP = List Price

NP = Net Price

$\quad d$ = Trade Discount Rate   Converted to a decimal equivalent.

NCF = Net Cost Factor

$\quad = (1 - d)$

Thus, bringing all the terms together, the expression for the amount of a trade discount and the net price (NP) paid can be written as:

$$\text{Amount of Trade Discount} = d(LP) \qquad \textbf{Formula 5.2}$$

$$NP = LP(1 - d) \qquad \textbf{Formula 5.3}$$

EXAMPLE 5.4

Auto Van Repairs buys parts from AB Supplies. Using the trade discounts applicable, compute the net price for the following parts.

(a) One fuel injector, list price $54.00, less trade discount of 35%;

(b) One electronic ignition system, list price $269.40, less trade discount of 40%;

(c) One box of spark plugs, list price $60.00, less trade discount of 25.5%;

(d) Three cases of lubricants, list price $29.09 per case, less trade discount of 20%.

Solution
(a) List price, LP = $54.00, trade discount, d = 0.35 (decimal equivalent of 35%); applying Formula 5.3, Net Price, $NP = LP(1 - d)$. Substituting each value gives:

$NP = \$54(1 - 0.35)$

$NP = \$54(0.65)$

$NP = \$35.10$, the net price of the injector;

(b) LP = $269.40, d = 0.40 (decimal equivalent of 40%); applying Formula 5.3:

$NP = LP(1 - d)$

$NP = \$269.40(1 - 0.40)$

$NP - \$269.40(0.60)$

$NP = \$161.64$, the net price of the ignition system;

(c) LP = $60.00, d = 0.255 (decimal equivalent of 25.5%); applying Formula 5.3:

$NP = LP(1 - d)$

$NP = \$60.00(1 - 0.255)$

$NP = \$60.00(0.745)$

$NP = \$44.70$, the net price of a box of spark plugs;

(d) LP = $29.09, d = 0.20 (decimal equivalent of 20%); applying Formula 5.3:

$NP = LP(1 - d)$

$NP = \$29.09(1 - 0.20)$

$NP = \$29.09(0.80)$

$NP = \$23.27$, the net price of one case of lubricants

NP of three cases = $\$23.27 \times 3$

$\qquad\qquad\qquad = \$69.81.$

On occasion a supplier may specify the trade discount in dollar terms rather than as a percentage. If this occurs, a buyer may wish to compute the percent or decimal equivalent of the trade discount. Such a calculation would permit a comparison between different suppliers. This comparison is important when quotations are in dollars by one supplier and percentages by another supplier. The method we would use to compute the trade discount rate, d, would be:

$$\text{Trade Discount Rate, } d = \frac{\text{Dollar Amount of Discount}}{\text{List Price}} \qquad \textbf{Formula 5.4}$$

EXAMPLE 5.5

Marathon Books has just received an invoice for an order of books it recently received. The list price of the books was \$1,234.50 and the trade discount offered was \$411.67. Compute the trade discount rate that has been applied by the supplier.

Solution   Using Formula 5.4, we first define the terms we know:

Dollar Amount of Discount = \$411.67

List Price = \$1,234.50

Applying Formula 5.4, the trade discount rate, d, is:

$$d = \frac{\$411.67}{\$1,234.50}$$

$$= 0.3335, \text{ or } 33.35\%$$

B. Multiple or Chain Discounts

It is not uncommon for more than one trade discount to be offered by a wholesaler or manufacturer to a buyer. The reason multiple discounts are offered by a supplier are varied. Some usual reasons are overstock of a product, a special manufacturer's promotion on a new or discontinued good, or the size of the order (and sometimes the size of the buyer). When the order is large or the customer is large, in general, the greater the discount. One way to handle an additional discount is to offer buyers multiple discounts.

The term **chain discount** is used to describe multiple discounts. A chain discount is a more descriptive term for applying multiple discounts since they are applied in sequence, or in a chain of calculations. Study Example 5.6, which shows how a buyer computes the net price after applying multiple trade discounts:

EXAMPLE 5.6

Acme Software offers trade discounts of 25% and 20% to Heller Computer Sales. If Heller has just purchased a selection of software that has a list price of \$7,500, find the net price of the purchase.

Solution   In finding the net price, we must understand how the trade discounts are applied in sequence.

Applying the <u>first</u> discount gives the first net price (NP_1):

$$NP_1 = LP(1 - d_1) \qquad d_1 \text{ is the first trade discount.}$$
$$NP_1 = \$7,500(1 - 0.25)$$
$$NP_1 = \$5,625$$

Applying the <u>second</u> discount gives the final net price (NP_2):

$$NP_2 = NP_1(1 - d_2) \quad d_2 \text{ is the second trade discount.}$$
$$NP_2 = \$5,625(1 - 0.20)$$
$$NP_2 = \$4,500$$

The final net price that Heller Computer Systems would pay for software that has a list price of \$7,500, given trade discounts of 25% and 20%, is \$4,500.

In the solution of Example 5.6, we cannot simply add the trade discounts, (i.e., 25% + 20%), since this would not yield the correct list price. However, we can combine the discounts if we use the following method:

LP = list or catalogue price
d_1 = the first trade discount
d_2 = the second trade discount
d_3 = the third trade discount
d_n = the nth trade discount

Now for each trade discount we can formulate an expression for the Net Cost Factor for each trade discount as:

$$NCF_1 = (1 - d_1)$$
$$NCF_2 = (1 - d_2)$$
$$NCF_3 = (1 - d_3)$$
$$\cdots$$
$$NCF_n = (1 - d_n)$$

Bringing the discounts and NCF's together we can find a single *NCF* that incorporates all the trade discounts. This is done by multiplying the individual *NCF*'s as:

> **Net Cost Factor For Multiple Discounts** $= (1 - d_1)(1 - d_2)(1 - d_3) \ldots (1 - d_n)$ **Formula 5.5**

From Formula 5.5 it is possible to specify the Net Price when multiple or chain discounts are available as:

> Net Price $= LP(1 - d_1)(1 - d_2)(1 - d_3) \ldots (1 - d_n)$ **Formula 5.6**

Applying Formula 5.6 to the list price in Example 5.6, the net price can be found directly by applying the *NCF* based on all the discounts. This is done as:

Net Price $= \$7,500(1 - 0.25)(1 - 0.20)$
$$= \$4,500$$

EXAMPLE 5.7

Venture Sporting Goods has just placed an order with its primary supplier. Since Venture is a major buyer of sporting goods, it receives multiple trade discounts. For each of the following purchases compute the net price directly by using Formula 5.6.

(a) Three dozen pairs of ski boots, listed at $350.95 per pair, less trade discounts of 20%, 25%, and 30%;

(b) Thirty-two sets of ski poles, listed at $75.45 per pair, less trade discounts of 30%, 15%, and 10%.

Solution (a) Find the net price of the ski boots:

Total List Price: $LP = 36 \times \$350.95$

$$= \$12,634.20$$

$d_1 = 0.20$, $d_2 = 0.25$, $d_3 = 0.30$

Applying Formula 5.6:

Net Price $= \$12,634.20(1 - 0.20)(1 - 0.25)(1 - 0.30)$

$$= \$12,634.20(0.80)(0.75)(0.70)$$

$$= \$12,634.20(0.42)$$

Net Price $= \$5,306.36$

(b) Finding the net price of the ski poles:

Total List Price: $32 \times \$75.45 = \$2,414.40$

$d_1 = 0.30$, $d_2 = 0.15$, $d_3 = 0.10$

Now, applying Formula 5.6:

Net Price $= \$2,414.40(1 - 0.30)(1 - 0.15)(1 - 0.10)$

Net Price $= \$1,292.91$

5.3 Terms of Payment: Cash Discounts

If cash discounts are offered they will be specified on the invoice. In the invoice presented in Section 5.1, there was a box on the invoice with the label "**Terms**". The **Terms** section of the invoice outlines the terms of payment that are offered to the buyer. To encourage early payment, suppliers sometimes offer a **cash discount**. In the Terms section of the invoice (see Figure 5.1), the expression "3/10, 1/20, n/30" appeared. The meaning of the first term is that if the invoice is paid within 10 days of the invoice date, the buyer is entitled to a 3% cash discount from the net price (i.e., 3/10). Further, if the buyer pays after 10 days of the invoice date, but on or before 20 days after the invoice date, the buyer is entitled to a 1% cash discount off the net price (i.e., 1/20). After 20 days, the total of the invoice is due, with the full payment expected 30 days after the invoice date (i.e., n/30 — the n stands for the net amount of the invoice).

As mentioned, one reason a cash discount is offered by suppliers is to encourage early payment. This early payment greatly helps a supplier since it increases its cash flow and minimizes the need for the supplier to borrow monies for its day-to-day operations.

There are different ways that the terms of payment may be offered by a supplier. These differences depend upon the type of invoice dating that is used for the terms. The three most common methods of dating are:

1. Ordinary Dating

2. End of Month Dating

3. Receipt of Goods Dating

A. Ordinary Dating

The terms 3/10, n/30 are examples of ordinary dating. The first number, 3, represents the percentage discount and the second number, 10, indicates how long after the date of the invoice the discount will be permitted. The term, n/30, simply means that the net amount of the invoice is due in 30 days.

EXAMPLE 5.8

Volk Transport in British Columbia orders parts for its trucks from Acme Parts in Ontario. On the last invoice from Acme, the net price was $2,345.60. The terms of payment were 2/10, n/30. Answer the following questions.

(a) If the invoice is paid within 10 days of the invoice date, what will be the cash discount? What will be the amount paid to Acme Parts?

(b) If the invoice is paid 15 days after the date of the invoice, what will be the cash discount?

Solution (a) If payment is made in 10 days the size of the cash discount is 2% of the net price of $2,345.60, therefore:

$$\text{Cash Discount} = 2\% \times \$2,345.60$$
$$= 0.02 \times \$2,345.60$$
$$= \$46.91$$

$$\text{Amount Paid} = \text{Net Price} - \text{Cash Discount}$$
$$= \$2,345.60 - \$46.91$$
$$= \$2,298.69$$

(b) If the payment is made after 10 days of the invoice date the cash discount is zero. Since the payment is 15 days after the invoice date there is no cash discount.

EXAMPLE 5.9

An invoice with a net price of $1,225.50 was dated September 30, 1992. The terms of payment are 3/10, 1/20, n/30. Calculate the amount paid and the cash discount if:

(a) the invoice is paid October 6, 1992;
(b) the invoice is paid October 15, 1992;
(c) the invoice is paid October 21, 1992.

Solution

(a) October 6: The payment is within 10 days of the invoice date. Therefore, the cash discount is 3% (3/10) of the net price:

$$\text{Cash Discount} = 0.03 \times \$1,225.50$$
$$= \$36.77$$
$$\text{Amount Paid} = \$1,225.50 - \$36.77$$
$$= \$1,188.74$$

(b) October 15: The payment is made after 10 days but within 20 days of the invoice date. Therefore, the cash discount is 2% (2/10) of the net price:

$$\text{Cash Discount} = 0.02 \times \$1,225.50$$
$$= \$24.51$$
$$\text{Amount Paid} = \$1,225.50 - \$24.51$$
$$= \$1,200.99$$

(c) October 21: The payment is made after the periods where cash discounts are available. The amount due will be $1,225.50, the full amount of the invoice.

B. End of Month Dating

End of month dating (E.O.M.) implies that the terms of the payment are extended and are available from the end of the month shown on the invoice. For example, if an invoice is dated September 5 and has the terms 2/10, n/30 E.O.M., the discount of 2/10 is available from the end of the month plus 10 days, or October 10. In effect, end of month dating means that the invoice is treated as if it were dated at the end of the month, and is due for payment in the month or months following.

Another way a supplier may specify E.O.M. dating is to use the word **prox** in the terms of payment, such as 2/10/prox. The word prox is an abbreviation for the Latin word **proximo** meaning next or following month. For example, an invoice dated March 16 with terms 3/10/prox is eligible for the cash discount until April 10.

There is an important exception to E.O.M. if the invoice is dated after the 26th day of a month. When this occurs some firms will permit the discount to apply for an additional month. For example, if an invoice was dated August 27, the discount period would commence on October 1. This practice is more common in the United States than in Canada.

The use of the E.O.M. method is usually found in industries where the buyer may not be able to sell the goods for some period after receipt of the goods. This could arise if there are assembly or processing requirements before the goods can be sold.

EXAMPLE 5.10

An invoice with a net price of $225.50 was dated October 4. The terms of payment are 2/10, 1/20, n/30 E.O.M. Calculate the amount paid and the cash discount if:

(a) the invoice is paid October 16;
(b) the invoice is paid November 8;
(c) the invoice is paid November 15.

Solution Since the invoice terms are E.O.M., the discount period for the cash discount 2/10 will apply to November 10 and the terms 1/20 will apply to November 20.

(a) October 16: If the invoice is paid on or before this date the cash discount is 2% of the net price.
Therefore:

$$\text{Cash Discount} = 0.02 \times \$225.50$$
$$= \$4.51$$
$$\text{Amount Paid} = \$225.50 - \$4.51$$
$$= \$220.99$$

(b) November 8: If the invoice is paid on this date, the cash discount is also 2% of the net price, as in part (a).
Therefore:

$$\text{Cash Discount} = 0.02 \times \$225.50$$
$$= \$4.51$$
$$\text{Amount Paid} = \$225.50 - \$4.51$$
$$= \$220.99$$

(c) November 15: If the invoice is paid on this date, the cash discount is 1% of the net price.
Therefore:

$$\text{Cash Discount} = 0.01 \times \$225.50$$
$$= \$2.26$$
$$\text{Amount Paid} = \$225.50 - \$2.26$$
$$= \$223.24$$

C. Receipt of Goods Dating

Another method that is sometimes applied to cash discounts is referred to as receipt of goods dating, abbreviated as R.O.G. If the terms provide for R.O.G., this means that the cash discount period begins when the goods are received. For example, 2/10, n/30 R.O.G. means that a 2% discount is available up to and including 10 days after receipt of the goods. Otherwise, the net price on the invoice is due 30 days after receipt of the goods.

Often the R.O.G. method of dating is used where delivery time is substantial — usually involving rail, water, or truck transport.

EXAMPLE 5.11

An invoice with a net price of $125.00 is dated June 10 and the goods are received on July 2. The terms of payment are 3/10, n/30 R.O.G. Calculate the amount paid and the cash discount if the invoice is paid July 12.

Solution The discount period will commence from the date of receipt of the goods. Here, 10 days from the receipt is 10 days from July 2. Since the invoice is paid on July 12, it is the last day of the discount period. Therefore the cash discount the amount paid is:

$$\text{Cash Discount} = 0.03 \times \$125.00$$
$$= \$3.75$$

$$\text{Amount Paid} = \$125.00 - \$3.25$$
$$= \$121.25$$

D. Partial Payments

The terms of payment are important since the cash discounts do represent substantial savings to the buyer. Sometimes, even when the terms are very favourable, the buyer may not be able to raise the full amount of the payment within the cash discount period. Yet, the buyer may be able to provide a partial payment within the cash discount period. When a partial payment is made, the buyer should be able to take advantage of a cash discount on the portion of the invoice paid.

Before turning to an example, one thing that should be noted is that some suppliers may not permit a cash discount on partial payments. If this is the case, the invoice will generally make it clear that the terms of the cash discount apply to only a full payment. The following example shows how the cash discount is accounted for when partial payments are made:

EXAMPLE 5.12

An invoice for the purchase of a computer for $2,500 was dated August 1 with the terms 2/10, n/30. If a partial payment of $1,000 is made on August 10, what amount is owing on the due date?

Solution To find the value of the partial payment, it is important to remember that a payment of $1,000 within the cash discount period has a value of more than $1,000. Since there is a cash discount of 2%, the amount of $1,000 is 98%

of its cash value when paid within the cash discount period (i.e., $1,000 is "98% of the value of a $1,000 payment in the discount period"). Thus the value of the $1,000 payment must be:

$$\frac{\$1,000}{0.98} = \$1,020.41$$

Therefore, a payment of $1,000, within the cash discount period, has the equivalent value of $1,020.41.

Therefore, the amount owing after 30 days is:

Invoice Amount – Equivalent Cash Payment

or

$$\$2,500 - \$1,020.41 = \$1,479.59$$

Thus, $1,479.59 will be the amount owing at the end of 30 days.

5.4 Retail Pricing — Markup and Markdown

Each firm has a method it uses to arrive at a selling price. The method used to determine a selling price will vary depending upon the demand for the product, the competition, as well as the cost of the good or service being sold. Although these factors have a role in the pricing decision, the emphasis in the following discussion will be on cost and profit.

Costs and revenue are the basis for another important aspect of operating a business — profit. Thus, we can say that the price a business establishes for a good or service it sells must reflect:

- the cost for the good or service;
- the operating cost of the business — these include wages, storage, cost of borrowed money, and other things necessary to carry on the business operation;
- the profit necessary to make it worthwhile to stay in business.

The terms markup and markdown are used to describe the process used to set the price of goods and services offered by businesses.

A. Markup

Markup is the difference between the selling price of the good and the cost of the good to the retailer. Markup can be based on either the cost of the good or the selling price of the good.

Despite the method used, each has one thing in common: pricing goods must consider the cost of the good, the business overhead, and the profit that the business expects to earn. This relationship can be stated as:

Selling Price = Cost of the Good + Overhead + Profit

If we use the following definitions:

$$SP = \text{Selling Price}$$
$$C = \text{Cost of the good}$$
$$O = \text{Overhead}$$
$$P = \text{Profit}$$
$$M = \text{Markup}$$

The statement for selling price can then be expressed by the formula:

$$SP = C + O + P \qquad \text{Formula 5.7}$$

Now, if we think about overhead and profit as the components that are used to determine the markup, we can further express the above as:

$$M = O + P \qquad \text{Formula 5.8}$$

The selling price will be determined by the cost of the good and the markup or:

Selling Price = Cost of the Good + Markup

In general, we think about markup as being overhead and profit combined. Thus, the selling price is normally expressed as:

$$SP = C + M \qquad \text{Formula 5.9}$$

It is also common to see the terms **margin** or **gross profit** used instead of markup. So, if you see a question asking you to determine the gross profit or gross margin on a good or service, the question is asking you to find the markup.

EXAMPLE 5.13

A computer costs the computer store $1,250. If the overhead costs per computer sold is $125 and the profit expected on each computer is $200, find:

(a) the selling price;
(b) the markup.

Solution   (a) To find the selling price of the computer we first define the terms:

$$C = \$1,250, \ O = \$125, \text{ and } P = \$200$$

Applying Formula 5.7 to find the selling price, *SP*:

$SP = C + O + P$

$SP = \$1,250 + \$125 + \$200$

$SP = \$1,575$

(b) To find the markup we use Formula 5.8:

$M = O + P$

$M = \$125 + \$200$

$M = \$325$

Normally markup is expressed as a percentage or rate, rather than in dollars and cents. When percentages or rates are used to determine the markup, the percentages are either based on the cost of the good or the selling price of the good. Let's examine each method.

(i) Markup Rate Based on Cost

To find the markup rate, or percentage based on cost, requires us to set up a ratio of markup to cost. We will use the terms:

M for markup

C for cost of the good

R_{mc} for the rate of markup

The rate of markup based on cost would be:

$$R_{mc} = \frac{M}{C} \qquad \textbf{Formula 5.10}$$

From Formula 5.10 we also can see that markup can be expressed in terms of the rate of markup and the cost. This would give us:

$$M = R_{mc}C \qquad \textbf{Formula 5.11}$$

To use Formula 5.11 to find the selling price of a good, *SP*, apply the markup rate to the cost to find *M*, and add this to the cost *C*. Example 5.14 shows how to use the rate of markup based on cost:

EXAMPLE 5.14

What is the selling price of a compact disk player costing \$250 to a store if the store uses a 25% markup based on cost?

Solution We know from Formula 5.10 that selling price *SP* is found as:

$SP = C + M$

From Formula 5.11 we know that $M = R_{mc}C$. Therefore, substituting this for M in Formula 5.10 gives:

$$SP = C + M \qquad\qquad \text{Substitute } M = R_{mc}C$$
$$SP = C + R_{mc}C$$

And, we know $C = \$250$ and $R_{mc} = 25\%$, or 0.25. Therefore, substituting these values we have:

$$SP = \$250 + 0.25(\$250)$$
$$SP = \$312.50$$

Therefore, the selling price of a compact disk player that costs $250 and has a 25% rate of markup applied to the cost is $312.50.

EXAMPLE 5.15

Find the selling price of a good that costs the retailer $450 if it is marked up by $33\frac{1}{2}\%$ over cost.

Solution   We know $C = \$450$ and $R_{mc} = 0.335$.
Now using $SP = C + R_{mc} \cdot C$, and substituting the values we have:

$$SP = \$450 + 0.335(\$450)$$
$$SP = \$600.75$$

Therefore, the selling price is $600.75.

EXAMPLE 5.16

A product was purchased by a retailer for $6,000 and sold for $8,500. What was the rate of markup, based on the cost of the good?

Solution   This problem can be solved by directly applying Formula 5.10, or:

$$R_{mc} = \frac{M}{C}$$

Where:

$M = \$8,500 - \$6,000$, or $2,500, and $C = \$6,000$
Thus, the rate of markup is:

$$R_{mc} = \frac{\$2,500}{\$6,000}$$
$$= 0.41666, \text{ or } 41.67\% \qquad \text{To two decimal places.}$$

Often the markup rates produce prices that are different from the price the retailer decides to charge. For example, suppose a good costs $14.10 and a markup rate of 50% over cost is applied. Thus, the price charged would be 150% of cost (cost = 100%, markup = 50% over cost), or 1.5 × $14.10, or $21.15. What a retailer may do to try to make the good more appealing to the consumer is to set the price at $20.99. Consequently, markup based on cost may only provide an estimate of actual price charged.

Sales or reductions in selling price also may be anticipated by a retailer. Consequently, in this circumstance the initial price set for a good may be higher than given by applying a markup over cost. The reason for this is that when the item is placed on sale, it appears as if the savings at the sale price are greater and thus is a better deal for the consumer.

In the first part of the chapter, it was noted that invoices offer trade discounts. Sometimes, a business will use the trade discount as the basis for the markup. That is, if a good has a list price of $100 and a trade discount of 30%, the net price would be $70. Sometimes retailers will use the list price as the retail price. Thus, a good purchased for a net price of $70 (after the 30% trade discount) would be sold at a retail price of $100. In fact, it is common for retailers to receive a computer print-out from a supplier that specifies the retailer cost as well as a suggested retail price — the list price.

Another approach to pricing products by retailers is to reduce the markup on certain high demand items to attract consumers to their store. This practice is common in the retail grocery business. Although we have set up the formula to determine a selling price based on a markup over cost, this may only be an approximate price since many other factors must be considered by a business in setting the price of a particular good.

(ii) Markup Rate Based on Selling Price

In the previous section, the selling price of a good was based on the cost of the good, plus a fixed percentage of cost (markup). However, often businesses offer a large range of products called a product line. What businesses often do is set a markup rate for a product line, where the markup rate is based on the **selling price**.

Consider a stereo store that handles a large range of products. In this circumstance, assume the markup on stereo receivers is 35%, 30% on compact disk (CD) players, 40% on receivers, and 35% on tape decks. To find the selling price for the stereo equipment, using a markup based on selling price, requires us to find a selling price for which the markup is 30% of the selling price, 35% of the selling price, and so on, for each product line the stereo store sells. Work through Example 5.17, which outlines how the selling price can be found when the markup is based on a percentage of the selling price.

EXAMPLE 5.17

A and B Stereo purchased a Panasonic receiver for resale at a cost of $310.50. A and B apply a markup rate of 35% of the **selling price** on all receivers. Find the selling price of the stereo receiver.

Solution   Since the markup percentage is 35% of the selling price, the cost will be the remaining percentage, or 65%. Put another way, the cost will be 65% of the selling price. We know:

$$C = \$310.50$$

$$SP = \text{Selling Price}$$

Since 65% of the selling price is cost, we can say:

65% of $SP = \$310.50$

$\quad 0.65SP = \$310.50$ Convert to decimal equivalents.

$\quad\quad SP = \dfrac{\$310.50}{0.65}$ Divide each side by 0.65 to find SP.

$\quad\quad SP = \$477.69$ Round to the nearest cent.

Therefore, we can say that if the stereo receiver is sold at a price of $477.69, the percentage markup is 35%, based on the selling price.

To check this, find M, the markup, using the relation:

$$M = SP - C$$

$$M = \$477.69 - \$310.50$$

$$M = \$167.19$$

Now find the percent that the markup, M, represents of the selling price, SP. Therefore:

$$\frac{M}{SP} = \frac{\$167.19}{\$477.69}$$

$$\doteq 0.35, \text{ or } 35\% \quad \text{The sign} \doteq \text{means approximately}$$

$$\text{equal to.}$$

From Example 5.17 we can formulate an expression to find the selling price, SP, when the markup percentage is based on the selling price. If we define R_{mp} as the markup rate based on the selling price we have:

$$R_{mp} = \text{the markup percentage based on selling price}$$

$$100\% - R_{mp} = \text{the percentage of the price that the product cost represents}$$

$$(100\% - R_{mp})SP = C \quad \text{the dollar cost of the good}$$

Now solving for SP we have:

$$SP = \frac{C}{(100\% - R_{mp})}$$

If decimal equivalents are used, then the selling price would be found by:

$$SP = \frac{C}{(1 - R_{mp})} \qquad \textbf{Formula 5.12}$$

And since $SP = C + M$ thus, $C = SP - M$.

$$R_{mp} = \frac{M}{SP} \qquad \textbf{Formula 5.13}$$

In Formula 5.12, R_{mp} is expressed as a decimal equivalent. To see how this formula works, let's take the information from Example 5.17.

In Example 5.17 we found the selling price (SP) of the stereo receiver when the cost was \$310.50 (C), under the condition that the product line was marked up at a rate of 35% of the selling price. Using Formula 5.12, the selling price can be found directly as follows:

$$C = \$310.50$$
$$R_{mp} = 35\%, \text{ or } 0.35$$

Now substituting these values into Formula 5.12, we have:

$$SP = \frac{C}{(1 - R_{mp})}$$

$$SP = \frac{\$310.50}{(1 - 0.35)}$$

$$SP = \frac{\$310.50}{(0.65)}$$

$$SP = \$477.69$$

The use of Formula 5.12 makes finding the selling price straight forward when markup is based on selling price. Also, if the selling price and the markup rate, based on selling price, are known, it is possible to find the cost, C. Similarly, if SP and C are known we can find R_{mp}. Example 5.18 shows where we can use Formula 5.12:

EXAMPLE 5.18

Given the following information about stereo products offered by A and B Stereo, find the required information.

(a) If a stereo receiver costs \$275 and the markup is 35% based on selling price, find the selling price.

(b) A compact disk player retails at a selling price of \$250.95 and the markup is 30% based on selling price. Find the cost to the store of the compact disk player.

(c) A compact disk sells for $24.95. The store's cost to purchase the compact disk is $18.95. What is the markup rate if markup is based on price? What would the markup rate be if the markup was based on cost?

Solution   (a) Defining the terms we have:

$$C = \$275$$

$$R_{mp} = 35\%, \text{ or } 0.35$$

We are looking to find SP given C and R_{mp}. Applying Formula 5.12 we have:

$$SP = \frac{C}{(1 - R_{mp})}$$

$$SP = \frac{\$275}{(1 - 0.35)}$$

$$SP = \$423.08$$

Thus, the selling price of the stereo receiver is $423.08.

(b) Defining the terms we have:

$$SP = \$250.95$$

$$R_{mp} = 30\%, \text{ or } 0.30$$

We are looking to find C given SP and R_{mp}. Applying Formula 5.12 we must rearrange the formula to find C. This would be done as:

$$SP = \frac{C}{(1 - R_{mp})}$$ Rearrange by multiplying both sides of the equation by $(1 - R_{mp})$.

$$SP(1 - R_{mp}) = C$$ Rearranging gives C.

$$C = SP(1 - R_{mp})$$ Now substitute the values.

$$C = \$250.95(1 - 0.30)$$

$$C = \$175.67$$

The cost of the compact disk player must have been $175.67.

(c) Defining the terms we have:

$$SP = \$24.95$$

$$C = \$18.95$$

First we find M by using Formula 5.9, and then use Formula 5.13 to find R_{mp}, which gives:

$$SP = C + M$$ Rearranging to find M.

$$M = SP - C$$ Substituting for $SP = \$24.95$ and $C = \$18.95$.

$$M = \$24.95 - \$18.95$$

$$M = \$6.00$$

$$R_{mp} = \frac{M}{SP}$$ Using Formula 5.13 and substituting for M and SP:

$$R_{mp} = \frac{6.00}{24.95}$$

$$R_{mp} = 0.2405$$

The markup rate is 24.05% of the selling price.

This question also asks us to compute the markup rate using the markup based on cost approach. To find this markup rate we turn to the earlier Formula, 5.10, which allows us to find R_{mc}, the markup rate based on cost. Therefore:

$$R_{mc} = \frac{M}{C} \qquad \text{Formula 5.10.}$$

Finding M, the markup, we have:

$SP = M + C$ Rearranging to find M.

$M = SP - C$

$M = \$24.95 - \$18.95$

$M = \$6.00$

Substituting the values we have:

$$R_{mc} = \frac{\$6.00}{\$18.95}$$

$$R_{mv} = 0.3166, \text{ or}$$

31.66%   Markup based on cost.

B. Markdown

Often you will open your local newspaper and find retailers offering a variety of products and services on sale at a "reduced price" — a SALE. Many reasons are given for special prices offered by merchants. These range from inventory clearances, going out of business (and you can never understand how they have been going out of business for as long as you recall), making room for a new product line or the current year's products, as well as a variety of other reasons. In all cases, where a merchant reduces the normal selling price, the reduction in price is called a **markdown**. A markdown is the dollar amount the normal price has been reduced. A markdown rate is the percentage the price has been reduced. In practice, retailers simply talk about markdown and use dollars and percentages interchangeably, since the consumer knows what is meant by the sale.

Firms have different pricing practices. For example, some retailers bring in special merchandise for a sale and say that it is being offered at a special price, such as 50% off the normal price. The problem is that there never has been a normal price, since this merchandise has not been sold before. Whether this is a markdown or not is debatable. One example of where this practice occasionally occurs is with apparel products (both men and women's apparel). Here, special clothing is brought in for a sale, and the consumer is advised of the large discounts which are being made off the "regular price".

Before turning to an example, one thing to remember is that markdown implies a reduction in the selling price. If the markdown is in dollars, it is subtracted from the normal selling price to find the new price. If a percentage markdown is being applied, the percentage is applied to the normal selling price to determine the new price.

EXAMPLE 5.19

An art store advertises that a particular artist's prints have been selling for $500. However, a special offer is being made and the prints have been marked down to $425 per print. What is the dollar amount and the rate of the markdown?

Solution   Dollar Amount of Markdown = $500 – $425
$$= \$75$$

Rate of the markdown is found by the ratio:

$$\frac{\text{Dollar Amount of Markdown}}{\text{Normal Selling Price}}$$

In this example we have:

$$\text{Rate of Markdown} = \frac{\text{Dollar Amount of Markdown}}{\text{Normal Selling Price}}$$

$$= \frac{\$75}{\$500}$$

Rate of Markdown = 0.15, or 15%

EXAMPLE 5.20

A Panasonic Laser Partner printer was purchased by a computer store for $1,500.50 and then marked up 30% based on selling price. The store has just been notified that this printer will be discontinued and replaced by a new printer, the Laser Plus. The computer store decides to discount the Laser Partner by a 25% markdown. What is the markdown price of the printer? Also, find the dollar amount of the markdown.

Solution   First find the selling price using Formula 5.12:

$$SP = \frac{C}{(1 - R_{mp})}$$

$$SP = \frac{\$1,500.50}{(1 - 0.30)}$$

$$SP = \$2,143.57$$

Therefore, if the selling price is \$2,143.57, and the markdown rate is 25%, the dollar amount of the markdown is:

$$\text{Markdown} = \$2,143.57(0.25)$$
$$= \$535.89$$
$$\text{Markdown Price} = \$2,143.57 - \$535.89$$
$$= \$1,607.68$$

SUMMARY OF FORMULAS

Formula 5.1   Net Price = List Price (Catalogue Price) – Trade Discount

Formula 5.2   Amount of Discount = $d(LP)$ Used to find the dollar amount of a trade discount. LP is the list price and the d is a single, decimal equivalent, trade discount.

Formula 5.3 $NP = LP(1 - d)$ The net price, NP, given the list price, LP, and a single trade discount d. (d is a decimal equivalent.)

Formula 5.4   Trade Discount Rate
$d = \dfrac{\text{Dollar Amount of Discount}}{\text{List Price}}$ The value of the trade discount, d, given the dollar amount of the discount and the list price.

Formula 5.5 NCF
For Multiple $= (1 - d_1)(1 - d_2)(1 - d_3) \ldots (1 - d_n)$
Discounts   Used to find the NCF, (net cost factor), given the different trade discounts d_1, $d_2 \ldots d_n$. The NCF is a single discount factor to be applied to the list price.

Formula 5.6   Net Price $= LP(1 - d_1)(1 - d_2)(1 - d_3) \ldots (1 - d_n)$
Used to find the net price by applying the NCF to the list price, LP, of a good.

Formula 5.7 $SP = C + O + P$ Used to find the selling price when cost per unit, C, overhead per unit, O, and profit, P, per unit are known.

Formula 5.8	$M = O + P$	Markup, M, in dollars is found by adding the overhead per unit, O, and profit per unit, P.
Formula 5.9	$SP = C + M$	Selling price, SP, is found by adding the cost per unit, C, plus the markup per unit, M. Each term in this formula is in dollars.
Formula 5.10	$R_{mc} = \dfrac{M}{C}$	The rate of markup, R_{mc}, based on cost, is found by dividing the ratio of dollar markup, M, by the cost per unit, C. This formula applies when the markup is based on the cost.
Formula 5.11	$M = R_{mc}C$	Used to find the markup, M, in dollars, when the rate of markup, R_{mc}, and the cost per unit, C, are known.
Formula 5.12	$SP = \dfrac{C}{(1 - R_{mp})}$	Used to find the selling price, SP, when the markup rate is applied to the selling price. R_{mp} is the markup rate based on selling price.
Formula 5.13	$R_{mp} = \dfrac{M}{SP}$	Used to find the rate of markup based on selling price.

GLOSSARY OF TERMS

Cash Discount   a discount based on early payment of an invoice. This discount is shown in the terms of payment section of the invoice.

Catalogue Price   the price quoted by a supplier for a product, exclusive of any trade discounts. The catalogue price is adjusted by the trade discount to determine the price paid by a buyer — this adjusted catalogue price is sometimes referred to as the wholesale price.

Chain Discounts   when a series of trade discounts are provided by a supplier to a buyer. Normally chain discounts are applied as one discount, called the net cost factor.

End of Month Dating(E.O.M.)   when the period for the cash discount does not commence until the end of the month of the date of the invoice. In some circumstances, the term proximo dating is used for E.O.M.

Invoice   the record of sale of goods that includes unit price, quantities ordered, buyer and seller names, trade discount applicable, shipping charges, and taxes.

List Price   see catalogue price.

Markup   is the difference between the selling price of a good and the costs associated with the sale of the good.

Markup Rate   the percentage applied to either the cost or the percentage of selling price to find the dollar value of the markup. When price is used as the basis it will always produce a lower markup rate than when cost of the good is used to find the markup rate.

Markdown   the amount the price of a good has been reduced for sale purposes. The rate of markdown is the dollar amount of the markdown divided by the normal selling price.

Multiple Discounts   see chain discounts.

Net Cost Factor   the percentage of list price the buyer will pay for a good. The net factor cost is a single percentage that incorporates all the trade discounts offered to a buyer.

Net Price   the net price is the price paid by a buyer once the trade discount has been subtracted from the list or catalogue price.

Ordinary Dating   when the basis of a cash discount is from the date on the invoice for the number of days specified.

Partial Payment   when only a part payment for an invoiced amount is paid, but paid within the period in which the cash discount applies.

Receipt of Goods Dating   when the time period for the cash discount is based upon the date the goods are received.

Terms of Payment   the section of an invoice that tells the buyer what type of cash discount is offered for early payment of an invoice.

Trade Discount   the discount provided to a buyer who is purchasing goods from a wholesaler or supplier for resale. Trade discounts are percentages applied to the list or catalogue price.

CHAPTER 6

Simple Interest

This chapter introduces you to some commonly used terms in business and finance. These concepts, principal, maturity value, present value, and equivalent value, are the most common applications of simple interest in business and in your personal finances.

The ideas presented in this chapter form the basis of most topics in later chapters. A thorough understanding of how interest works is an important prerequisite for carrying out many financial transactions in the business world.

It is common for each of us to need to borrow money for purchases such as a car, a house, major appliances, and other goods that require large expenditures from the average person's income. Businesses, from small one-person operations to huge conglomerates, also borrow money to finance various stages of growth. When one uses someone else's money there is always an associated cost called **interest**. The cost of borrowing, interest, depends on such things as:

- interest rate,
- length of time the money is borrowed,
- method used to calculate the interest, and
- amount borrowed.

The type of loan an individual negotiates with a bank, credit union, or finance company also is important since different loan arrangements, such as promissory notes and demand loans, have different conditions for repayment.

It is important to understand the ideas presented in this chapter, since they form the building blocks for the financial topics in the remaining chapters of the text.

6.1 Simple Interest

In this first section we'll look at the three components that are needed to calculate simple interest: **principal, interest rate,** and **time**. During our discussion of time, we'll examine two different kinds of time, **exact time** and **approximate time,** and how the measure of time affects the calculation of interest.

A. Basic Simple Interest

The borrowing of money is something that each of us will do over our lifetime — some more than others! Borrowing funds as a means of purchasing a car, a boat, paying for an education, or for other major expenditures, is done regularly by all Canadians and Canadian businesses. **When we borrow money we are expected to pay for the use of the money — this is called interest.**

One way of thinking about interest is to compare it to the rent paid for an apartment, or, in the case of a business, the rent paid for an office or building space. In each case, the payment of a rent compensates the owner for the use of an asset. The same principle applies when you are paid interest on your savings account or Canada Savings bond — the interest you are paid is a rent for the use of your money by the bank or government, respectively.

When we borrow money, the amount we borrow is called the principal. For example, if we borrow $20,000 for a new car, $20,000 would be the principal. To determine how much interest must be paid for money borrowed, the interest rate must be known. **The interest rate refers to the percentage that will be used to calculate the cost of borrowing.** The interest rate is quoted on an annual basis. For example, if the car loan of $20,000 has a cost of 15% per year, then we would pay $3,000 ($20,000 × 0.15) interest for one year's use of the money.

Often payments are made toward the repayment of a loan; generally, payments are monthly. In these cases, the principal of the loan will not be $20,000 for a full year since the payments generally reduce some of the outstanding principal each month. Thus, there must be a measure that accounts for how long a principal has been outstanding — **this measure is called time**.

The time a principal may be outstanding can be expressed in days, months, or years. However, in all cases, the interest rate and the time will always be measured in the same terms. For example, a loan that has been outstanding for 35 days would have to be measured in terms of a year, that is, 35/365, where the 365 days is equivalent to one year. Note that the interest rate is expressed annually and the time is also expressed as a fraction of a year.

To calculate simple interest, the following formula is used:

$$I = Prt \qquad \textbf{Formula 6.1}$$

Where:

I = interest
P = principal
r = interest rate (per year)
t = time (in years or fraction of a year)

EXAMPLE 6.1

Brian Robson went to his bank and borrowed $10,000 to purchase a used car. Brian agreed to pay the full amount of the loan in seven months, plus simple interest, at an interest rate of 15% per annum (year).

(a) If Brian repays the full amount of the loan in seven months, what is the cost of the loan? (i.e., what is the interest paid?)

(b) If Brian had arranged to repay the loan in fifteen months, what would be the cost of the loan? (Cost of the loan is the simple interest.)

Solution   (a) In this example:

$$P = \$10,000$$

$$r = 0.15 \text{ (15\% per year)}$$

$$t = \frac{7}{12} \qquad \text{Note that } \frac{7}{12} \text{ is a fraction of a year.}$$

Thus, the calculation for interest is:

$$I = \$10,000(0.15)\left(\frac{7}{12}\right)$$

$$= \$875$$

(b) For fifteen months, the only change is with time.

$$t = \frac{15}{12}$$

Thus, the calculation for interest is:

$$I = \$10,000(0.15)\left(\frac{15}{12}\right)$$

$$= \$1,875$$

B. Calculating the Number of Days

Since time is often expressed in days rather than in months, the number of days in the year must be determined prior to any interest calculations. For example, a loan made on July 10 for 60 days can be interpreted two ways:

• Does one assume that 60 days is equivalent to two months? In that case, the loan would be due on September 10.

• Does one take the exact number of days and calculate that the loan is due on September 8?

The answer to these two questions depends upon whether **exact time** or **approximate time** is being used. In Canada, the practice is to use exact time, that is, the exact number of days for time (for either a loan or an investment). If the calculations use the exact number of days for interest calculations, the interest is referred to as **exact interest**. However, if one uses the rule that each month has 30 days, and a year has 360 days, then the **approximate time** is being used. If one has a problem where only the number of months is specified, without any dates, then the approximate time must be used to find the interest.

(i) Exact Time

Exact time, as the name implies, uses the precise number of days for time of the loan or investment. Thus a period of 180 days, for example, will be less than six months. The easiest way to calculate exact time is to use a table (see Table 6.1) that numerically identifies each day of the year from 1 to 365. This table permits the easy measurement of the exact number of days for interest computations.

Table 6.1   Number of Days in the Year

Day of month	Jan.	Feb.	Mar.	April	May	June	July	Aug.	Sept.	Oct.	Nov.	Dec.	Day of month
1	1	32	60	91	121	152	182	213	244	274	305	335	1
2	2	33	61	92	122	153	183	214	245	275	306	336	2
3	3	34	62	93	123	154	184	215	246	276	307	337	3
4	4	35	63	94	124	155	185	216	247	277	308	338	4
5	5	36	64	95	125	156	186	217	248	278	309	339	5
6	6	37	65	96	126	157	187	218	249	279	310	340	6
7	7	38	66	97	127	158	188	219	250	280	311	341	7
8	8	39	67	98	128	159	189	220	251	281	312	342	8
9	9	40	68	99	129	160	190	221	252	282	313	343	9
10	10	41	69	100	130	161	191	222	253	283	314	344	10
11	11	42	70	101	131	162	192	223	254	284	315	345	11
12	12	43	71	102	132	163	193	224	255	285	316	346	12
13	13	44	72	103	133	164	194	225	256	286	317	347	13
14	14	45	73	104	134	165	195	226	257	287	318	348	14
15	15	46	74	105	135	166	196	227	258	288	319	349	15
16	16	47	75	106	136	167	197	228	259	289	320	350	16
17	17	48	76	107	137	168	198	229	260	290	321	351	17
18	18	49	77	108	138	169	199	230	261	291	322	352	18
19	19	50	78	109	139	170	200	231	262	292	323	353	19
20	20	51	79	110	140	171	201	232	263	293	324	354	20
21	21	52	80	111	141	172	202	233	264	294	325	355	21
22	22	53	81	112	142	173	203	234	265	295	326	356	22
23	23	54	82	113	143	174	204	235	266	296	327	357	23
24	24	55	83	114	144	175	205	236	267	297	328	358	24
25	25	56	84	115	145	176	206	237	268	298	329	359	25
26	26	57	85	116	146	177	207	238	269	299	330	360	26
27	27	58	86	117	147	178	208	239	270	300	331	361	27
28	28	59	87	118	148	179	209	240	271	301	332	362	28
29	29		88	119	149	180	210	241	272	302	333	363	29
30	30		89	120	150	181	211	242	273	303	334	364	30
31	31		90		151		212	243		304		365	31

Note: For leap year add 1 to the tabulated number after February 28.

EXAMPLE 6.2

Colwood Paints takes out a business loan to purchase new inventory. Using exact time, find the number of days the loan is outstanding if the loan period is from September 20, 1991, to December 25, 1991.

Solution   There are two methods one can use to find the exact number of days. Using the first method, take a calendar and identify the number of days for each month. (*Note:* Remember, you include the first or the last day of the loan, but not both.)

	Number of Days	
September	10	September 21–30 <u>inclusive</u>. (September 20, is not included.)
October	31	
November	30	
December	<u>25</u>	December 25 is included.
Total	96 days	

The second and easier method is to use Table 6.1. First we find the number in the table (day of the year) for September 20 — 263. Then, we find the number for December 25 — 359. Subtract the two:

	Day of the Year
December 25	359
September 20	<u>263</u>
Difference	96 days

It is important to recognize that when 263 is subtracted from 359 it excludes the start date (or end date) as part of the calculation.

(ii) Approximate Time

The second procedure for calculating time uses approximate time, where each year is assumed to have 360 days and each month is considered to have 30 days. This basis is used to determine how long money has been borrowed or invested. This measurement is called **approximate time**. Example 6.3 demonstrates this situation:

EXAMPLE 6.3

Alec Lindsay took out a loan on March 20 for five months. Find the number of days Alec had the loan outstanding using approximate time.

Solution   From March 20 to August 20 is five months. Now, treating each month as 30 days, the approximate time is 30×5, or 150 days.

EXAMPLE 6.4

A small store took out a loan of $1,500 on March 10, 1991, and agreed to repay the loan in full in four months. If the simple interest rate being charged is 12%, determine the interest using (a) exact time and (b) approximate time.

Solution (a) To calculate interest using exact time, we must find the number of days, using Table 6.1:

July 10 (four months later)	191
March 10	69
Difference	122 days

Applying the formula, $I = Prt$, where

$$P = \$1,500$$

$$r = 0.12$$

$$t = \frac{122}{365}$$

Now calculating simple interest:

$$I = \$1,500(0.12)\left(\frac{122}{365}\right)$$

$$I = \$60.16$$

(b) Using approximate time, $t = \frac{4}{12}$, or $\frac{120}{360}$.

With approximate time each month is treated as having 30 days. Therefore, the interest is calculated as follows:

$$I = Prt$$

$$I = \$1,500(0.12)\left(\frac{4}{12}\right)$$

$$I = \$60.00$$

Although there is only a difference of $0.16 in this example, a larger principal will cause the difference to be larger.

If you have ever borrowed money in the United States you may have found that the number of days for the year was 360 rather than 365 days. When the exact number of days a loan or investment is computed, one may end up with two interest calculations. If the exact time money is borrowed is measured as a fraction of 365 days, the calculations give **exact time and exact interest**. When the exact time money is borrowed is measured as a fraction of 360 days per year, then we have **exact time with ordinary interest**. Note how the term exact time is being used; it refers to the exact number of days money is borrowed (or invested). When the approximate time is used the interest can be either ordinary or exact interest, depending on how the number of days money has been outstanding is measured. As a consequence, when the two measures of interest (ordinary and exact) and the two measures of time (approximate and exact) are combined, it actually produces a combination of four possible ways to compute interest. These are:

Exact interest using exact time;
Exact interest using approximate time;
Ordinary interest using exact time; and
Ordinary interest using approximate time.

EXAMPLE 6.5

A loan of $8,000 is taken out on August 31 and repaid on December 15. Find the interest due under each of the methods noted above, if the simple interest rate on the loan is 15% per annum.

Solution First, let's find the two measures of time:

Exact Time
December 15	349	From Table 6.1.
August 31	243	
Number of days (exact)	106	

Approximate Time
Number of days in December	15
Number of days for Sept.–Nov. (3 × 30)	90
Number of days (approximate)	105

Using the formula $I = Prt$ to calculate the interest, we have:

Exact interest, using exact time:

$$I = \$8,000(0.15)\left(\frac{106}{365}\right)$$

$$I = \$348.49$$

Exact interest, using approximate time:

$$I = \$8,000(0.15)\left(\frac{105}{365}\right)$$

$$I = \$345.21$$

Ordinary interest, using exact time:

$$I = \$8,000(0.15)\left(\frac{106}{360}\right)$$

$$I = \$353.33$$

Ordinary interest, using approximate time:

$$I = \$8,000(0.15)\left(\frac{105}{360}\right)$$

$$I = \$350.00$$

As can be seen from the above example, the method used to calculate the interest makes a substantial difference in how much interest is paid (charged to a borrower). The combination of ordinary interest and exact time produces the largest interest payment and, as you might guess, is known as the **Banker's Rule**. The Banker's Rule is more common in the United States. **In Canada, the rule applied is exact time and exact interest, providing the actual number of days can be determined.** If the time is specified in months then ordinary interest with approximate time is used. When the dates are given, we will use the Canadian approach to calculate interest, that is, using the exact time.

When calculating the number of days, there are two things that must be kept in mind. First, when determining the number of days between two dates, count either the beginning date or the end date, but not both. The subtraction of numbers in the day of the year in Table 6.1 takes this into account.

Second, when using Table 6.1 to calculate the exact time, the table must be adjusted for **leap years**. Leap years are years divisible by 4, such as 1992 and 1996. In leap years, February has an extra day. Therefore, you must add 1 to each value in Table 6.1, starting with February 28, to adjust for the leap year.

6.2 Determining the Maturity Value (Amount, Future Value), Rate, and Time

In this section we will determine the future value of money, called the **maturity value or amount**, as well as explain the formulas for determining time and the interest rate, and in particular, how these formulas can be used in simple business problems.

A. Maturity Value (Amount)

The maturity value or amount of money refers to the sum of interest and principal. What is important to understand is that money has different values at different points in time. The difference in value comes about through the accumulation of interest. The expression **time value of money** is used to recognize that money has a different value at different points in time. The term maturity value comes from the idea of growth over time, where maturity value is the value of money plus any accumulated interest.

In most discussions, the sum, S, is used for maturity value or the amount because it represents the sum of two terms, principal (P) and interest (I). To use the example of a loan, when you repay a loan you pay the principal plus the interest owing, which is the maturity value of the loan.

To calculate the sum or amount, the following formula is used:

$$S = P + I$$

Since $I = Prt$,

$$S = P + Prt$$

Factoring out the common term:

$$S = P(1 + rt)$$ **Formula 6.2**

Formula 6.2 can be used to determine, in one calculation, the amount or maturity value of a loan or a deposit.

EXAMPLE 6.6

A loan of $1,800 is arranged at 18% for four months. Find (a) the interest and, (b) the amount or maturity value of the loan.

Solution (a) To find the interest we use $I = Prt$, where:

$$P = \$1,800$$
$$r = 0.18$$
$$t = \frac{4}{12}$$

Thus, the interest is:

$$I = \$1,800(0.18)\left(\frac{4}{12}\right)$$
$$I = \$108$$

(b) To find the amount, or maturity value, of the loan we use:

$$S = P + I$$
$$S = \$1,800 + \$108$$
$$S = \$1,908$$

or

$$S = P(1 + rt)$$
$$S = \$1,800\left[1 + (0.18)\frac{4}{12}\right]$$
$$S = \$1,908$$

B. Finding the Time

Suppose you need $15,000 for a down payment on a house and you have only $12,000. To determine how long it will take the $12,000 to accumulate to the sum, $15,000, we need to be able to calculate the time, t. Based on the formulas we have learned so far, the easiest way to find the time is to rearrange the interest formula $I = Prt$.

To find t:

Divide both sides of $I = Prt$ by Pr to obtain $\dfrac{I}{Pr} = t$

Rearrange the formula to put t on the left hand side of the equation:

$$t = \frac{I}{Pr} \qquad \textbf{Formula 6.3}$$

EXAMPLE 6.7

John Adams wants to accumulate $50 in simple interest and invests $500 today. If the interest rate is 8%, how long will it take to accumulate $50?

Solution In this example:

$$I = \$50$$
$$P = \$500$$
$$r = 0.08$$

The calculation for time is:

$$t = \frac{I}{Pr}$$

$$t = \frac{\$50}{(\$500)(0.08)}$$

$$t = 1.25 \text{ years}$$

EXAMPLE 6.8

Noel Stevens borrows $5,000 to furnish her new apartment. If she wishes to pay a maximum of $100 interest, when must she repay the loan if the simple interest rate is 10%?

Solution In this example:

$$I = \$100$$
$$P = \$5,000$$
$$r = 0.1$$

Now, applying Formula 6.3 and substituting:

$$t = \frac{I}{Pr}$$

$$t = \frac{\$100}{(\$5,000)(0.1)}$$

$$t = 0.2 \text{ years, or 73 days}$$

Noel must repay the loan in 73 days.

C. Finding the Interest Rate

The interest rate can be found by manipulating the original interest formula ($I = Prt$) in the same manner as we rearranged it to find the time.

To find r:

Divide both sides of $I = Prt$ by Pt to obtain $\dfrac{I}{Pt} = r$

Rearrange the formula to put r on the left hand side of the equation:

$$r = \frac{I}{Pt} \qquad\qquad \textbf{Formula 6.4}$$

EXAMPLE 6.9

What simple interest rate is necessary to yield $150 on a $1,600 investment in eight months?

Solution   In this example:

$$I = \$150$$

$$P = \$1,600$$

$$t = \frac{8}{12}$$

Thus, the calculation for the interest rate is:

$$r = \frac{I}{Pt}$$

$$r = \frac{\$150}{\left[(\$1,600)\dfrac{8}{12}\right]}$$

$$r = 0.1406, \text{ or } 14.06\% \text{ per year}$$

EXAMPLE 6.10

A friend offers to lend you $5,000 under the condition that you will repay $5,200 in two months. What is the interest rate being charged?

Solution To solve this problem we must first find the interest payment. This is done by subtracting $5,000 (money borrowed) from $5,200 (amount to be repaid), which yields $200. Substituting the known values into Formula 6.4 we have:

$$r = \frac{I}{Pt}$$

$$r = \frac{\$200}{\left[(\$5,000)\frac{2}{12}\right]}$$

$$r = 0.24, \text{ or } 24\% \text{ per year}$$

6.3 Principal and Present Value

In this section we will examine the widely used concept of present value. Instead of beginning with the principal that is borrowed or invested it may be more appropriate to start from what you want to accumulate in the future, and then work backward to see what you must invest to reach the required amount. This is like someone deciding how much they will need to retire in so many years, then working in reverse to figure out what amount must be invested today to have the desired amount for the retirement in the future.

A. Principal

As you will recall from our earlier discussion, the principal refers to the initial amount of money borrowed or deposited. To find the value of the principal, we again use the formula $I = Prt$ and solve for P. Dividing both sides of the expression by rt yields:

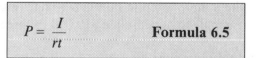

$$P = \frac{I}{rt} \qquad \textbf{Formula 6.5}$$

Another way of expressing the principal is to use the expression

$$S = P + I$$

and substitute Prt for I. Remember that S is the maturity value or amount.

$$S = P + Prt$$

or

$$S = P(1 + rt)$$

Then rearrange the expression to solve for *P.*

$$P = \frac{S}{(1 + rt)}$$ **Formula 6.6**

EXAMPLE 6.11

You are advised that you can receive $100 interest in two months. If the simple interest rate is 8%, what principal must be invested to earn this interest?

Solution In this example:

$$I = \$100$$

$$t = \frac{2}{12}$$

$$r = 0.08$$

Thus, the calculation for principal is:

$$P = \frac{I}{rt}$$

$$P = \frac{\$100}{\left[(0.08)\dfrac{2}{12}\right]}$$

$$P = \$7,500$$

Therefore, the required principal to be invested is $7,500.

EXAMPLE 6.12

Jerry and Anne need $10,000 in three years for a down payment on a house. If the simple interest rate is 6%, how much would they have to deposit today (principal) to accumulate $10,000 in three years?

Solution In this example:

$$S = \$10,000 \text{ (amount or maturity value)}$$

$$t = 3 \text{ years}$$

$$r = 0.06$$

The calculation for principal is:

$$P = \frac{S}{(1 + rt)}$$

$$P = \frac{\$10,000}{[1 + (0.06)3]}$$

$$P \doteq \$8,474.58$$

Therefore, if they deposit $8,474.58 today at 6%, they will have $10,000 in three years.

B. Present Value

One important concept used in business is present value. **Present value refers to today's value of a future amount.** For example, if a piece of land will have a value of $20,000 in three years and the simple interest rate is 10%, what is the price that should be paid for the land today? The answer to this question is called the present value (today's value) of the future amount of $20,000.

Using a time diagram, we can see the problem visually (Figure 6.1).

Figure 6.1 Bringing back a future value to find today's value (present value)

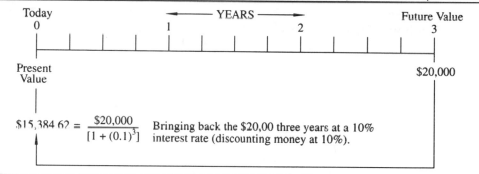

What we need to figure out is how to bring the $20,000, in three years, back in time to today. To perform this calculation, we simply find what principal, P, would have to be invested today to yield $20,000 in three years, when the simple interest rate is 10%. Therefore, we use:

$$P = \frac{S}{(1 + rt)}$$

$$P = \frac{\$20,000}{[1 + (0.1)3]}$$

$$P \doteq \$15,384.62$$

Thus, the present value of $15,384.62 will yield the future value of $20,000 in three years at an interest rate of 10%. Therefore, a fair price today for the land is $15,384.62.

Note that the formula for present value is the same formula as used to find the principal, P (Formula 6.6), namely:

$$P = \frac{S}{(1 + rt)}$$

Figure 6.2 summarises the discounting idea as shown on a timeline.

Figure 6.2   Moving the future value of $20,000 back in time (i.e., discounting) three years to find today's value

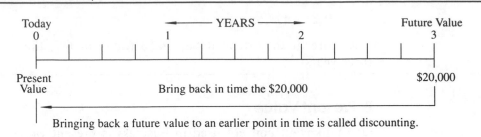

Bringing back a future value to an earlier point in time is called discounting.

EXAMPLE 6.13

What is the maximum price that one should pay today (the present value) for a piece of land forecasted to have a value of $35,000 in two years if the simple interest rate is 6%?

Solution   Using the formula $P = \dfrac{S}{(1 + rt)}$ and substituting:

$S = \$35,000$ Future value.

$r = 0.06$

$t = 2$

$P = \dfrac{\$35,000}{[1 + (0.06)2]}$

$P = \$31,250$

Based on this calculation one would not want to pay any more than $31,250, today, for land expected to be worth $35,000 in two years, if the simple interest rate is 6%.

A time diagram for this problem would look as follows:

Figure 6.3

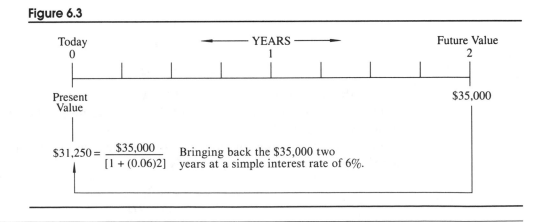

EXAMPLE 6.14

(*Note:* This real life example is fairly complicated. Work through each step of the solution slowly, making sure that you understand why each formula is used.)

A car rental agency has the cash available to buy five new cars for its fleet. After asking for quotes from different dealers, the best obtainable price per car is $15,000. One year from now, the price on the same car is expected to be $16,500 per car because of a factory price increase (inflation). The company can wait until next year to purchase the cars since the current fleet is in reasonably good shape. At present, the company has the cash in the bank and can collect simple interest at 12% per year.

(a) What is the most cost-effective decision (which is better, buy now or wait for a year)?
(b) Find the savings of the best decision.

Solution   (a) The approach that most people would use to solve this problem would be to calculate the amount of money the company would have in one year by leaving the principal in the bank and compare this amount to the amount required to purchase the cars in one year's time.

STEP 1   Determine the principal:

$$P = \$15,000 \times 5$$
$$P = \$75,000 \qquad \text{5 cars @ \$15,000 each.}$$

STEP 2   Find the amount or future value of the principal in one year, assuming it is left in the bank at the 12% interest rate:

$$S = \$75,000[1 + (0.12)1]$$
$$S = \$84,000$$

STEP 3   Determine the cost of purchasing the cars in one year's time:

$$\$16,500 \times 5 = \$82,500$$

STEP 4   Comparing the two amounts, the best decision is to purchase the cars next year and save $1,500 ($84,000 minus $82,500). The conclusion is correct but the $1,500 savings does not measure the savings today. Rather, it measures a future savings.

(b) To find the savings <u>today</u>, we must use the concept of present value. That is, we must compare today's value of the future cost ($82,500) with the actual cost today ($75,000). The difference between these two values will give us <u>today's</u> savings.

STEP 1   To calculate today's value for the future amount of $82,500 we use the present value formula:

$$P = \frac{S}{(1 + rt)}$$

Substituting: $S = \$82,500$; $r = 0.12$; $t = 1$ year

$$P = \frac{\$82,500}{[1 + (0.12)1]}$$

$$P \doteq \$73,660.71$$

STEP 2
Comparing the current price of $75,000 with today's value of the future cost, $73,660.71, the savings today of purchasing next year are:

$$\$75,000 - \$73,660.71, \text{ or } \$1,339.29$$

The savings generated in each case, $1,500 one year from now and $1,339.29 today, both express the equivalent savings but at different points in time. The relationship between the two values can be seen if we accumulate today's savings, $1,339.29, for one year at 12% simple interest. Let's see what happens if we accumulate the savings for one year:

Using Formula 6.2, finding the amount or future value gives:

$$S = P(1 + rt)$$

Substituting: $P = \$1,339.29$; $r = 0.12$; $t = 1$ year:

$$S = \$1,339.29[1 + (0.12)1]$$

$$S \doteq \$1,500 \qquad \text{Any difference is due to rounding.}$$

6.4 Equivalent Values

We already know that when money is put to work (for example, by being invested) its value grows to maturity. This process is continuous so that it is possible to calculate the value of the money at any point in time. In the case of an investment, we can find its accumulated value at any time. Each of the amounts calculated would be directly comparable and of equivalent value. For example, $1,000 invested (or borrowed) at 12% has different values over time. The changing nature of money at a given interest rate can be seen in Figure 6.4. In particular, $100 invested at 12% has a value of $106 in six months and a value of $112 in a year. Each of these three values is considered **equivalent to each other** since each is based on the same principal and interest rate, but, evaluated at different points in time.

Sometimes there is a need to change the due date of a loan, for example, when one cannot meet a particular payment. When the due date is changed, the value of the debt is also changed. The value of the debt when changed is called an **equivalent value** — a new value that is equivalent to the old debt.

Suppose that a debt of $500 is due today and the payment cannot be paid as agreed. The credit manager of the institution from which the loan was taken permits an extension of the debt for two months, providing interest is paid at the simple rate of 12%. Therefore, in two months one would pay $500 plus interest at 12% for two months, yielding a final payment of $510.

Figure 6.4   Equivalent Values

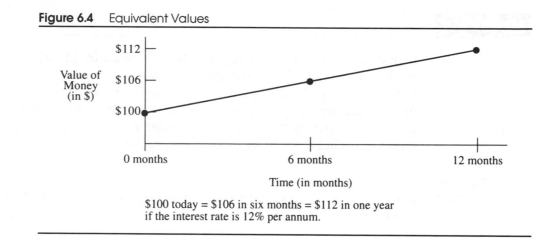

$100 today = $106 in six months = $112 in one year
if the interest rate is 12% per annum.

The payment of $510 in two months is referred to as an equivalent value, since either $500 now or $510 in two months repays the debt.

EXAMPLE 6.15

A debt of $1,000 (principal and interest) is due today. Assume the debtor doesn't have enough money to repay the loan today, and the creditor agrees that the debt can be replaced by a new debt due in three months. If the money is worth 15% simple interest, what will be the value of the new debt?

Solution   The new debt is found by solving for S, where:

$$S = P(1 + rt)$$

Substituting: $P = \$1,000$; $r = 0.15$; $t = \dfrac{3}{12}$

$$S = \$1,000\left[1 + (0.15)\,\frac{3}{12}\right]$$

$$S = \$1,037.50$$

Thus, $1,037.50 in three months is equivalent to $1,000 due today when the interest rate is 15%.

Unfortunately the calculation of equivalent payments becomes more complicated when more than one payment occurs. The problem is that a sum of money will have different values at different points in time. To resolve the problem we MUST select a focal point. **A focal point (also called a comparison point) is a common point in time when the new and old debt can be compared.** When using simple interest, different focal points will yield slightly different payments, so always be sure to use the focal date specified in the problem. The only time a focal point is understood, unless otherwise stated, is when only one payment is to be found in the future. That is, if there is only a single final payment and the focal date is not specified, use the last period as the focal point.

EXAMPLE 6.16

In Example 16.15 it was suggested that the loan of $1,000 would be repaid in three months with a single payment. Suppose it was decided to repay the debt in two equal payments — one at month three, the other at month six. Assume the focal date is agreed to be month three. (*Note:* That we could have selected any period to be the focal point; month three was simply for convenience.) What is the value of these two payments?

Solution

STEP 1 Let X be the value of each equal payment, one at month three and one at month six.

STEP 2 Move the old debt and the new debt to the focal date:

Old Debt: $\$1,000\left[1 + (0.15)\,\dfrac{3}{12}\right]$

New Debt: One payment at focal date = X

Second equal payment at month six brought back to

$$\text{focal date} = \frac{X}{\left[1 + (0.15)\,\dfrac{3}{12}\right]}$$

STEP 3 Set the old debt equal to the new debt and solve for X.

Old Debt $=$ New Debt

$$\$1,000\left[1 + (0.15)\,\frac{3}{12}\right] = X + \frac{X}{\left[1 + (0.15)\,\dfrac{3}{12}\right]}$$

$$\$1,000(1.0375) = X + \frac{X}{(1 + 0.0375)}$$

$$\$1,037.50 = X\left[1 + \frac{1}{(1.0375)}\right]$$

$$\$1,037.50 \doteq X(1.963855)$$

$$X \doteq \frac{\$1,037.50}{1.963855}$$

$$X \doteq \$528.30$$

The required answer is two equal payments of $528.30, one at month three and the other at month six.

The time diagram shows this graphically:

Figure 6.5

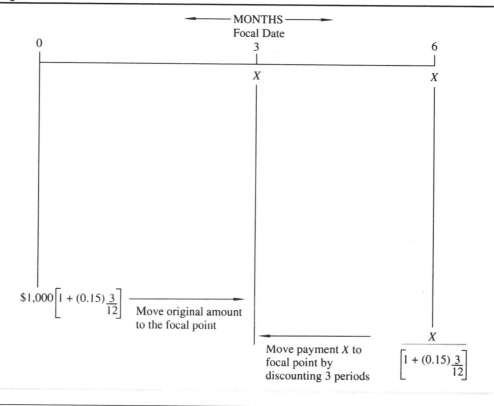

EXAMPLE 6.17

Bob Harris owes the Royal Bank $800, due in five months, and $1,000 plus 10% simple interest, due in eight months. If money is worth 12%, what single payment at month ten would be equivalent to the two original debts and satisfy the bank?

Solution Since there will only be one payment at month ten, the focal date becomes month ten. Let X be the value of the single payment. See Figure 6.6 below:

STEP 1 X is our value of the single payment at month ten.

STEP 2 Move the old debt and the new debt to the focal date.

$$\text{Old Debt} = \$800\left[1 + (0.12)\,\frac{5}{12}\right] + \$1,066.67\left[1 + (0.12)\,\frac{2}{12}\right]$$

(*Note:* $1,066.67 resulted from the accumulation of $1,000 at 10% from the beginning to month eight, when it is due.)

$$\text{New Debt} = X = \text{single payment at month ten}$$

STEP 3 Set the new debt equal to the old debt and solve for X.

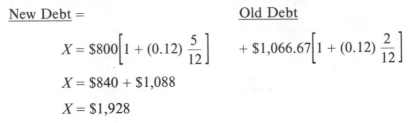

$$X = \$800\left[1 + (0.12)\,\frac{5}{12}\right] \quad + \$1,066.67\left[1 + (0.12)\,\frac{2}{12}\right]$$

$$X = \$840 + \$1,088$$

$$X = \$1,928$$

Therefore, the single payment at month ten, which is equivalent to the old debt, is $1,928.00. The time diagram is:

Figure 6.6

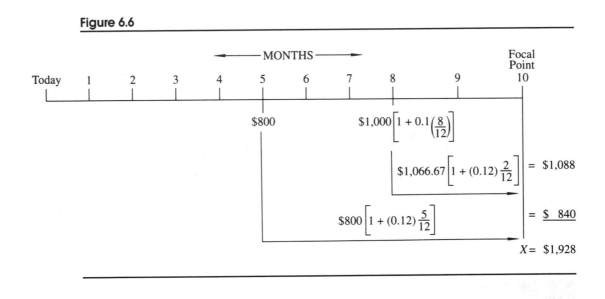

Equivalent payments are very important since they allow us to move debt to different points in time, while still satisfying the original debt.

6.5 Partial Payments

Partial payments refer to the practice of repaying a debt in a series of payments rather than in a lump sum. When we have debt that is retired (that is, to be repaid) with partial payments, there must be an agreement between the creditor and debtor on how the partial payments will be credited to the debt. The most accepted method is the **Declining Balance method**.

The Declining Balance method requires the payment to be used to pay off the interest accumulated on the debt (called accrued interest). Any of the payment remaining after the interest is deducted is then used to reduce the principal. Therefore, each time a payment is made, a separate calculation for interest payment and principal reduction must occur.

EXAMPLE 6.18

Suppose you took out a $2,000 loan at 15% to be repaid in one year. You decide to make payments of $600 after four months and $400 at the end of ten months. What is the outstanding balance of your loan at the end of the year? Use approximate time to solve the problem. (*Note:* The solution to this problem is fairly complex. Work through it slowly and methodically, making sure you understand exactly how each figure is calculated.)

Solution

Original Debt		$2,000.00
First payment, fourth month	$600.00	

Deduct:

Interest on $2,000 for four months $100.00 ⟵ $(2,000)(0.15)\left(\dfrac{4}{12}\right)$

Amount to apply to principal $500.00   500.00 ⟵ $(600 - 100)$

Balance at end of the fourth month $1,500.00

Second payment, ten months $400.00

Deduct:

Interest on $1,500 for six months $112.50 ⟵ $(1,500)(0.15)\left(\dfrac{6}{12}\right)$

Amount to apply to principal $287.50   287.50 ⟵ $(400 - 112.50)$

Balance at end of the tenth month $1,212.50

Add:

Interest for remaining two months   30.31 ⟵ $(1,212.50)(0.15)\left(\dfrac{2}{12}\right)$

Balance at the end of the year $1,242.81

6.6 Demand Loans, Promissory Notes, and Discounting

Now that you are familiar with the terms associated with simple interest, such as principal, rate, time, maturity value, and equivalent values, it's time to examine two of the most common applications of simple interest: **demand loans** and **promissory notes**. If you have ever borrowed money from a bank or entered into an agreement with a merchant for the purchase of goods, you may have used one of these loan instruments yourself, perhaps without realizing it.

We also will examine the practice of **discounting**. One example of this common financial transaction occurs around income tax time, when firms offer immediate cash for your income tax refund, often demanding a hefty discount.

A. Demand Loans

A demand loan is a loan that is payable on demand. Demand loans are often taken out for consumer purchases such as a boat, an automobile, a holiday, and other expenditures for which we cannot afford the full payment at the time of purchase. Businesses often use demand loans as a method to acquire inventory or other necessities associated with running the business. This is especially true for small businesses.

When a demand loan is taken out, the borrower will need to sign a demand note that is a promise to pay the loan. In general, demand loans do not have regular payments, rather, interest is usually paid once a month with an understanding between the borrower and lender as to when the full amount of the loan is to be repaid. This type of agreement is made at the time the loan is taken out. However, the term demand loan means that it can be called at any time while the loan is outstanding, regardless of when the borrower agreed to repay the loan.

A demand loan is usually not a secured loan. To secure a loan means offering an asset to the bank or credit union as "protection" should one have problems in meeting the terms of the loan. The need for security is influenced by many factors. For example, if a person or business has been a reliable customer with an excellent financial record, a lending institution may not require any security, providing the loan is not too large.

The interest rate charged on a demand loan will reflect the risk involved. That is, the higher the risk perceived by the lender, the higher the rate charged on the loan. One feature about the interest rate on a demand loan is that the rate is generally based on an interest rate called the prime rate. **The prime rate is the rate of interest banks and credit unions charge their very best customers and is the lowest borrowing rate.** Often the interest rate on a demand loan is quoted at 2% or 3% above the prime rate. Thus, if the prime rate changes, the rate charged on a demand loan will also change.

The phenomenon of changing interest rates is common. Most people with loans listen to the news on Thursdays to find out if there has been a change in interest rates because the Bank of Canada sets the bank rate on that day. This action determines the interest rates at chartered banks, credit unions, and other financial institutions for the following week.

Remember, the name demand loan means exactly what it states — payable upon demand. Consequently, when one enters a loan agreement that is a demand loan, the institution has the right to "call" the loan (ask you to make the full payment) at any time, for any reason.

Consider the following example of a simple interest calculation for a demand loan:

EXAMPLE 6.19

The owners of Naylor's Garage took out a demand loan on June 1 for $1,500, at a simple interest rate of 15%, to purchase some badly needed equipment. On June 14, the prime rate increased and the rate on the demand loan was changed to 16%. If the loan is repaid on June 30, how much interest is due?

Solution Using the interest formula $I = Prt$ where:

$P = $1,500$

$r = 0.15$ from June 1 to June 14 and 0.16 thereafter

$t = 13$ days from June 1 to June 14, and 16 days from June 14 to June 30

Calculation for June 1 to June 14:

$$I = \$1,500(0.15)\left(\frac{13}{365}\right)$$

$$\doteq \$8.01$$

Calculation for June 14 to June 30:

$$I = \$1,500(0.16)\left(\frac{16}{365}\right)$$

$$\doteq \$10.52$$

Thus, the total interest is $8.01 + $10.52, or $18.53.

B. Promissory Notes

Another type of loan transaction involves the use of a promissory note. **A promissory note is a written promise by the debtor, referred to as the maker of the note, to pay to the creditor, called the payee, a sum of money on the specified date with or without interest.** Promissory notes are sometimes used by banks and credit unions when the borrower wishes the loan to be outstanding for a definite period of time. It is similar to an I.O.U. you might write to a friend who has lent you a few dollars.

Promissory notes are legal promises to pay and have a very precise set of procedures for the borrower and the lender. An important feature of a promissory note is that it will have a **specific maturity date** and a **specific maturity value**. In Canada there is a requirement that, unless otherwise specified, the borrower be allowed three extra days, beyond the maturity date, to repay the promissory note. We call these **three days of grace**. The law that adds the three days of grace is the Bills of Exchange Act. Most financial institutions provide more than three days of grace — not by law — but simply as a matter of good business. That is, if someone cannot meet the obligation on the specified date, financial institutions often extend the period of repayment beyond three days. As a consequence, the notion of three days of grace is something that is not commonly discussed in financial circles — unless of course there is a legal issue with respect to its use.

A promissory note is negotiated for a particular time period. This time period is referred to as the **term** of the note. The term of a promissory note may be written in days, months, or years. In each case, there will be a maturity date. However, the legal repayment date will not actually be until three days after the maturity date. This is referred to as the **legal due date**. It may be helpful to visualize the three separate dates involved:

Figure 6.7 Promissory Note Dates

Legal Due Date

Date of Issue

Maturity Date

If the promissory note is marked "NO GRACE", three days of grace is not required and the maturity date and the legal due date will be the same.

The sample note, below, is one form of a promissory note:

Figure 6.8 Sample Promissory Note

PROMISSORY NOTE

$14,000   Victoria, July 2, 1992

Eighty days after date I promise to pay to the order of
                    John Murray Higginbottom

the sum of $_____ Fourteen thousand _____ .00
for value received, with interest at 18 % per annum.

                                        Signed John Doe

The following information can be determined from the sample promissory note:

Face value:	$14,000
Date of note:	July 2, 1992
Term of the note:	80 days
Interest rate:	18%
Maturity date:	80 days after July 2, 1992, that is, September 20
Legal due date:	September 23, 1992 (maturity date plus three days of grace)
Maturity value:	$14,000 + \$14,000(0.18)\left(\dfrac{83}{365}\right)$, or $14,573.04
Maker:	John Doe
Payee:	John Murray Higginbottom

In order to understand the terms, let's look at an example:

EXAMPLE 6.20

A promissory note is signed by Capital Drywall for $2,500 (called the face value of the note) at an interest rate of 16%. The date of the note is October 15, 1991, and the term is 60 days. Find (a) the maturity date, (b) the legal due date, and (c) the maturity value of the note.

Solution   (a) Sixty days after October 15, 1991, is December 14, 1991 (see Table 6.1). The maturity date is therefore December 14, 1991.

(b) The legal due date is three days after the maturity date, or December 17, 1991. This accounts for the three days of grace.

(c) The maturity value includes principal ($2,500) plus interest.

Using the simple interest formula $I = Prt$ where:

$P = \$2,500$

$r = 0.16$

$t = \dfrac{63}{365}$

Although the note is for 60 days, the period of grace is included in the interest calculation because one must pay for the use of the money for the full period it is used.

Substituting from above:

$$I = \$2,500(0.16)\left(\frac{63}{365}\right)$$

$$\doteq \$69.04$$

The maturity value is $2,500 + $69.04, or $2,569.04.

C. Discounting

The term discounting was briefly defined earlier as the process that brings a maturity value back in time. This process is often used to allow for an early payment on a loan or provide for the resale of a note. Notes are resold when the holder of a note — the one who lent the money originally — needs cash before the note is due. An example of discounting a promissory note is when one wishes to repay a note earlier than the legal due date. However, because the note is a binding contract one must first find the maturity value, then discount the maturity value to find out the amount needed to repay the loan early.

For example, if a note for $1,500 is due in three months but is paid off one month early, what is the payment to satisfy the note? We must discount the maturity value of the note (the amount due in three months) to find the final payment. **The interest rate used to find the early payment is referred**

to as the discount rate. When we discount there is often a need to calculate the dollar value of the discount; this is called the simple discount and is found by subtracting the discounted value of the note from the maturity value of the note.

It is important to understand that the rate of interest used in discounting a note **does not have to be the same as the interest rate on the note.** One reason that the discount rate and the interest rate on a note are different is that discounting takes place at a different point in time. Thus, the rate of interest that prevails in the market at the time of the discount will often be used for discounting. Another reason the discount rate may be different from the interest rate on the note is risk. For example, if the ability of the maker of a note is at all questionable, then the one who was purchasing the note would apply a very high discount rate to compensate for the risk.

The term "simple" is used to recognize that we are using simple interest procedures to perform the discount.

Promissory notes can be sold, for cash, if the maker of the note requires the money early. For example, suppose you loaned a friend $10,000 and shortly afterward discovered that you needed the money. The note cannot be called so you are forced to sell the note to someone. The price you get will depend on the discount rate used. Sometimes this can be very expensive if the purchaser of the note uses a very large discount rate. Next time you're reading the newspaper, look in the business classified section to see if you can find someone wanting to sell a promissory note. Other credit instruments besides notes are also negotiable.

When discounting, there will always be a **discount period**. In our example above, the note is being discounted one month early. This one month is called the discount period.

The discount rate refers to the rate used to discount notes and other credit instruments, or to an interest rate agreed upon to be used in determining the discount. When discounting a note, the monies received by the holder of the note (payee) at the date of the discount are referred to as the **proceeds**. The difference between the maturity value and the proceeds is the simple discount.

To calculate the simple discount and proceeds we must always determine the maturity value of the note. However, this step may be avoided in some circumstances since there are two types of promissory notes — **non-interest bearing** and **interest bearing**. Depending upon the type of note, the maturity value and thus our calculations to find the proceeds and simple discount will be different.

(i) Non-Interest Bearing Notes

A non-interest bearing note refers to a note whose maturity value is simply the face value on the note. For example, suppose we are advised that a debt is due in two years and will be retired by a note that specifies a payment of $2,500 (assume no grace period). In this example, the maturity value is $2,500 because we are advised that the note calls for the $2,500 payment in two years. Suppose we wish to settle the note today, what would be the proceeds and the simple discount? To answer this question we must know what the appropriate discount rate is; let's assume 15%. Now we must discount the maturity value of $2,500. Therefore, since we are bringing back a future value (we are bringing back the value two years before the due date) we use our formula to discount the future maturity value of $2,500. This yields:

$$P = \frac{S}{(1 + rt)}$$

$$P = \frac{\$2,500}{[1 + (0.15)2]}$$

$$\doteq \$1,923.08$$

Thus, the proceeds to the lender will be $1,923.08. The simple discount is found by subtracting the proceeds from the maturity value. Therefore:

$$\text{Simple Discount} = \$2,500 - \$1,923.08$$
$$= \$576.92$$

EXAMPLE 6.21

A note with a maturity value of $5,000 is due in $1\frac{1}{2}$ years. If the note is discounted today and the discount rate is 18%, what are (a) the proceeds and (b) the simple discount?

Solution   (a) Using the formula $P - \dfrac{S}{(1 + rt)}$ and substituting:

$$S = \$5,000$$

$$r = 0.18$$

$$t = 1.5 \text{ years}$$

$$P = \text{Proceeds}$$

$$= \frac{\$5,000}{[1 + (0.18)1.5]}$$

$$\doteq \$3,937.01$$

(b) Simple discount $= \$5,000 - \$3,937.01$
$$= \$1,062.99$$

(ii) Interest Bearing Notes

An interest bearing note implies that the face value of the note must be repaid plus accumulated interest — at the specified rate.

To find the proceeds and simple discount for an interest bearing note one must first calculate the maturity value of the note. The maturity value is then discounted to obtain proceeds. The simple discount is found as above, by subtracting the proceeds from the maturity value. Consider the following example.

EXAMPLE 6.22

A person borrowed $10,000 on February 15, 1991, and signed a promissory note, agreeing to repay the $10,000 in six months plus 18% simple interest. Four months later, the loan is settled by discounting the note at an interest rate of 20% (simple discount rate). If the note has specified no grace, what are the proceeds?

Solution

STEP 1   Find the maturity value of the debt on August 15. Substituting:

$$P = \$10,000$$
$$r = 0.18$$
$$t = \frac{181}{365} \qquad \text{From Table 6.1 } (227 - 46 = 181)$$

Computing the maturity value using the amount formula:

$$S = P(1 + rt)$$
$$S = \$10,000\left[1 + (0.18)\frac{181}{365}\right]$$
$$= \$10,892.60$$

STEP 2   The second step is to find the proceeds, at month four (June 15), when the debt is settled.

Substituting:

$$S = \$10,892.60$$
$$r = 0.2$$
$$t = \frac{61}{365} \qquad \text{From Table 6.1 } (227 - 166 = 61)$$

The interest rate r is 0.2 since we are told the loan is discounted at 20%. The reason $t = \frac{61}{365}$ is that the discount period is two months (June 15 to August 15), that is, it is being paid off two months before the due date.

The proceeds, P, are:

$$P = \frac{S}{(1 + rt)}$$
$$P = \frac{\$10,892.60}{\left[1 + (0.2)\frac{61}{365}\right]}$$
$$\doteq \$10,540.30$$

Therefore, the proceeds are $10,540.30 when this loan is discounted two months early at a simple interest rate of 20%.

(iii) Use of the Present Value Formula

Before ending this section there is an important point that should be remembered. When a note is discounted on a simple discount base, we use the present value formula, namely:

$$P = \frac{S}{(1 + rt)} \qquad \textbf{Formula 6.6}$$

Remember, the procedure of discounting requires us to move a future value (maturity value) back in time to the date of discount.

SUMMARY OF FORMULAS

Formula 6.1	$I = Prt$	Finding simple interest, when principal, rate, and time are known.
Formula 6.2	$S = P(1 + rt)$	Finding the amount or future value using simple interest.
Formula 6.3	$t = \dfrac{I}{Pr}$	Finding the time period when simple interest, principal, and rate are known.
Formula 6.4	$r = \dfrac{I}{Pt}$	Finding the simple interest rate when principal, time, and interest are known.
Formula 6.5	$P = \dfrac{I}{rt}$	Finding the principal when simple interest, rate, and time are known.
Formula 6.6	$P = \dfrac{S}{(1 + rt)}$	Finding the principal when the amount, rate, and time are known.
"	$P - \dfrac{S}{(1 + rt)}$	This expression finds the present value of a future amount — it is the same as the expression to find the principal.
"	$P = \dfrac{S}{(1 + rt)}$	This expression is used to find the proceeds of a discounted note, where $P =$ proceeds and $S =$ maturity value.
Simple Discount	$= (S - P)$	S refers to the maturity value, P refers to the proceeds.

GLOSSARY OF TERMS

Amount   the future value of money, which is found by adding principal plus interest.

Approximate Time   when time is computed using 30 days per month and 360 days per year.

Declining Balance Method   the process of subtracting accumulated interest from any partial payments on a loan. Any of the payment remaining is then subtracted from the outstanding principal.

Demand Loan   a loan that is payable on demand and usually requires the signing of a demand note.

Discounting   the process of bringing the value of money back in time.

Discount Rate   the rate of interest used to discount future values.

Equivalent Value   the value of money at different points in time.

Exact Time   when time is computed using the exact number of days money has been outstanding. Each year has 365 days and each month the exact number of days.

Focal Point   the point in time to which all values of money are brought. It refers to a reference point for calculating equivalent values.

Interest   the "rent" paid for the use of money.

Interest Bearing Note   the face value of the note accumulates interest until the maturity date.

Leap Years   years when February has one additional day.

Legal Due Date   the date a note or loan comes due. The legal due date for a promissory note is three days beyond the maturity date.

Maker   the person who makes the promise to pay when using a promissory note.

Maturity Date   the date a loan or investment matures.

Maturity Value   the same as amount. It refers to the principal plus interest at some point in the future.

Non-Interest Bearing Note   a note where the maturity value and the face value are the same and any interest to be paid has already been included in the face value of the note.

Partial payments   payments made toward repaying a loan.

Present Value   today's value of a future amount.

Principal   the original value borrowed or invested.

Proceeds   what one receives after discounting a note.

Promissory Note   a written promise to pay a sum of money plus interest at a specific time (date) in the future.

Simple Discount   the dollar value of the discount, which is found by subtracting the proceeds from discounting a note from the maturity value of the note.

Simple Interest   the amount that will be repaid for the use of money, calculated on principal only.

Time Value of Money   the fact that money has a different value at different points in time.

Compound Interest

Chapter 7 introduces you to the concepts and calculations used with compound interest. Fortunately, many of the procedures for compound interest are similar to the topics discussed in Chapter 6. Topics such as finding the time, present value, equivalent values, and discounting interest and non-interest bearing notes will be examined using compound interest procedures. In addition, a more detailed discussion will be given to interest rates and, in particular, finding the "real" or **effective** rate of interest and its importance when comparing rates quoted or advertised by financial institutions.

Compound interest differs from simple interest in the procedure used to compute the interest. With simple interest we applied the annual interest rate and time to the principal to calculate the interest. The most important feature of simple interest was that the principal was always the original balance with which we started. That is, the principal did not change, regardless of the time involved.

Compound interest, on the other hand, requires the principal to change. The changing principal reflects the interest accumulated from previous periods. Two ways to think about compound interest are:

- a person who borrows is paying rent on the unpaid interest as well as a rent for the use of the initial (principal) amount borrowed;
- a depositor or a lender earns interest on unpaid interest as well as the principal.

Consequently, when compound interest is used it will yield more interest dollars than the same rate applied as simple interest.

The use of compound interest in business and government is most common where money is tied up for long periods of time. The best example is a residential mortgage. Other examples include some types of consumer loans, such as outstanding credit card balances.

Before proceeding with Chapter 7 you may wish to review:

- basic algebraic concepts (Chapters 3 and 4),
- the laws and rules of exponents (Chapter 3).

It's important that you thoroughly understand **the laws of exponents** before proceeding with this chapter. (See Chapter 3.)

7.1 Compound Interest

As explained in Chapter 6, interest refers to the cost of using money. **Compounding interest means that the interest cost will include interest calculated on interest, since the interest rate is applied to both the principal and interest for all previous periods.** For example, if a loan of $1,000 is outstanding for two years and the interest rate is 12%, compounded yearly:

- at the end of the first year, the interest would be $1,000 × 0.12, or $120; and,
- in the second year the interest rate of 12% will be applied not just to the $1,000, but also to the $120 interest of the first year. Thus, in the second year the interest due would be 0.12 × $1,120, or $134.40.

Unless simple interest is stated, one assumes interest is compounded. If simple interest of 12% was used, the second year's interest would only be $120, since the simple interest rate always applies to the original principal and not to any accumulated interest. As you can see, the effects of compounding cause the interest cost to be $14.40 higher with compounding in the second year over a simple interest rate.

When compound interest is used we must **always** know how often the interest rate is calculated each year. That is, the interest rate, as with simple interest, is quoted annually, e.g., 10% per annum. However, with simple interest the calculation of interest was only once a year or fraction of a year, and only on the original principal. Compound interest, on the other hand, may involve calculations more than once a year, each using a new principal (interest plus principal).

The first term we must understand when dealing with compound interest is conversion period. The term **conversion period** refers to how often the interest is calculated over the term of the loan or deposit. The conversion period must be determined for each year or fraction of a year relevant to the problem at hand.

For example, if the interest rate is compounded semiannually (this means calculated twice a year), then the number of conversion periods per year would be two. If the loan or deposit was for two years then the total number of conversion periods would be four.

Another example would be where interest is compounded monthly. Here, the number of conversion periods would be twelve per year. The total number of conversion periods would depend upon how long the term was. **To figure out interest using compound interest, the total number of conversion periods must be determined before any computation of interest can occur.**

The method used to find the total number of conversion periods is simply to multiply the number of conversion periods per year by the number of years (or fractions of a year).

Examine Figure 7.1, which outlines some conversion periods:

Figure 7.1

Interest Period	Compound Period	Time	Total Number of Conversion Periods
18%	yearly	5 years	5 (5 × 1)
12%	semiannually	5 years	10 (5 × 2)
10%	quarterly	5 years	20 (5 × 4)
16%	monthly	5 years	60 (5 × 12)

From Figure 7.1 you can see that as the number of compound periods per year changes the total number of conversion periods changes. Now let's turn to the formula used in compound interest to see how everything fits together.

7.2 Finding the Amount

A. Finding the Amount by Using the Compound Interest Formula

In Chapter 6, the **amount** referred to the principal plus interest and was defined as S. The same is true for compound interest calculations. Before we look at the formula, let's consider an example that will help us understand the compound method.

Suppose you visit your local credit union with a $10,000 inheritance and wish to invest the money in a term deposit for five years. To your surprise the credit union offers two options: the first option offers you 8% simple interest; the second option offers you 7.5% compounded quarterly. Which one would yield the most interest and how much interest could you expect to receive?

The best way to answer the question is to calculate the interest you will receive under each option. First let's consider the option offering simple interest.

$$\text{Using } S = P(1 + rt), \text{ from Chapter 6 where:}$$
$$P = 10,000$$
$$r = 0.08$$
$$t = 5$$
$$\text{Thus, } S = \$10,000[1 + 0.08(5)]$$
$$= \$14,000$$

The simple interest option would provide you with $4,000 in interest at the end of five years.

Now let's examine the second option offered by the credit union. To use compound interest we must first define some new terms:

n = the total number of conversion periods, that is, how often the interest is calculated over the entire time period;

i = the interest rate <u>per</u> conversion period;

P = the principal;

S = the amount.

Sometimes you will see the term compound period used in place of conversion period — both mean the same.

In our example, the value of n is found by multiplying the number of conversion periods per year by the number of years, or 4×5, which gives us a total of twenty conversion periods over the five year period.

The next step is to determine the interest rate per conversion period, i. **In all compound interest problems the interest per conversion period is found by dividing the annual rate by the number of conversion periods (compound periods) per year.** In our example, the annual rate is 7.5% compounded quarterly. The interest rate per conversion period is $\dfrac{(7.5\%)}{4}$, or 1.875%, per quarter. We will use a decimal equivalent in the formulas to come, i.e., 0.01875.

In compound interest we must calculate the interest every conversion period and add it to the principal. The interest and principal become the basis on which to compute the interest for the next period. Consider the following:

Interest and principal in the first quarter is based on the calculation:

$$\$10,000\left[1 + \left(\frac{0.075}{4}\right)(1)\right] = \$10,187.50$$

Using the simple interest formula,

$S = P(1 + rt)$ where $r = 0.01875$ and $t = 1$ for one quarter.

The \$10,187.50 is the principal and interest after the first quarter.

In the second quarter the interest and principal calculations go as follows:

$$\$10,187.50\left[1 + \left(\frac{0.075}{4}\right)(1)\right] \doteq \$10,378.52$$

As you can see, the principal used each period to compute the amount (interest + principal) changes by the interest accumulated over the previous interest period. Consequently, the number of calculations will be repeated twenty times over to find the total of interest and principal using compound interest. To say the least, this involves a lot of calculations!

Fortunately, the compound interest formula makes the computation very easy and quick. The compound formula to find the **compound amount** is:

$S = P(1 + i)^n$ **Formula 7.1**

Where:

S = amount
P = principal
i = interest rate per conversion period
n = total number of conversion periods

In our problem we want to find S, where we know the following:

$P = \$10,000$

$i = \dfrac{0.075}{4}$, or 0.01875

$n = 4 \times 5$, or 20, conversion periods over the five years

Therefore, the amount, S, is:

$$S = \$10,000(1 + 0.01875)^{20}$$
$$\doteq \$14,499.48$$

As we can see, although the annual rate of 7.5% is less than the 8% simple interest, the effects of compounding certainly produce more interest. In particular, the compounding of interest in this problem produces $499.48 more interest and generates a total of $4,499.48 in interest over the five year period.

It should be clear that the compound interest formula saves a great deal of work, since it performs all the separate additions in one step. The mathematics involved in this formula are based on a topic called geometric progressions. If you are interested in this topic, take a look in Chapter 4, which explains the concepts of arithmetic and geometric series.

EXAMPLE 7.1

Fenstar Office Services has just invested $50,000 in computing equipment and software. Based on past performance, the company expects to have to replace the equipment in five years. If estimates of costs are correct, the company expects to pay $75,000 for the new equipment in five years. If the company has $50,000 cash, today, and can invest it at 10%, compounded semiannually, how much would be accumulated toward the equipment replacement in five years?

Solution To solve this problem, there are three steps:

STEP 1   Determine what is being sought. In this problem what is wanted is how much accumulates in five years, or S.

STEP 2   Identify the value of each term:

S = unknown

$P = \$50,000$

$n = 2 \times 5$, or 10   2 times a year for five years.

$i = \dfrac{0.10}{2}$, or 0.05   Annual rate divided by number of compound periods.

STEP 3   Substitute the values into the compound interest formula (Formula 7.1) as follows:

$$S = P(1 + i)^n$$
$$S = \$50,000(1 + 0.05)^{10}$$
$$\doteq \$81,444.73$$

Therefore, Fenstar will accumulate more than it requires at the end of five years, namely, $81,444.73 – $75,000, or $6,444.73 more than required.

7.3 Finding the Present Value and Compound Discount

A. Present Value

As discussed in Chapter 6, **present value refers to today's value of a future amount**. For example, suppose a friend offers you a deal that pays you $5,000 in five years, based on a certain payment being made today. If you know that the interest rate being offered at the bank is 10% compounded semiannually, can you determine the maximum price you should pay for the investment?

To answer this question we need to develop a formula for **present value** using the compound procedures. In Chapter 6 we used the term P for present value. The same applies to compound interest. The formula is simply a re-arrangement of Formula 7.1 to find P. We begin with:

$$S = P(1 + i)^n \qquad \text{Formula 7.1}$$

Rearranging this formula to solve for P yields:

$$P = \frac{S}{(1 + i)^n}$$

Using negative exponents to represent division, the expression can be rewritten as:

$$P = S(1 + i)^{-n} \qquad \textbf{Formula 7.2}$$

Formula 7.2 is the method we use to compute present value using compound interest. (*Note:* If you are unclear about negative exponents please refer to Chapter 3, where there is a discussion of this topic.) Now let's apply this formula to our problem.

The first step requires us to identify all the values for the terms in our formula:

$S = \$5,000$ This is the future amount.

$n = 2 \times 5 = 10$ Compounded semiannually for five years.

$i = \dfrac{0.1}{2} = 0.05$

Using the formula $P = S(1 + i)^{-n}$, and making the appropriate substitutions we have:

$$P = \$5,000(1 + 0.05)^{-10}$$
$$\doteq \$3,069.57$$

Thus, if your friend wants you to pay any more than $3,069.57, you would be better off to put your money in the bank, since you would earn more interest.

B. Compound Discount

In Chapter 6 we introduced the concepts of discounting and simple discount. We used the term discounting to describe the process that moves a maturity value back in time to permit an early payment or to provide for the sale of a note. The dollar value of the discount, called the simple discount, was found by subtracting the discounted value from the maturity value. The monies received by the holder of the note at the date of discount were called the proceeds.

In financial transactions involving discounting and compound interest, **compound discount refers to the difference between the compound amount and the present value (or the discounted value).** For example, if a future amount is $5,000 and the present value of this future amount is $3,500 then the compound discount would be $1,500 ($5,000 – $3,500).

In terms of the symbols used in Chapter 6, the method is defined by:

$$\text{Compound Discount} = S - P$$

EXAMPLE 7.2

Find the present value and the compound discount of $2,000 due in four years, if the discount rate (interest rate used to discount) is 15% compounded quarterly.

Solution First we find the present value of the $2,000 due in four years using our present value formula:

$$P = S(1 + i)^{-n}$$

Where:

$$S = \$2,000$$

$$i = \frac{0.15}{4} = 0.0375 = 3.75\%$$

$$n = 4 \times 4 = 16$$

$$P = \$2,000(1 + 0.0375)^{-16}$$
$$\doteq \$1,109.74$$

Now calculating the compound discount we have:

$$S - P = \$2,000 - \$1,109.74$$
$$= \$890.26$$

7.4 Compound Discount for Interest Bearing and Non-Interest Bearing Notes

A. Interest Bearing Notes

When the topic of interest bearing notes was introduced in Chapter 6, it was emphasized that discounting of an interest bearing note would be based on the maturity value of the note. The maturity value of the note was found by adding principal and the accumulated interest.

For example, an interest bearing note for $3,000 is signed and will be repaid in six months. If the interest rate is 24% compounded monthly, what is the maturity value of the note?

As can be seen, the concept of interest bearing implies that there is an interest rate attached to the note. To find the maturity value, we must first accumulate the $3,000 at the specified interest rate. Therefore, the maturity value would be found by using the formula:

$S = P(1 + i)^n$, where S is the maturity value.

$$i = \frac{0.24}{12} = 0.02$$

$n = 6$ Interest is compounded monthly.

Now making the substitutions we have:

$S = \$3,000(1 + 0.02)^6$

$S \doteq \$3,378.49$

The value of the note, if held to maturity, would be $3,378.49. However, suppose that the note is repaid early, three months before it is due, and the discount rate to be applied is 18%, compounded monthly. What is the value of the discount? The problem becomes a simple matter of discounting the **maturity value**, $3,378.49, for three months, and subtracting this discounted value from the maturity value. That is:

$P = S(1 + i)^{-n}$

Now substituting:

$$P = \$3,378.49\left(1 + \frac{0.18}{12}\right)^{-3}$$

$P \doteq \$3,230.91$

Using a time diagram, the problem looks as follows:

Figure 7.2

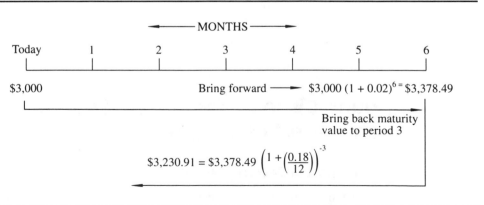

The compound discount is found by using the expression, developed above, namely, $S - P$. Again, substituting:

$3,378.49 - \$3,230.91 = \$147.58$

Please be sure that you understand the three steps involved in determining the compound discount.

1. Compute the maturity value. Remember this is a contracted amount and will be the amount to be discounted.
2. Discount the maturity value at the specified <u>discount rate</u>.
3. Compute the compound discount by subtracting the discounted value from the maturity value of the note.

Before leaving this section, recall that when we discount a note we are generally seeking to find one or both of the following:

- Compound Discount
- Proceeds, P, the dollars received after the discount.

B. Non-Interest Bearing Notes

In Chapter 6 we stated that a non-interest bearing note is a note where the maturity value of the note includes interest and principal. (Remember from our previous discussion that the interest is added to the principal to determine the value of the note.)

Suppose that a loan is repaid by signing a note that requires a \$5,000 payment in three years. In this case, all we know is that \$5,000 is the maturity value that includes interest and principal. Consequently, when we discount a non-interest bearing note we simply discount the face value of the note. For a non-interest bearing note, this is the maturity value of the note. It is important to realize that there is no need to accumulate interest, as was required with an interest bearing note.

Returning to the \$5,000 note, suppose that it is discounted at 18%, compounded monthly, two years before it is due. What are the proceeds? In this case, the discounted value of the note will give us the proceeds or the amount received after the note has been discounted.

To discount the non-interest bearing note two years early requires us to use our present value formula:

$P = S(1 + i)^{-n}$

Now making all the substitutions:

$S = \$5,000$

$n = 2 \times 12 = 24$ Two years early, compounded monthly.

$i = \dfrac{0.18}{12} = 0.015$

$P = \$5,000(1 + 0.015)^{-24}$

$P \doteq \$3,497.72$

Therefore, the proceeds are \$3,497.72 when the note is discounted two years before it is due.

7.5 The Interest Rate

When using compound interest there are three terms used to describe the interest rate. It is important that you understand and are able to calculate each. These terms are:

- the **NOMINAL** rate of interest,
- the **EQUIVALENT** rate of interest, and
- the **EFFECTIVE** rate of interest.

A. The Nominal Rate of Interest

The nominal rate of interest refers to the rate quoted annually, regardless of the number of times the rate may be compounded. For example, if the rate is quoted as 12% compounded monthly then the nominal rate is 12%. If the rate is 16% compounded quarterly then the nominal rate is 16%.

An important point to note is that the nominal rate does not tell you what you are really being charged, since you now know that if you are quoted 12% compounded quarterly it would actually cost you more than, for example, 12% compounded annually. We will calculate this "real" rate when we examine the effective rate of interest later in this section.

EXAMPLE 7.9

Jennifer applied for a loan at the Bank of B.C. She was advised that the loan would be granted and the interest rate would be 18% compounded monthly. What is the nominal rate of interest on the loan?

Solution Based on the previous explanation, we would respond that the nominal rate of interest being charged on Jennifer's loan is 18%.

B. The Equivalent Rate of Interest

The equivalent rate of interest is a rate of interest that produces the same interest per year as a different interest rate, both being applied to the same principal. For example, the equivalent rate of interest can be used to find a rate of interest, compounded semiannually, which is equivalent to another rate, compounded monthly. This seems like a lot of double talk, so let's use an example to see what is meant.

Suppose a credit union currently charges 15% compounded monthly and now wishes to compound its rates semiannually, as currently done by local competing banks. However, the credit union wants the total interest calculated to be the same when the new compounding period is introduced, that is, they want the same amount of interest to be paid before and after the change in interest compounding periods. The question is, what would the rate of interest be, compounded semiannually, that is equivalent to the old rate of 15% compounded monthly? To answer this question, we turn to the equivalent rate of interest.

To compute equivalent rates of interest we must set up **equations of equivalence,** somewhat similar to those we used in equivalent payments in Chapter 6. In the compound interest formula, the term $(1 + i)^n$ is sometimes called the **accumulation factor**, since this term determines how large S is in the formula $S = P(1 + i)^n$.

To see how the accumulation factor is used in an equation of equivalence, let's consider the problem the credit union is trying to solve. What we need to figure out is how $(1 + i)^n$ can turn out to be the same, whether the rate is compounded monthly or semiannually — do you have any ideas?

First we must summarize what we know about the two accumulation factors.

- One of the factors is known to be based on 15% compounded monthly, or $\left[1 + \left(\frac{0.15}{12}\right)\right]^{12}$ each year.

- The other accumulation factor to be found will be compounded semiannually, $(1 + i)^2$.

Next, we must set the two accumulation factors equal to each other and determine what value of i yields the same as 15% compounded monthly. The reason that one year was selected was because this was the period over which the interest was quoted (15% per annum compounded monthly). Let's calculate the accumulation factor for one year based on the current practice of charging 15% compounded monthly.

Using the expression $(1 + i)^n$:

$$n = 12, \text{ the number of conversion periods for one year.}$$

$$i = \frac{0.15}{12}, \text{ or } 0.0125$$

Substituting these into the expression we have:

$$(1 + 0.0125)^{12} = 1.160754518$$

The new interest rate must raise the same interest per year. Therefore, taking a similar position as above, we have:

$n = 2$	This results from the semiannual compounding.
$i = \text{unknown}$	This is what we are trying to figure out. Remember, we are looking for an interest rate that, when compounded semiannually, will raise the same money as 15% compounded monthly.

Now, as above, we substitute and get:

$$(1 + i)^2$$

The only thing we know is that the value of i must give us 1.160754518, as calculated above. To find this value of i we set the two expressions equal to each other and solve for i. Therefore:

$$(1 + i)^2 = (1.160754518)$$

Using our knowledge of exponents we have:

$$(1 + i) = (1.160754518)^{\frac{1}{2}}$$

Next isolate i on the left hand side of the expression and solve for i.

$$i = (1.160754518)^{\frac{1}{2}} - 1$$

$$i = 0.077383181$$

This is the rate to be applied semiannually. The annual rate will be $(0.077383181 \times 2) = 0.154766361$, approximately 15.4766% per year. Therefore, an interest rate of 15.476,6% compounded semiannually, is **equivalent** to a rate of 15% compounded monthly.

If you are skeptical, let's look at a loan for $7,500 that has been outstanding at a credit union for one year. How much interest is due under the two situations? If everything goes according to plan, the amount of interest should be identical for both interest rates.

First, let's consider the current practice of charging 15% compounded monthly:

$P = \$7,500$

$i = \dfrac{0.15}{12}$, or 0.0125

$n = 12$ Since it's for one year.

Solving for S we have:

$$S = \$7,500(1 + 0.0125)^{12}$$

$$\doteq \$8,705.66$$

The second case involves calculating the interest for the same period at the equivalent rate of 15.4766% compounded semiannually. As above, let's make the appropriate substitutions:

$P = \$7,500$

$i = \dfrac{0.154766}{2}$, or
0.077383   The rate applied every six months.

$n = 2$ Two compounding periods per year.

Now solving for S, we have:

$$S = \$7,500(1 + 0.077383)^{2}$$

$$S \doteq \$8,705.66$$

Please note that it was necessary to use sufficient decimal places to ensure we have the same answer for the two calculations. Any rounding may have caused a slight difference in the final answer. In the real world, calculations would be done by computer to get an exact rate but the rate quoted to the public would be 15.48%. (The frequency of compounding would appear in the fine print.)

C. The Effective Annual Rate of Interest

In Canada it is required by law that when we borrow money the effective rate of interest must be stated clearly in the loan agreement. In other words, borrowers must be told the true cost of borrowing.

For example, if you were taking out a loan at 14% compounded monthly or compounded semiannually, which one would you choose? With your current knowledge you would select 14% compounded semiannually since it will cost you less money.

Although you know which is the least costly, what is not stated is the actual interest cost per year. Rather, only the **nominal** rate is being quoted. The requirement that every loan have a disclosure of the "real rate" of interest means that there must be a rate stated, which, if calculated only once a year, would yield the same interest as the loan agreement requires, regardless of how often the institution compounds the interest each year. This annual rate is called the **effective rate**. Let's consider the problem at hand:

To compute an effective rate of interest we must find *i*, which, if calculated once a year, yields exactly the same interest as the rate quoted, but compounded more than once a year. In our problem we have:

$$14\% \text{ compounded monthly}$$

This rate can be converted into an equivalent annual rate, compounded once a year. This converted annual rate is the effective rate. Using the procedure we learned in the previous section, set the two accumulation factors equal to each other:

$$(1 + i)^1 = \left[1 + \frac{0.14}{12}\right]^{12}$$

This expression states, in mathematical terms, "there is a rate *i*, calculated once a year, which is equivalent to 14% compounded monthly".

Solving for *i* we get:

$$(1 + i) = (1 + 0.011666667)^{12}$$
$$i = (1 + 0.011666667)^{12} - 1$$
$$i = 0.149342$$

Therefore, 14.9342% calculated once a year gives you the same interest as the 14% compounded monthly.

The rate of 14.9342% is referred to as the effective rate since this is the annual cost of 14% compounded monthly. The same procedure can be used to compute the effective rate of 14% compounded semiannually. That is:

$$(1 + i)^1 = \left[1 + \frac{0.14}{2}\right]^2$$

$$i = \left[1 + \frac{0.14}{2}\right]^2 - 1$$

$$i = 0.1449, \text{ or } 14.49\% \text{ per annum}$$

EXAMPLE 7.3

Marilyn Anderson has been comparing the cost of a loan between two companies. One loan company has offered her a loan at 16% compounded monthly. The other company has offered her a loan at 16.5% compounded semiannually. If Marilyn were to ask you for advice, what would you recommend?

Solution This problem can be answered directly by calculating the effective rate of interest for each company. Let's do the first company:

OPTION 1

$$(1 + i)^1 = \left[1 + \frac{0.16}{12}\right]^{12}$$

$$i = (1 + 0.013333)^{12} - 1$$

$$i = 0.172270798, \text{ or } 17.23\% \text{ per year}$$

Now, turning to the second offer, we compute the effective rate as:

OPTION 2

$$(1 + i)^1 = \left[1 + \frac{0.165}{2}\right]^2$$

$$i = (1 + 0.0825)^2 - 1$$

$$i = 0.17180625, \text{ or } 17.18\% \text{ per year.}$$

Based on the above you would recommend that she take the 16.5% compounded semiannually since it is the loan that costs the least. Remember the effective rate tells you what rate, **calculated once a year**, is equivalent to the nominal rate compounded however many times the interest is compounded per year.

Often a formula is used to calculate the effective rate of interest. This formula is a simple way of transforming the quoted rate to an annual rate, equivalent to the old rate. The formula is:

Effective Rate = $(1 + i)^m - 1$ **Formula 7.3**

Where:

i = the interest rate per conversion period
m = the number of conversion periods per year

Reconsidering the example above, where Marilyn was having a problem, it becomes quite an easy matter to help her. Let's see how the formula would work for the first option, 16% compounded monthly:

OPTION 1

$$i = \frac{0.16}{12} \text{ or } 0.01333 \quad \text{This is the first interest rate quoted.}$$

$$m = 12 \qquad \text{The number of conversion periods per year.}$$

Substituting for each of the terms:

$$\text{Effective Rate} = \left[1 + \left(\frac{0.16}{12} \right) \right]^{12} - 1$$
$$\doteq 0.172271$$

Now doing the same for the rate of 16.5% compounded semiannually:

OPTION 2

$$i = \frac{0.165}{2} \text{, or } 0.0825$$

$$m = 2 \qquad \text{The interest is compounded only twice a year.}$$

Substituting the information into Formula 7.3 yields:

$$\text{Effective Rate} = (1 + 0.0825)^2 - 1$$
$$\doteq 0.17181$$

Based on these calculations we arrive at the same conclusion as before. You may ask yourself, "Which method do I use?" Either is acceptable, so use the method you understand best.

Next time you see a special ad for financing, for example, a car, which includes something about interest rates, look closely to see if the effective rate is quoted.

7.6 Fractional Periods

Up to now, all our time calculations have involved time periods that have been complete periods, that is, whole numbers for n. However, imagine a situation where a note is being discounted three and a half months before it is due, and assume the interest rate for discounting is compounded monthly. The solution to such a problem is to let $n = 3.5$ in our calculations. Moreover, it sometimes occurs that the period is something other than a half a period. For example, suppose a note is discounted twenty days before it is due. What would we do then?

A few years ago the answer would have been to calculate as many periods as one could with compound interest and then finish off the remaining period using an approximate method involving simple interest. Today, because of electronic calculators and computers, we can calculate the exact interest regardless of the fraction of a period involved.

For example, if there were only twenty days involved in the discount and the interest was compounded monthly for the discount, then the fraction used would be $\frac{20}{30}$ or .667. If the month is known, for example, March, then the time would be $\frac{20}{31}$. Remember, when there is no date specified and the interest rate is monthly we must treat the year as having 360 days and each month as having 30 days.

It will be of interest to note that financial institutions calculate the exact days in the month to determine the interest charge by computing a daily equivalent rate — for example, 12% compounded monthly can be converted to an equivalent rate, compounded daily. There are differences in each financial institution as to how the interest is calculated; the differences depend on company policy.

The use of exact fractional periods is common. One exception is calculations involving bond prices and bond interest. In the bond market an approximation method that uses simple interest has become the accepted procedure for calculations involving fractional periods. We shall examine this topic in a later chapter. Let's consider some examples of fractional periods and see how the calculations are done:

EXAMPLE 7.4

A note is discounted one month before it is due. The note is for a five year period. If the face value of the note is $6,500 and the interest rate on the note is 14% compounded semiannually, find the proceeds if the note is discounted at 12% compounded semiannually.

Solution

STEP 1   Since the note is an interest bearing note we must first find the maturity value. Use the formula:

$$S = P(1 + i)^n$$

Where:

$P = \$6,500$

$i = \dfrac{0.14}{2}$, or 0.07

$n = 2 \times 5$, or 10   Compounded semiannually for five years.

$S = \$6,500(1 + 0.07)^{10}$

$S \doteq \$12,786.48$

STEP 2   Next, we use the discount formula to discount the maturity value one month before it is due. In our example:

$$n = \frac{1}{6}$$

The note is being discounted one month before it is due; the discount period is for one month. Since the discount rate is calculated every six months, the discount period is for only a fraction of the period, or $\frac{1}{6}$ months.

$$i = \frac{0.12}{2}, \text{ or } 0.06$$

Remember this is the discount rate.

$$S = \$12,786.48$$

Now using the discount formula:

$$P = S(1 + i)^{-n}$$

Substituting we have:

$$P = \$12,786.48(1 + 0.06)^{-\frac{1}{6}}$$

$$P \doteq \$12,662.91$$

Thus, if the note is discounted one month early the proceeds are $12,662.91.

7.7 Finding the Number of Periods, *n*

When we discussed simple interest we developed a method for finding how long it would take a principal to accumulate. We called this finding the time. The similar problem in compound interest involves finding the number of conversion periods it will take a principal to accumulate. From this, we can determine the length of time it will take to accumulate a sum in the future.

The formula we use is a little more complicated to develop since to find the value of *n*, an exponent, requires the use of logarithms. Please don't panic, you can review the subject of logarithms at your leisure (see Chapter 4 for a complete discussion). For now we'll show you how to perform the calculations.

Before we get too far along, look on your calculator for a key that has **ln** or **log** on it. Although you might have both, use only one; it does not matter which one. We will use **ln** in our examples only because this is the most common one programmed into business calculators.

To understand what we are about to do we must refer to the compound formula to find the amount, *S*:

$$S = P(1 + i)^n$$

Our objective is to isolate n so that if we know S, P, and i we can determine n. The first step is to rearrange the formula by dividing both sides by P:

$$\frac{S}{P} = (1 + i)^n$$

Rearranging this expression so that the term with n is on the left hand side of the expression gives:

$$(1 + i)^n = \frac{S}{P}$$

As can be seen, it is not possible to solve directly for n because it is an exponent. In order to get the value of n isolated, we must take the natural logarithm of both sides of the expression. This process yields:

$$n[\ln(1 + i)] = \ln\left[\frac{S}{P}\right]$$

Solving for n requires us to divide both sides of the expression by $\ln(1 + i)$ giving:

$$n = \frac{\ln\left(\dfrac{S}{P}\right)}{\ln(1 + i)} \qquad \textbf{Formula 7.4}$$

In using this formula we must make sure we follow a precise set of steps to perform the computations. Study the steps in the following example:

EXAMPLE 7.5

How long will it take for \$1,500 to accumulate to \$2,146 if the interest rate is 12% compounded monthly?

Solution The first thing we must do is to identify the values for each term in our formula:

$S = \$2,146$

$P = \$1,500$

$i = \dfrac{0.12}{12}$, or 0.01   Since we know the interest rate is calculated each month.

Substituting the above into Formula 7.4 gives us the following:

$$n = \frac{\ln\left[\dfrac{\$2,146}{\$1,500}\right]}{\ln(1 + 0.01)}$$

$$n = \frac{\ln(1.43066666)}{\ln(1.01)}$$

To work out this last expression the following calculator steps are needed:

1. Enter 1.01. **Before** you depress the ln key (or the log key) check to see if the ln key operates as a second function key (this means you have to depress 2nd to operate the ln function).

2. After depressing the ln key you should get 0.009950331 — place this number in memory.

3. Now repeat Step 1 for 1.4306666. You should see 0.358140536 on the display.

4. Depress:

   - the division sign, followed by
   - recall memory, and finally,
   - the equals sign.

5. If all went according to plan you should see 35.99283 on your display, which represents the number of periods that the principal of $1,500 would have to accumulate for to amount to $2,146.

Note: If you are using Log your solution will look as follows:

$$\text{Log}(1.01) = 0.004321374$$

$$\text{Log}\left(\frac{\$2,146}{\$1,500}\right) = 0.155538459$$

$$n = 35.9928$$

In most cases you would round the answer to $n = 36$.

You may have wondered why the $\ln(1 + i)$ was entered first. This was simply because we needed this number to divide into $\ln\left(\dfrac{S}{P}\right)$. Starting with $\ln(1 + i)$ and using the memory saved us writing the numbers down and reentering them into the calculator.

7.8 Finding the Interest Rate

In some financial transactions, we know the amount we are going to invest or borrow and for how long. We also know how much we can expect to earn or pay. One example is being offered a chance to purchase an investment today knowing that you will receive a specified amount in the future. Although it may sound like a good deal, the interest rate is not specified, only the beginning and end values. What we need to do is to compute the interest rate, given this information. The procedure to find the interest rate simply requires us to manipulate the amount formula to solve for i. We, therefore, begin with Formula 7.1:

$$S = P(1 + i)^n$$

Then, we divide both sides of the formula by P:

$$\frac{S}{P} = (1 + i)^n$$

The next step requires us to take the nth root of both sides so that we can isolate i. Taking the nth root simply means we divide the exponent n by n and divide the exponent for $\left(\dfrac{S}{P}\right)$ by n. Remember the exponent for any number when not stated is 1. Let's see how this all comes together:

$$\left[\frac{S}{P}\right]^1 = (1 + i)^n$$

Dividing each exponent by n gives:

$$\left[\frac{S}{P}\right]^{\frac{1}{n}} = (1 + i)^{\frac{n}{n}}$$

Therefore:

$$\left[\frac{S}{P}\right]^{\frac{1}{n}} = (1 + i)$$

Finally we rearrange the expression so that i is on the left hand side:

$$(1 + i) = \left(\frac{S}{P}\right)^{\frac{1}{n}}$$

$$i = \left(\frac{S}{P}\right)^{\frac{1}{n}} - 1$$

Therefore, the formula to find i, the rate of interest, is:

$$i = \left(\frac{S}{P}\right)^{\frac{1}{n}} - 1 \qquad \textbf{Formula 7.5}$$

EXAMPLE 7.6

At what nominal interest rate, compounded monthly for 6.5 years, will $1,500 accumulate to an amount of $2,500?

Solution To solve the problem we must first determine the values for each term in Formula 7.5.

$S = \$2,500$

$P = \$1,500$

$n = 6.5 \times 12$, or 78

The value for n comes from the knowledge that the interest rate is compounded monthly. Now substituting into the formula:

$$i = \left(\frac{\$2,500}{\$1,500} \right)^{\frac{1}{78}} - 1$$

$$i \doteq (1.006571) - 1$$

$$i \doteq 0.006571$$

Therefore, the interest rate per month is 0.006571. To find the nominal rate per year we multiply this monthly rate by 12, which yields 0.078852, or 7.885% per year. To see if this is correct, let's find the value of S, using the amount formula:

$$S = P(1 + i)^n$$

$$S = \$1,500(1 + 0.006571)^{78}$$

$$S \doteq \$2,500$$

7.9 Equivalent Payments Using Compound Interest

In Chapter 6 we introduced the concept of equivalent payments. The concept was used in problems requiring us to reschedule payments when loan or debt obligations couldn't be met. The methods used in compound interest are the same as for simple interest except we now move payments to different points in time using the compound formula.

It's interesting to note that our compound amount formula:

$$S = P(1 + i)^n$$

is an equation that expresses value at different points in time. In fact, S is the equivalent value of P after n periods at an interest rate i. Think about it this way. If we have $50 today and the interest rate is 6% compounded annually, and the money is invested for two years, then:

$$S = \$50(1 + 0.06)^2$$
$$= \$56.18$$

From the above we can say that $50 today is equivalent to $56.18 in two years at 6% compounded annually. A similar relation can be set up for our present value formula:

$$P = S(1 + i)^{-n}$$

Again, it will be necessary to have a focal point or comparison date. If no focal date is given select a focal date that falls on one of the dates of the new payments. If there is only one unknown payment, which is at the end of a future period, then use this future period as the focal point.

EXAMPLE 7.7

A debt of $8,400 is due in seven years. If the value of money is 9.75% compounded monthly, what is the payment if the debt is paid off in five years?

Solution The following time diagram will help us visualize how we compute equivalent payments:

Figure 7.3

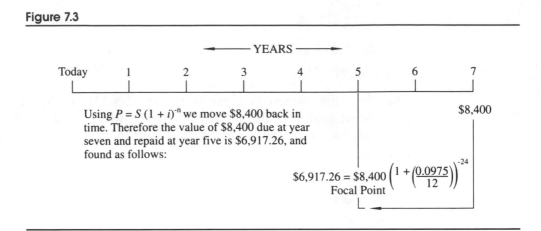

Now setting up the equations:

$S = \$8,400$

$i = \dfrac{0.0975}{12}$, or 0.008125

$i = 0.008125$

$n = 12 \times 2$, or 24   Since we are paying the loan off two years before the due date.

Using the present value formula to move the payment in year seven back to year five gives:

$P = S(1 + i)^{-n}$

$P = \$8,400(1 + 0.008125)^{-24}$

$P \doteq \$6,917.26$

Therefore, we can conclude that a $6,917.26 payment at year five, two years early, will be equivalent to $8,400 in year seven.

SUMMARY OF FORMULAS

Formula 7.1 $S = P(1 + i)^n$ Used to find the amount S using compound interest. n refers to the number of conversion periods and i refers to the interest rate per conversion period.

Formula 7.2 $P = S(1 + i)^{-n}$

Used to find the present value using compound interest. The $-n$ is another way of expressing division of S by the term $(1 + i)^n$.

$S - P$ = Compound Discount

Formula 7.3   Effective Rate $= (1 + i)^m - 1$

Used to find the effective rate of interest. m refers to the number of conversion periods per year and i refers to the rate per conversion period.

Formula 7.4

$$n = \frac{\ln\left(\dfrac{S}{P}\right)}{\ln(1 + i)}$$

Used to find the number of compound or conversion periods to accumulate to a sum, S, in the future.

Formula 7.5 $i = \left[\dfrac{S}{P}\right]^{\frac{1}{n}} - 1$

Used to find i, the interest rate per conversion period. If i is multiplied by the number of conversion periods per year, this produces the nominal interest rate per year.

GLOSSARY OF TERMS

Amount   the sum of interest and principal. When compound interest is used, the amount includes accumulated interest on interest as well as interest on the original principal.

Compound Discount   the difference between the maturity value of a note and the discounted value of the note when compound interest procedures apply to the interest calculations.

Compound Period   the time between each successive interest calculation.

Conversion Period   also called the compound period. It refers to the time between each interest calculation. (e.g., compounded monthly implies that the conversion period is each month.)

Effective Interest Rate   a rate of interest compounded once a year that yields the same interest as another rate compounded n times a year. The effective rate is often called the real rate of interest.

Equivalent Rates   the converting of an interest rate from one conversion period to another interest rate with a different conversion period, both yielding the same annual interest and both having the same effective rate.

Fractional Conversion Periods   when the value of n is a mixed number or a number less than one. Fractional periods refer to partial conversion periods. For example, two months would be two-thirds of a conversion period if the interest rate is compounded quarterly.

Nominal Interest Rate   the annual quotation of the interest rate, regardless of the number of times the interest is compounded. (e.g., for 12% compounded quarterly, the nominal rate is 12%.)

CHAPTER 8

Annuities

Most loans and some investments in business involve periodic payments, made at regular intervals, for a fixed number of periods. These financial arrangements are called **annuities**. One common example of an annuity is the mortgage used in the financing of a real estate purchase. A familiar example of an investment plan that meets the annuity criteria is a pension fund that makes regular payments.

Remember that in Chapter 7 we were only concerned with "fixed" values at different points in time. In this chapter, and in Chapters 9 and 10, attention is focused on business situations that involve a series of periodic payments made over time.

As you will learn, there are many kinds of annuities. The difference between each type is based on how or when the interest is calculated or when the payments occur. Consequently, you will need to examine each problem and situation to decide the annuity method that is appropriate for the problem at hand.

In this chapter, we will discuss in detail the ordinary simple annuity. In addition, an overview of some other annuities, the annuity due, the deferred annuity, and a general annuity, are briefly mentioned and will be discussed in detail in later chapters.

In this chapter, the common element for each annuity question is that the interest (compounding) period and the payment period will be the same.

We will begin with a brief discussion of ordinary simple annuities. We'll learn how to calculate the amount, present value, periodic payment, and the term. We'll also learn how to compute the value of a final payment when it's different from the regular payments. You'll be pleased to know that the calculations you'll be doing are extensions of the compound interest procedures you learned in Chapter 7.

8.1 Annuities: The Basic Idea

A. Terminology of Annuities

An annuity refers to a financial transaction that involves a series of periodic payments made over time at regular intervals. The original meaning of annuity referred to payments over an annual period. The only annual reference that remains is that the interest rate is quoted annually.

To understand the topic of annuities there are two terms that you must become familiar with before proceeding. They are:

- **the payment interval**
- **the term of an annuity**

The payment interval refers to the period of time that separates two successive payments. For example, a mortgage with monthly payments would have a payment interval of one month. A mortgage with quarterly payments would have a payment interval of three months.

The term of an annuity refers to the time from the beginning of the first payment interval to the end of the final payment interval. For example, a mortgage taken out today and due to be repaid over sixty months at a constant interest rate is said to have a five year term.

Before we turn to the formulas associated with annuities, there is a need to understand the differences that may occur between annuities. The following two sections describe in detail more about the financial instrument of the annuity.

B. Different Types of Annuities

Annuities can be classified according to their term, the payment period, and the interest rate. The following descriptions will help explain the different ways to consider annuities.

(i) Classifying Annuities by the Term

Classifying annuities by their term provides the basis for three types of annuities. The first is called an **annuity certain**. An annuity certain is an annuity with a precise start date and end date. One example of an annuity certain is a loan agreement that requires 60 monthly payments starting at a specific time and ending five years later (60 payments). Here one would know the start and end date, thus making it an annuity certain.

Another way the term of an annuity may be structured is to have a specific start date but no ending. When this occurs the type of annuity is called a **perpetuity**. The name perpetuity refers to payments going on forever. A perpetuity requires that only interest be paid, leaving the principal untouched to allow it to continue to generate interest for the payments indefinitely.

An annuity also may be classified as a **contingent annuity**. To be a contingent annuity, the annuity will have a definite start date, but the ending point will be unknown. The typical type of contingent annuity is pension plans, which are designed to provide payments until the death of the recipient. This uncertainty over the ending of the payments makes the annuity a contingent annuity.

(ii) Classifying Annuities by Payments

In business it is common to consider annuities by when the payments are made in each payment period. On the one hand, there is the annuity that has payments at the end of each payment period, for example, at the end of each month or the end of each quarter. When an annuity has payments at the end of the payment period, the annuity is called an **ordinary annuity**. Consider a situation where a loan agreement is signed on August 1 and requires monthly payments at the end of each month. The first payment would be due on September 1 — the end of one month after August 1. Note that the date is not important, it is the time that must pass before the first payment is made that is important. Unless told otherwise, assume that the annuity you are working with is an ordinary annuity.

Some annuities require payments at the beginning of each period. The most common examples are rent and lease payments in real estate. When the payments come at the beginning of each period the annuity is called an **annuity due**. For example, if you rent an apartment today, September 1, and the owner requires payment today, and on the first of each month hereafter, the annuity is an annuity due because the payments start immediately and occur at the beginning of each payment period.

Another annuity, which can be either an ordinary annuity or an annuity due, is a **deferred annuity**. A deferred annuity is an annuity that does not commence payments until some point in the future. An example of a deferred annuity is when a retailer has a sale in the fall and advertises that there are no payments until spring. Since the payments are deferred until spring, the annuity is called a deferred annuity. Also, the payments could come at the end or the beginning of the period. Deferred simply refers to when the annuity commences the flow of payments.

(iii) Annuities Classified by the Interest Period

Annuities that have the interest conversion period and payment period coinciding are called **simple annuities**. For example, a loan that has monthly payments and an interest rate, compounded monthly, would be called a simple annuity. Thus an ordinary simple annuity would mean an annuity that has payments at the end of each payment period, with the interest conversion period and the payment period being the same. On the other hand, a simple annuity due means the payments come at the beginning of each period, and the interest rate and the payment period coincide. In business, and in this book, unless otherwise stated, when the word annuity is used in a problem it will mean ordinary annuity. An annuity due requires a clear statement in the financial contract before it occurs. Any problems requiring the application of an annuity due will make it clear that the payments are at the beginning of each period.

Another type of annuity is the **complex or general annuity**. Here the payment period and the interest period need not coincide. An example is a loan with monthly payments and the interest rate compounded semiannually. In this instance, since the payment period and interest period are different, the annuity is called a complex or general annuity. As well, the complex annuity may be an ordinary annuity, an annuity due, or a deferred annuity. In the real world, the most common example of a complex or general annuity is the standard home mortgage. If you call a bank and ask them how interest is calculated on mortgages you will be advised that the rate is compounded semiannually with payments being made monthly or biweekly.

8.2 Ordinary Simple Annuities

An ordinary simple annuity refers to an annuity that has the following characteristics:

- The payments are always made at the end of <u>each</u> payment interval.
- The interest rate will compound at the same interval as the payment interval.

A. The Amount of an Ordinary Simple Annuity

Let's consider an example. Suppose you want to save $15,000 and agree to make regular monthly deposits at the end of each month to accumulate the desired sum of $15,000 over a period of 48 months. The time, 48 months, is called the term of the annuity. Assume the interest rate you are being paid is 18%, compounded monthly. In this example we note that:

- There are regular payments (deposits) each month over 48 months. It is the regular payments that make this an annuity. The one month time period between payments is referred to as the payment interval.
- The payment (deposit) is made at the **end** of each month, which makes the annuity an ordinary annuity.
- The monthly payments (deposits) coincide with the interest period. Since the payment period and the interest period are the same, the annuity is a simple annuity.

When we combine the facts that the payments (deposits) are at the end of each period and that the interest compound period coincides with the payment (deposit) period you see why this type of annuity is called an <u>ordinary simple annuity</u>.

To see how an annuity works, let's consider another example. Suppose a couple decides to set aside $450 at the end of each month toward the purchase of a new home. If the interest rate is 8% compounded monthly, how much will they have after three months? How much will they have at the end of one year?

If we consider the first problem, how much is accumulated at the end of three months, we could use the amount formula for compound interest from Chapter 7

$$S = P(1 + i)^n$$

to calculate the value of S for each deposit as follows:

S_1 will be the first deposit at the end of month one, accumulated for two months (remember that the first payment does not occur until the end of the first month). Thus, the first payment will have two months to accumulate:

$$S_1 = \$450\left[1 + \frac{0.08}{12}\right]^2$$

$$= \$456.02$$

S_2 will be the accumulated second deposit made at the end of the second month. By the end of the third month only one month of interest will have accumulated, thus:

$$S_2 = \$450\left[1 + \frac{0.08}{12}\right]^1$$

$$= \$453.00$$

The time diagram shown below should help you visualize the process:

Figure 8.1

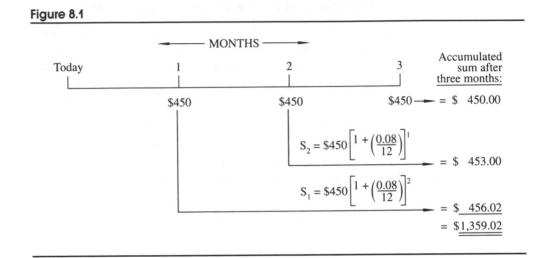

Now, since the third payment is made at the end of the third month, there will be no interest, thus S_3 is $450.

Combining the three payments plus the interest tells us how much money would have accumulated at the end of three months, or:

$$S_1 + S_2 + S_3 = \$456.02 + \$453 + \$450$$

$$= \$1,359.02$$

Therefore, if $450 is deposited at the end of each month for three months, and interest is 8% compounded monthly, there will be $1,359.02 in the account.

The second part of the problem requires us to compute how much would be accumulated at the end of one year. If we follow the method above we will have twelve separate calculations — one heck of a lot of calculations! Fortunately, the problem can be easily handled using annuities.

Before we get too far, we must define some new terms that are generally used in most finance books. The first is the **amount** of an ordinary simple annuity, S_n. The remaining terms can be defined in terms of our example:

R = the regular payment. In our example it is $450.

i = the interest per payment period. In our problem it will be $\frac{0.08}{12}$.

n = the number of payments over which we wish to calculate the amount (sum) of the annuity; in this problem n would be 12.

S_n = the amount of an ordinary simple annuity.

Bringing these terms together, a formula can be stated that will calculate the sum of a series of regular payments. This sum will include accumulated interest and payments under the condition that each payment is made at the end of each payment period, and that interest is calculated coincidental with each payment period. The formula that computes this sum is:

$$S_n = \frac{R[(1 + i)^n - 1]}{i} \qquad \textbf{Formula 8.1}$$

Now considering the problem at hand, we wish to calculate the amount of twelve payments of $450, made each month, when the payments are made at the end of each month and the interest rate is 8% compounded monthly. Substituting into our formula we have:

$R = \$450$

$i = \dfrac{0.08}{12}$

$n = 12$ Since we are interested in the amount at the end of twelve payments.

Using Formula 8.1:

$$S_n = \frac{R[(1 + i)^n - 1]}{i}$$

$$S_n = \frac{\$450\left[\left(1 + \dfrac{0.08}{12}\right)^{12} - 1\right]}{\dfrac{0.08}{12}}$$

$$S_n \doteq \$450(12.449926)$$

$$\doteq \$5,602.47$$

Thus, in twelve months there will be $5,602.47 in the account.

It is important to recognize that Formula 8.1 uses the method of geometric progressions referred to in Chapter 4. If you are interested in understanding how this procedure is used to compute the formula for S_n you may want to review the topic in geometric progression in Chapter 4.

If we recalculate the first part of the problem, where n was 3, using Formula 8.1, we should get the same answer that we found using the method of finding three values for S using compound interest. Substituting we have:

$R = \$450$

$i = \dfrac{0.08}{12}$

$n = 3$ Since we were interested in only the amount after three payments.

Now applying the formula:

$$S_n = \frac{\$450\left[\left(1 + \frac{0.08}{12}\right)^3 - 1\right]}{\frac{0.08}{12}}$$

$S_n \doteq \$450(3.02004444)$

$S_n \doteq \$1,359.02$ The same answer as first found using the compound interest method.

EXAMPLE 8.1

Maxwell Baker decides to set aside $20 at the end of each month for his daughter Amanda's college education. If Amanda turns one year old today, how much will be available for her college education when she turns nineteen years old? Assume that the interest rate is 5% compounded monthly.

Solution   First we assign all the terms:

$R = \$20$

$i = \dfrac{0.05}{12}$, or $0.004166\dot{6}$

$n = 18 \times 12$, or 216 This assumes the last payment falls on the girl's nineteenth birthday.

Now substituting into our Formula, 8.1, we have:

$$S_n = \frac{R[(1 + i)^n - 1]}{i}$$

$$S_n = \frac{\$20\left[\left(1 + \frac{0.05}{12}\right)^{216} - 1\right]}{\frac{0.05}{12}}$$

$S_n = \$20(349.2020206)$

$S_n = \$6,984.04$

Thus, if Mr. Baker makes these monthly deposits for 216 months he will have $6,984.04 set aside for Amanda's education when she turns nineteen.

B. The Present Value of an Ordinary Simple Annuity

In Chapters 6 and 7 we used the concept of **present value** to determine today's value of a future amount. The same concept is often used with annuities. Remember that the process used to bring back a series of future payments to find the present value is called **discounting**. This value is often referred to as the **discounted value** or present value of an annuity. An example of when one would want to find the present or discounted value of an annuity is the purchase of a retirement annuity. A retirement annuity is designed to provide one with a monthly income, upon retirement, for a specified number of years.

Suppose your friend Barbara asks you to help her determine the appropriate price to pay for an annuity offering a retirement income of $1,000 a month for ten years. Assume the interest rate is 6% compounded monthly. To help in solving the problem, first identify the terms to be used:

R = the regular payments, in our problem this would be $1,000 per month.

i = the interest rate per payment period. In our example it would be $\left(\dfrac{0.06}{12}\right)$, or 0.005.

n = the number of payments. In this problem there are twelve payments per year for a period of ten years, or $10 \times 12 = 120$ payments.

A_n = the present value of an ordinary simple annuity.

Combining the terms, the present value of an annuity is found by the following formula:

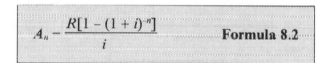

$$A_n = \frac{R[1 - (1 + i)^{-n}]}{i} \qquad \textbf{Formula 8.2}$$

Note: Formula 8.2 uses a geometric progression outlined in Chapter 4.

If we make all the substitutions we have:

R = $1,000

i = 0.005

n = 12×10, or 120

$$A_n = \frac{\$1,000[1 - (1 + 0.005)^{-120}]}{0.005}$$

$A_n \doteq \$90,073.45$

Therefore, if Barbara wants to have a monthly income of $1,000 for the next ten years, under the conditions of the problem, you would recommend that she pay no more than $90,073.45, at the interest rate of 6% compounded monthly.

EXAMPLE 8.2

Calculate the present value of an annuity that offers to pay you $1,000 every four months for one year using (a) the compound interest method and (b) the annuity formula. Assume the interest rate is 12% compounded every four months.

Solution (a) **Using the Compound Interest Method**

This method requires us to calculate the present value of each payment separately and add the present values to find the present value of the payments. Therefore:

$P = S(1 + i)^{-n}$ will be calculated for each payment.

Starting with the first payment:

$P_1 = $ The present value of the first payment of $1,000 made at the end of the first four months.

$S_1 = \$1,000$

$i = \dfrac{0.12}{3}$, or 0.04

$n = 1$

$P_1 = \$1,000(1 + 0.04)^{-1}$

$\doteq \$961.54$

Calculating for the second payment:

$P_2 = $ The present value of the second payment made at the end of the second four months.

$n = 2$

$S = \$1,000$

$P_2 = \$1,000(1 + 0.04)^{-2}$

$\doteq \$924.56$

Now doing the same for the last payment in twelve months or three interest periods away:

$P_3 = \$1,000(1 + 0.04)^{-3}$

$\doteq \$889$

Adding the three present values we have:

$$\$961.54 + \$924.56 + \$889 = \$2,775.10$$

You may find it helpful to examine this example visually:

Figure 8.2

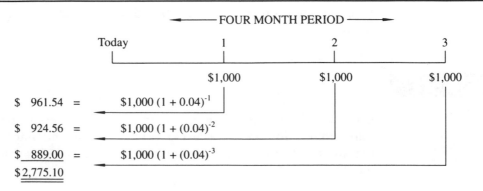

(b) Using the Annuity Method

As you will see, this method is much more direct in finding the present value of the payments. Assign values to the terms in Formula 8.2:

$$A_n = \frac{R[1 - (1 + i)^{-n}]}{i}$$

Where:

A_n = present value of the annuity (the unknown)

R = \$1,000

$i = \dfrac{0.12}{3}$, or 0.04, every four months

n = 3 Since there are three payments for the year.

Substituting:

$$A_n = \frac{\$1,000[1 - (1 + 0.04)^{-3}]}{0.04}$$

$A_n = \$2,775.09$

This result is \$0.01 different from the compound interest approach and occurs because of rounding differences. It is important to recognize the advantage of the annuity formula for finding the present value of an annuity, since it saves so many calculations when compared with the compound interest method.

EXAMPLE 8.3

A house sells for \$15,000 cash plus monthly payments (excluding taxes) of \$750 for twenty-five years. If the interest rate being charged is 10% compounded monthly, what would have been the equivalent cash price for the house?

Solution To solve this problem, we must compute the present value of the monthly payments and add this to the down payment. Therefore:

$$A_n = \frac{R[1 - (1 + i)^{-n}]}{i}$$

Where:

R = \$750

$i = \dfrac{0.1}{12}$, or $0.008333\dot{3}$

n = 25 × 12, or 300

Therefore:

$$A_n = \frac{\$750 \left[1 - \left(1 + \frac{0.1}{12}\right)^{-300}\right]}{\frac{0.1}{12}}$$

$$A_n \doteq \$82,535.42$$

Thus, the purchase price must have been:

$\$15,000 + \$82,535.42 = \$97,535.42$

Just before leaving this problem, can you calculate the financing cost of the house if you made all the 300 payments?

The solution requires us to compare the cash price with the total value of the payments. The value of the monthly payments is $\$750 \times 300 = \$225,000$. Now subtract the actual amount financed, $\$82,535.42$, which gives $\$142,464.58$, the amount of interest paid! (Remember that there was a down payment of $\$15,000$, applied to the purchase price of $\$97,535.42$, which left an amount outstanding of $\$82,535.42$.)

8.3 Finding the Size of the Payment (R) for an Ordinary Simple Annuity

A. Finding R When the Amount Is Known

Often we wish to find the value of each periodic payment when a future amount is already known. For example, suppose a young couple decides to set aside money each month to accumulate the down payment on a house. If they need $\$10,000$ for the down payment, how much would they have to set aside each month for two years? If we know the interest rate it is possible to work backwards from our amount formula for an annuity to find the payment. Let's assume this young couple can earn 8% compounded monthly on their money.

To solve this problem we need to develop a new formula from Formula 8.1 to find R, the payment. Beginning with Formula 8.1,

$$S_n = \frac{R[(1 + i)^n - 1]}{i}$$

we must rearrange this expression to isolate R. The easiest way is to divide both sides of the equation by

$$\frac{[(1 + i)^n - 1]}{i}$$

which will leave R by itself on the right hand side of the equation. Thus:

$$\frac{S_n}{\frac{[(1 + i)^n - 1]}{i}} = R$$

Switching the two sides gives:

$$R = \frac{S_n}{\dfrac{[(1+i)^n - 1]}{i}} \qquad \textbf{Formula 8.3}$$

The most difficult part of the formula is sorting out the brackets.

Returning to the problem facing the young couple, let's see how this new formula makes our task simple. First we must identify the values of the known in our expression:

$R =$ Unknown monthly payment.

$i = \dfrac{0.08}{12}$

$n = 24$ The monthly payments for two years.

$S_n = \$10,000$ The amount they wish to have in two years.

Making the substitutions into Formula 8.3 we get:

$$R = \frac{\$10,000}{\dfrac{\left[\left(1 + \dfrac{0.08}{12}\right)^{24} - 1\right]}{\dfrac{0.08}{12}}}$$

$$R \doteq \frac{\$10,000}{25.93318973}$$

$$\doteq \$385.61$$

Thus, if this couple makes monthly deposits of $385.61 into an account that earns 8% compounded monthly, they will have accumulated $10,000 through interest and payments at the end of two years.

You may find that the payment will differ by a couple of cents depending on which calculator you use.

EXAMPLE 8.4

John Zilky is thinking about retiring in five years. He would like to have $50,000 in an account upon retirement. If he decides to make monthly deposits in his local credit union where he can earn 8.5% compounded monthly, what would be the required monthly deposit to accumulate $50,000 in five years?

Solution To solve this problem we need only apply Formula 8.3, after determining the values for each term in the formula. These are:

$R = $ unknown

$i = \dfrac{0.085}{12}$, or $0.00708333\dot{3}$

$n = 5 \times 12$, or 60   The number of payments over five years.

$S_n = \$50,000$

Substituting into our formula yields:

$$R = \frac{\$50,000}{\left[\frac{\left[\left(1 + \frac{0.085}{12}\right)^{60} - 1\right]}{\frac{0.085}{12}}\right]}$$

$$R \doteq \frac{\$50,000}{74.44243734}$$

$$R \doteq \$671.66$$

Therefore, if John makes regular payments of \$671.66 each month he will have \$50,000 in five years, providing the interest rate stays at 8.5% compounded monthly.

B. Finding *R* when the Present Value Is Known

The formula for R when the present value is known relies on the initial formula for finding the present value of an ordinary simple annuity. As you may recall the formula was:

$$A_n = \frac{R[1 - (1 + i)^{-n}]}{i}$$

We must rearrange this formula to obtain an expression that will give R directly, given that we know A_n, i, and n. The first step is to divide both sides of the expression by

$$\frac{[1 - (1 + i)^{-n}]}{i}$$

which will leave R on the right hand side of the equation, that is:

$$\frac{A_n}{\frac{[1 - (1 + i)^{-n}]}{i}} = R$$

Rearranging so that R is on the left hand side of the expression gives:

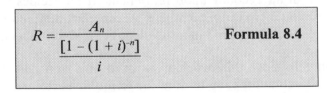

$$R = \frac{A_n}{\frac{[1 - (1 + i)^{-n}]}{i}} \qquad \textbf{Formula 8.4}$$

The best example of finding the payment when the present value is known is a personal loan. When someone borrows money they generally arrange to repay the loan with regular payments.

Two common types of personal loans are mortgages and loans for automobiles. In each case, when we borrow the money the present value of the money borrowed is the amount borrowed. Thus, if the present value, the interest rate, and the number of periods over which the loan will be repaid are known, it is a simple matter to work out the size of each payment. Let's see how it works with a specific example:

EXAMPLE 8.5

Shirley buys a new car and has to borrow $12,000 to complete the deal. Shirley's bank is happy to advance her the funds. If the interest rate is 18% compounded monthly and she makes monthly payments to repay the loan over 48 months, what would be the size of her monthly payments?

Solution   The solution to the problem requires us to use our new Formula, 8.4, that is:

$$R = \frac{A_n}{\dfrac{[1 - (1 + i)^{-n}]}{i}}$$

First we must assign the values to each term in our expression, therefore:

R = unknown

$i = \dfrac{0.18}{12}$, or 0.015

$n = 12 \times 4$, or 48   Four years.

$A_n = \$12,000$

The last term, A_n, is the most important part. The reason the loan is treated as a present value is that the money borrowed today has a value of $12,000, today, which is simply another way of looking at present value.

Now substituting into our formula:

$$R = \frac{\$12,000}{\dfrac{[1 - (1 + 0.015)^{-48}]}{0.015}}$$

$$R \doteq \frac{\$12,000}{34.04255365}$$

$$\doteq \$352.50$$

Thus, if monthly payments of $352.50 are made at the end of each month the loan of $12,000 will be paid off in 48 months.

8.4 Finding the Term (Number of Payments), *n*, for an Ordinary Simple Annuity

Finding the term of an ordinary annuity is a little more awkward since, as with compound interest, the procedure to find the value of *n* requires us to use logarithms. The formulas for finding the amount and present value are:

$$S_n = \frac{R[(1 + i)^n - 1]}{i} \qquad \text{finding the amount}$$

and

$$A_n = \frac{R[1 - (1 + i)^{-n}]}{i} \qquad \text{finding the present value.}$$

You will note that in each formula *n* is an exponent. Isolating an exponent requires us to use logarithms. It's not essential to understand how logarithms work — if you are interested, look in Chapter 4 section 4.6 for the explanation of logarithms. What you must understand is how to use the **log** or **ln** functions on your calculator.

The two sections following show you how to find *n* when you know all the other parts of the formula. The importance of this calculation can be seen when we discuss how a person can save a great deal of money by increasing a monthly mortgage payment by a few dollars.

A. Finding the Term, *n*, when the Amount Is Known

To find the value of *n* when the amounts *R* and *i* are known requires us to rearrange Formula 8.1 to isolate *n*. After a little algebra and the use of logarithms the expression to find *n* when *Sn* is known is:

$$n = \frac{\ln\left[1 + \dfrac{S_n i}{R}\right]}{\ln(1 + i)} \qquad \textbf{Formula 8.5}$$

If you would like to examine the steps involved in deriving this formula please review Chapter 4's section on the rules of logarithms.

To see the use of this formula let's consider an example:

EXAMPLE 8.6

If $100 is deposited at the end of each month into an account that pays 5% compounded monthly, how long will it take to accumulate $5,000?

Solution   The first thing that should be recognized is whether we have knowledge of the future value (amount) or the present value of an annuity. In this problem we are aware of the future value since we are advised that we want to have an <u>accumulated value</u> of $5,000, at some point in the future.

Turning to our formula, to find the value of n for a known amount we have:

$$n = \frac{\ln\left[1 + \frac{S_n i}{R}\right]}{\ln(1 + i)}$$

Now outlining the values we know from the problem:

$R = \$100$

$i = \frac{0.05}{12}$

$S_n = \$5,000$

Substituting into our formula gives:

$$n = \frac{\ln\left[1 + \frac{5,000\left(\frac{0.05}{12}\right)}{100}\right]}{\ln(1 + \frac{0.05}{12})}$$

$$n \doteq \frac{\ln[1 + 0.208333]}{\ln(1.00416666)}$$

$n = 45.5126$ Approximately 46 payments, where the 46th payment will be slightly less than the other payments.

Therefore, the length of time to accumulate the sum is:

$\frac{45.5126}{12}$, or 3.79 years   Approximately 3 years, 9 months, and 14 days, i.e., $0.79 \times 12 = 9.48$ months, $0.48 \times 30 = 14.4$ days.

Thus, if 46 payments are made with the first 45 at $100 and the 46th being slightly less, there will be $5,000 in the account. In a later section we will show you how to calculate the actual value of the 46th payment.

B. Finding the Term, *n*, when the Present Value Is Known

The procedure for finding n when the present value is known is very similar to finding n when the amount is known. The most significant difference is the use of a negative sign in the formula to follow. Unfortunately, solving for a negative exponent involves the use of negative signs, so please look carefully at the formula to see how these signs must be used to obtain the desired result. If you wish to study the algebra involved please review Chapter 4.

To find n when we know R, i, and A_n we will use the formula:

$$n = \frac{-\ln\left[1 - \dfrac{A_n i}{R}\right]}{\ln(1 + i)} \qquad \textbf{Formula 8.6}$$

Please note the negative signs. In particular, the negative sign in the front of the expression must be used since the remainder of the formula will give you a negative answer. The combination of the two negatives makes your final value for n a positive number.

EXAMPLE 8.7

Roger and Susan are negotiating a mortgage on a new home. They have decided that the maximum mortgage payment they can afford is $850 a month. If the interest rate is 10% compounded monthly and the size of the mortgage is $74,000, how many years will it take them to pay off the mortgage?

Solution To answer this question we are first going to find how many monthly payments of $850 it will take to repay the mortgage. Once we have the number of monthly payments we will then convert this into years by dividing n by 12, since there are twelve months in each year.

The first step in our solution is to make sure we lay out what we know. Based on the information, we know:

$R = \$850$

$i = \dfrac{0.10}{12}$, or $0.008333\dot{3}$

$A_n = \$74,000$

Substituting into the Formula 8.6 gives:

$$n = \frac{-\ln\left[1 - \dfrac{\$74,000\left(\dfrac{0.10}{12}\right)}{\$850}\right]}{\ln\left(1 + \dfrac{0.10}{12}\right)}$$

$$n \doteq \frac{-[-1.2927672]}{(0.0082988)}$$

$$n \doteq -[-155.7776]$$

$$n \doteq 155.78 \text{ months, or } \left(\frac{155.78}{12}\right), \text{ or } 12.9815 \text{ years}$$

Therefore, the number of years required to repay a $74,000 mortgage is approximately thirteen years, and requires 156 payments. The first 155 payments will be $850 and the last payment will be a smaller payment, under the condition that the interest rate is 10% compounded monthly. A later section of the text explains how to find the value of the different last payment (see Example 8.9).

8.5 Finding the Outstanding Balance of a Loan, the Balance in a Fund, and the Value of the Last Payment

As we saw in the previous section, when we calculate the term of an annuity, or n, we often find that the number of payments does not work out to be an even number. In Example 8.7, we found that it was necessary to make 155.78 payments. In the real world the actual number of payments would be 156. When this occurs the value of the final payment will be different from the other payments. In this section we will show you how to compute the value of the last payment.

To find the value of the last payment we must know how to find the outstanding balance or the accumulated amount at any time during the term of an annuity. To get started, let's see how we can find out how much of the loan we've paid off or how much we've accumulated in an account before the end of the term of the annuity.

A. Finding the Outstanding Balance or the Accumulated Sum of an Annuity

How often have you heard someone talking about how much they have remaining to pay on a loan? Perhaps you have wanted to determine how much money you have in a retirement fund at a certain point in time. The method relies on a combination of the techniques you've learned up to this point in the text. Let's look first at finding the balance of a loan.

(I) Finding the Outstanding Balance on a Loan: Using Present Value

The method used to find the outstanding balance on a loan requires us to compute the present value of the remaining payments. For example, if you have a loan that must be paid off with 60 monthly payments and you have just made the 38th payment, to find out how much is still owing immediately upon paying the 38th payment, you would need to calculate the present value of the remaining 22 payments. This will work because the value of the remaining payments — present value — is today's value of the future payments. This "today's value" is the outstanding balance of the loan, that is, today's value of the loan.

Suppose you had been making monthly payments of $133.47 on a loan of $6,000 at an interest rate of 12% compounded monthly. On the 38th payment you want to determine the outstanding balance. Since there are 22 payments remaining you would find the present value of these payments using the present value formula for an ordinary simple annuity. That is, using Formula 8.1:

$$A_n = \frac{R[1 - (1 + i)^{-n}]}{i}$$

Where:

$R = \$133.47$

$i = \dfrac{0.12}{12}$, or 0.01

$n = 22$ The remaining payments.

Substituting into the formula yields:

$$A_n = \frac{\$133.47[1 - (1 + 0.01)^{-22}]}{0.01}$$

$$A_n \doteq \$2,624.07$$

Thus, the balance of a $6,000 loan after making 38 monthly payments of size $133.47 is $2,624.07.

(ii) Using Future Value to Find the Outstanding Balance for a Loan

A second approach to finding the outstanding balance on a loan uses information on what has occurred, rather than turning to the present value of payments to occur in the future. This second approach uses the accumulation formulas for S and S_n and focuses on the payments <u>that have been made</u>, in addition to the initial amount of the loan. To see how this method works consider Example 8.8:

EXAMPLE 8.8

A loan is to be repaid over 25 years with monthly payments. The size of the loan is $160,000 and the interest rate is 14% compounded monthly. If monthly payments have been regularly made, how much is outstanding on the loan after three years of payments? Use the accumulation approach to find the outstanding balance.

Solution

STEP 1   First we must find R, the regular payment:

$$R = \frac{A_n}{\dfrac{[1 - (1 + i)^{-n}]}{i}}$$

Where:

$$A_n = \$160,000$$

$$i = \frac{0.14}{12}, \text{ or } 0.11666\dot{6}$$

$$n = 25 \times 12, \text{ or } 300$$

$$R = \frac{\$160,000}{\dfrac{\left[1 - \left(1 + \dfrac{0.14}{12}\right)^{-300}\right]}{\dfrac{0.14}{12}}}$$

$$R = \$1,926.02$$

STEP 2   Using the relation

Outstanding Balance $= S - S_n$

$$S = P(1 + i)^n \qquad \text{The amount formula from Chapter 7.}$$

Where:

$R = \$1,926.02$

$P = \$160,000$

$S_n = \$160,000$

$i = \dfrac{0.14}{12}$, or

$0.011666\dot{6}$

$n = 3 \times 12$, or 36

Note that n is 36, the number of payments <u>that have been made</u>. In the future value approach, n always refers to the number of payments that have been made when finding the outstanding balance.

Substituting everything:

Outstanding Balance $= P(1 + i)^n - \dfrac{R[(1 + i)^n - 1]}{i}$

$$\$160,000\left(1 + \frac{0.14}{12}\right)^{36} - \frac{\$1,926.02\left[\left(1 + \frac{0.14}{12}\right)^{36} - 1\right]}{\frac{0.14}{12}}$$

Outstanding Balance $= \$242,922.56 - \$85,559.20$

$= \$157,363.36$

Thus, the outstanding balance immediately after the 36th payment is $157,363.36. If you compare this to the answer found by computing the present value of the remaining payments ($n - 264$), you will get the same answer. There may be a slight difference due to rounding.

When you have need to find the outstanding balance, using either the present value or accumulation methods are acceptable. Each method has some advantage on certain types of problems. The choice by the writer to use the present value approach to find an outstanding balance is a personal preference.

(iii) Finding the Accumulated Amount at Any Point in Time

When we make regular payments to a retirement plan or some other fund, it may be necessary to figure out how much has accumulated in the fund at some point in time. The process is quite straight forward since we need only find the sum, S_n, for the number of periods for which payments have been made.

For example, suppose you have been making payments of $100 a month to an RRSP for the last eight years. If the interest rate is 8% compounded monthly, how much is in the fund at the end of eight years? To determine this we simply apply Formula 8.1, that is:

$$S_n = \frac{R[(1 + i)^n - 1]}{i}$$

Where:

$$R = \$100$$

$$i = \frac{0.08}{12}$$

$$n = 12 \times 8, \text{ or } 96$$

Substituting into our formula gives:

$$S_n = \frac{\$100\left[\left(1 + \dfrac{0.08}{12}\right)^{96} - 1\right]}{\dfrac{0.08}{12}}$$

$$S_n \doteq \$100(133.868583)$$

$$S_n = \$13,386.86$$

Therefore, after eight years of payments you would have accumulated $13,386.86 in the retirement plan.

B. Finding the Value of the Last Payment

As you may remember, when we found out how to calculate the number of payments we found that the value of n was not an even number. When this occurs we must adjust the annuity payments, resulting in a smaller last payment. To see how this problem can be handled with the tools you've learned so far let's recall an example from Section 8.5:

EXAMPLE 8.9	(from 8.7)

Roger and Susan were required to make 156 payments with the first 155 payments being $850 and the last payment being different. Now let's see how we can find the exact value of the last payment.

The first step is to determine the outstanding balance at the end of period 155. Then we figure out how much interest will be due on the outstanding balance from period 155 to period 156. This interest plus the outstanding balance from period 155 will be the payment at period 156 that will pay off the debt.

To find the outstanding balance at the end of period 155 we must calculate the present value of the remaining payment. In this problem the remaining payment is a fractional period, or 0.78. Using our present value formula and making the substitutions we have:

$$A_n = \frac{R[1 - (1 + i)^{-n}]}{i}$$

Where:

$$R = \$850$$

$$i = \frac{0.10}{12}, \text{ or } 0.008333\dot{3}$$

$$n = 0.78$$

Substituting we get:

$$A_n = \frac{\$850[1 - (1 + 0.008333\dot{3})^{-0.78}]}{0.008333\dot{3}}$$

$$A_n \doteq \$850(0.7742592)$$

$$A_n \doteq \$658.12$$

Thus $658.12 is outstanding at the end of the 155th period. If we figure out how much interest will be due on $658.12 at the end of the 156th period we need only add this interest to the $658.12 to find the value of the last payment.

To calculate the interest on the $658.12 for one period we simply multiply the rate times the outstanding balance for one period.

$$\$658.12 \times 0.008333\dot{3} = \$5.48$$

Therefore, the value of the last payment is:

$$\$658.12 + \$5.48 = \$663.60$$

If the owners make a payment of $663.60 at the end of period 156 they will have paid off the entire debt.

8.6 Finding the Rate of Interest for an Annuity

Up to this point we have not explored finding the interest rate for an annuity. Unlike the annuity methods we have discussed so far, there is some "guessing" involved with calculating the interest rate.

Those of you with financial calculators will find the calculation of i very easy and precise. If you don't have a financial calculator, you must find a procedure that will approximate i for any of the annuities discussed.

To make the process clear we will choose two examples, one involving the amount of an ordinary simple annuity and the other dealing with the present value of an ordinary simple annuity. The important thing to understand is that we can use the identical method for any type of annuity, including those to be examined in the next two chapters.

A. The Approximate Method

To find the interest rate when the amount, payment, and n are known we would begin with the formula:

$$S_n = \frac{R[(1 + i)^n - 1]}{i}$$

Since our goal is to find i we must rearrange the formula to isolate i or:

$$\frac{S_n}{R} = \frac{[(1 + i)^n - 1]}{i}$$

As you can see, the value of i cannot be isolated since there is no way to get i by itself on one side of the expression.

To solve this problem we can closely approximate the value of i by using the procedure outlined in the next example.

EXAMPLE 8.10

The District of Gray River is setting up a reserve fund that will accumulate to $5,000,000 in three years. The payments that the District makes are $345,018 every quarter. If the interest rate compounds every quarter, what is the nominal rate? (Remember, the nominal rate of interest refers to the rate quoted annually, regardless of the number of times the rate may be compounded.)

Solution The first thing we do is to set the equation up with the known values. These are:

$$S_n = \$5,000,000$$
$$n = 4 \times 3, \text{ or } 12$$
$$R = \$345,018$$

Now substituting these into our formula for S_n we have:

$$S_n = \frac{R[(1 + i)^n - 1]}{i}$$

or:

$$\frac{S_n}{R} = \frac{[(1 + i)^n - 1]}{i}$$

$$\frac{\$5,000,000}{\$345,018} = \frac{[(1 + i)^{12} - 1]}{i}$$

$$14.491998 = \frac{[(1 + i)^{12} - 1]}{i}$$

The approach we now have to take is to "guess" at a value of i such that the value of $\frac{[(1 + i)^{12} - 1]}{i}$, from the right hand side of the equation above, comes out to be 14.492020, the value of the left hand side of the equation.

GUESS 1 One approach to guessing is to assume an annual rate of 12%. In this problem 12% would yield a rate of 3% each quarter. The reason 12% per year was selected was to provide a reference point. From the initial value, one knows whether to increase or decrease the rate in the second guess — it's not scientific, but rather, an arbitrary reference point. In this case, we let i be 3% ($\frac{12\%}{4}$) to see whether the rate needs to be increased or decreased on the second guess. Substituting the value of $i = 0.03$ into $\frac{[(1 + i)^{12} - 1]}{i}$ yields:

$$\frac{[(1 + 0.03)^{12} - 1]}{0.03} \doteq 14.192030$$

Thus, 0.03 is too low so let's try another guess using the information from our last attempt. It would appear that if i increases then the expression $\frac{[(1 + i)^{12} - 1]}{i}$ will also rise.

Continuing our guessing, the next value we might choose is 3.5% since we need only increase the value of i slightly to reach 14.491998.

GUESS 2   Let i be 3.5%. Substituting we get:

$$\frac{[(1 + 0.035)^{12} - 1]}{0.035} \doteq 14.601962$$

As you can see we are very close to the value we are seeking. Our third guess will be just slightly less than the 3.5% we've just tried.

GUESS 3   Let i be 3.25%. Substituting into our expression yields:

$$\frac{[(1 + 0.0325)^{12} - 1]}{0.0325} \doteq 14.395285$$

FINAL SOLUTION   We can see that we have gone a little bit too far with $i = 0.0325$. However, note that the value of $\left(\frac{S_n}{R}\right)$, 14.491998, is about half way between the two values for i, 3.5% and 3.25%. Since the value we want is approximately between the two we can try 3.375%, which is exactly half way. This gives:

$$\frac{[(1 + 0.03375)^{12} - 1]}{0.03375} \doteq 14.498192$$

As we can see this value is still slightly too high, but it can be clearly concluded that the interest rate each quarter is somewhere between 3.25% and 3.375%. If you have a financial calculator you will find that the exact interest rate is 3.367505% per quarter.

As a result, we would say that the final answer is in a range of values, namely:

$$3.25\% < i < 3.375\%$$

The nominal rate of interest is therefore somewhere between 13% and 13.5% compounded quarterly. The nominal rate was found by: 3.25% × 4 (quarters) and 3.375% × 4 (quarters). Based on our calculations, the interest rate is closer to 13.5% compounded quarterly.

You may be surprised that we're not as precise as we have been in the other sections on annuities. However, with the availability of financial calculators, it is only necessary to be within a range for interest rates since technology can help us be more precise.

Remember, i refers to the rate per conversion period. To find the annual or nominal rate we must multiply i by the number of conversion periods per year.

B. Finding the Interest Rate by Interpolation

There may be an occasion where one needs to compute a precise measure of the interest rate for an annuity, and no financial calculator is available. This can be accomplished by the method of interpolation, sometimes called the method of averages.

Interpolation requires some initial guessing to find a range within which the correct rate falls. Once a range is found, the method of interpolation provides an algebraic approach to determine a good estimate of the interest rate. The words "good estimate" are used because the method of interpolation assumes that the expressions we are using are linear. As you know, the annuity formulas are not linear because they have an exponent. However, as you will see, the error is extremely minor. The one thing you must do to keep the error small is to find two interest rates whose range is 1% or less, and within this range the rate we are seeking to find must fall. Example 8.11 demonstrates the interpolation method for a given present value of an annuity.

Remember the initial rates selected will be our best guesses until we find two rates that we can average out to find the interpolated value of i.

EXAMPLE 8.11   Finding *i* for a Given Present Value

An income retirement annuity has been designed to make regular payments of $600 every quarter. The annuity can be purchased for $9,000, today. The payments will last for five years and be made every quarter. What is the nominal rate, compounded quarterly, that is being paid on the annuity?

Solution   To solve the problem, we first must substitute what we know into the formula:

$$A_n = \frac{R[1-(1 + i)^{-n}]}{i}$$

$$A_n = \$9,000$$

$$R = \$600$$

$$n = 4 \times 5, \text{ or } 20$$

Rearranging the formula and substituting we get:

$$\frac{A_n}{R} = \frac{[1 - (1 + i)^{-n}]}{i}$$

$$\frac{\$9,000}{\$600} = \frac{[1 - (1 + i)^{-20}]}{i}$$

$$15 = \frac{[1 - (1 + i)^{-20}]}{i}$$

What must be done now is to guess different values of i to get a value of $\frac{A_n}{R}$ as close to 15 as possible.

Guessing, set $i = 0.02$ as a first try (8% per year, compounded quarterly). Substituting $i = 0.02$ gives:

$$\frac{[1 - (1 + i)^{-n}]}{i} = \frac{[1 - (1 + 0.02)^{-20}]}{0.02}$$

$$= 16.35143334$$

Since the value of $\frac{A_n}{R}$ must be 15, the value of 16.35143334 is too high when $i = 0.02$. Thus, set $i = 0.03$ (12% per year, compounded quarterly) as a second guess and solve. This gives:

$$\frac{[1 - (1 + i)^{-n}]}{i} = \frac{[1 - (1 + 0.03)^{-20}]}{0.03}$$

$$= 14.87747486$$

This second guess is far closer and we can see that the correct value of i falls between 2% and 3% per quarter.

Now we turn to interpolation to assist us in finding the value of i. This is done by using a table, as below:

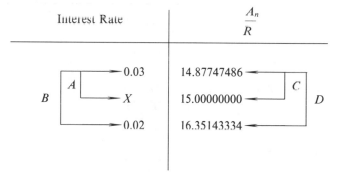

What we now do is figure out what proportion of the 1% difference in the two rates we either subtract from 3% or add to 2%. To do this we simply solve for X using ratios. Note how the ratio is constructed, using the reference letters A, B, C, and D beside the vertical lines in the above table. These show how we set up a ratio to solve for X.

$$\frac{A}{B} = \frac{C}{D}$$

$$\frac{0.03 - X}{0.03 - 0.02} = \frac{14.87747486 - 15.00000000}{14.87747486 - 16.35143334}$$

$$\frac{0.03 - X}{0.01} = \frac{-0.12252514}{-1.47395848} \quad \text{Now working through the steps to find } X.$$

$$0.03 - X = 0.01\left(\frac{-0.12252514}{-1.47395848}\right)$$

$$-X = 0.01\left(\frac{-0.12252514}{-1.47395848}\right) - 0.03$$

$$-X = 0.01(0.083126588) - 0.03$$

$$-X = 0.00083126588 - 0.03$$

$$-X = -0.029168734 \qquad \text{Multiply both sides by } -1.$$

$$X = 0.029168734 \qquad \text{The rate per quarter.}$$

As you can see, the process is very tedious, but unless you have a financial calculator, this is the method you must use to find a good estimate of i for a given present value. The method to find i for an amount is identical, except we use $\dfrac{S_n}{R}$.

SUMMARY OF FORMULAS

ORDINARY SIMPLE ANNUITIES

Formula 8.1	$S_n = \dfrac{R[(1 + i)^n - 1]}{i}$	Used to find the amount of an ordinary simple annuity.
Formula 8.2	$A_n = \dfrac{R[1 - (1 + i)^{-n}]}{i}$	Used to find the present value of an ordinary simple annuity.
Formula 8.3	$R = \dfrac{S_n}{\dfrac{[(1 + i)^n - 1]}{i}}$	Used to find the payment R when the amount, i, and n are known.
Formula 8.4	$R = \dfrac{A_n}{\dfrac{[1 - (1 + i)^{-n}]}{i}}$	Used to find the payment R when the present value, i, and n are known.
Formula 8.5	$n = \dfrac{\ln\left[1 + \dfrac{S_n\, i}{R}\right]}{\ln(1 + i)}$	Used to find the number of payments when the amount, i, and R are known.
Formula 8.6	$n = \dfrac{-\ln\left[1 - \dfrac{A_n\, i}{R}\right]}{\ln(1 + i)}$	Used to find the number of payments when the present value, i, and R are known.

GLOSSARY OF TERMS

Amortization Period   the time period over which a debt is paid off or retired.

Amount of an Annuity   the sum of the annuity payments plus accumulated interest.

Annuity   a financial instrument that requires periodic payments. In general, the payments are made at the same period in time.

Annuity Certain   annuities that have a definite start time and a definite end period.

Annuity Due   annuities that have the payments at the beginning of each period.

Complex Annuity   see General Annuity.

Contingent Annuity   an annuity that has an unknown start date and/or an unknown end date. A pension plan is an example of a contingent annuity with a definite start date but an unknown end date.

Deferred Annuity   when an annuity does not commence until some point in the future. Deferred annuities are only relevant when dealing with present values, e.g., a deferred loan.

General Annuity   an annuity that allows for the payment period and the interest period to be different.

Interpolation   the method used to find the interest rate for an annuity.

Lease Payment   the payment for use of equipment, real estate, and other types of assets. In general, lease payments occur at the beginning of each period.

Payment Interval   see Payment Period.

Payment Period   the time between each regular payment of an annuity.

Perpetuity   an annuity whose payments go on forever. The payments are always equal to the regular interest so that the original principal is never changed.

Ordinary Annuity   an annuity where the regular payments come at the end of each payment period.

Simple Annuity   an annuity that has the interest period (conversion period) and the payment period coinciding.

Term of an Annuity   the time from the start to the finish of the annuity payments. However, sometimes in business the term of an annuity also refers to the time period that the interest rate is fixed for the annuity.

CHAPTER 9

Due and Deferred Annuities

Two annuities that were briefly described in Chapter 8 were the annuity due and the deferred annuity. Both of these annuities are commonly used in business.

An annuity due means that the regular payment comes at the beginning of the period — sometimes referred to as a payment in advance. One example of an annuity due is a rent payment. The second type of annuity that will be discussed in this chapter is the deferred annuity, which means that the annuity payments do not start immediately. That is, they commence at some point in the future. An example of a deferred annuity is purchasing a stereo on a payment plan in September, where payments don't commence until January of the following year (many variants of this type of scheme are found in the advertisements of your local paper).

9.1 Simple Annuity Due

Up to this point our discussion of annuities has focused on ordinary simple annuities. We learned that for simple annuities, the interest (compound) period and the payment period always coincide. Also, recall that an ordinary annuity has payments that always come at the end of the payment period.

In this section we will learn about another type of simple annuity. As with our discussion in Chapter 8, the interest period and the payment period will coincide, but this is where the similarity ends. Let's examine the special features of an **annuity due**.

An annuity due is an annuity that has payments that occur at the beginning of the payment period. Since the payment comes at the beginning of the period there will always be one extra interest period for each payment when finding the amount, and one less discount period when finding the present value of an annuity due. For example, if you are depositing money at the beginning of a period you would expect to earn interest for that period. The computations for an annuity due rely on our previous formulas for an ordinary simple annuity, with an adjustment to recognize the extra interest period associated with each payment.

(i) Amount of an Annuity Due

Finding the amount of an annuity due is very straight forward. All that must be done is account for the additional interest period. For example, think of a person making three payments of $1,000 at the beginning of each month to a savings account that pays 6% compounded monthly. If we examine the difference in the interest calculations that occur between an ordinary annuity and an annuity due, it will help us to understand how we arrive at the new formulas for an annuity due.

Using an ordinary simple annuity means that the three payments come at the end of each month. The amount at the end of the three months would be found by using Formula 8.1, or:

$$S_n = \frac{R[(1 + i)^n - 1]}{i}$$

Where:

$$R = \$1,000$$

$$i = \frac{0.06}{12}, \text{ or } 0.005$$

$$n = 3$$

Substituting we have:

$$S_n = \frac{\$1,000[(1 + 0.005)^3 - 1]}{0.005}$$

$$S_n = \$3,015.03$$

Now look at the same problem when the payments are made at the beginning of each month.

With an annuity due the first payment is made at the start of the first month, the second at the beginning of the second month, and the third at the beginning of the third month. If we apply our compound interest formula from Chapter 7 we would find the amount of these three payments as follows:

$$\$1,000(1 + 0.005)^3 = \$1,015.08$$
$$\$1,000(1 + 0.005)^2 = \$1,010.03$$
$$\$1,000(1 + 0.005)^1 = \$1,005.00$$

If we total the payments and interest we see that the amount in the account at the end of three months is $3,030.11, which is higher than the amount when the payments came at the end of each month. In this problem, the difference is $3,030.11 – $3,015.03, or $15.08.

We can adjust our ordinary simple annuity formula to handle the change in the timing of the payments (to the beginning of each period) as follows:

$$S_n(\text{due}) = \frac{R(1 + i)[(1 + i)^n - 1]}{i} \qquad \textbf{Formula 9.1}$$

Diagrammatically the additional interest can be seen as a result of the payments (R_1, R_2, R_3) coming at the beginning of the month.

Figure 9.1 A Comparison of Amount Calculations for an Annuity Due and an Ordinary Annuity

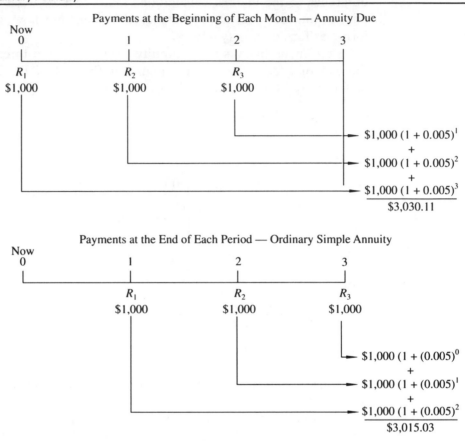

The first thing to note in Formula 9.1 is that we clearly show that we are looking at the amount of an annuity due by stating <u>due</u> after S_n.

The second thing you should notice is that there is an "extra" $(1 + i)$ on the right hand side of the equation to reflect the additional interest period associated with each payment in computing the amount. As well there will be one less interest period per payment for discounting.

Now applying this formula to the problem above:

$$S_n(\text{due}) = \frac{R(1 + i)[(1 + i)^n - 1]}{i}$$

Where:

$$R = \$1,000$$
$$i = 0.005$$
$$n = 3$$

Substituting into our formula we have:

$$S_n(\text{due}) = \frac{\$1,000(1 + 0.005)[(1 + 0.005)^3 - 1]}{0.005}$$

$$S_n(\text{due}) = \$1,000[3.030100]$$
$$S_n(\text{due}) = \$3,030.10$$

The $0.01 difference from the compound interest approach above is simply a rounding difference.

As you can see, the difference in this formula from our previous amount formula is the extra $(1 + i)$ portion.

It is important that you always read the problem looking for when the payment will occur — at the beginning or the end of the payment period. However, if it is not stated when the payments are made, assume an ordinary annuity. An annuity due requires a specific statement in the problem that the payments are in advance or at the beginning of the period.

EXAMPLE 9.1

Mark is starting an investment fund in which he plans to deposit $500 at the beginning of each month. If he can earn 10% compounded monthly, how much will be in the fund at the end of six years?

Solution   The solution to this problem requires the recognition that the payments are made at the beginning of each period. Thus, we must apply our annuity due formula for finding the amount. Using Formula 9.1 gives:

$$S_n(\text{due}) \quad \frac{R(1 + i)[(1 + i)^n - 1]}{i}$$

Where:

$$R = \$500$$

$$i = \frac{0.10}{12}, \text{ or } 0.008333$$

$$n = 12 \times 6, \text{ or } 72$$

Substituting into our formula yields:

$$S_n(\text{duc}) = \frac{\$500\left(1 + \frac{0.10}{12}\right)\left[\left(1 + \frac{0.10}{12}\right)^{72} - 1\right]}{\frac{0.10}{12}}$$

$$S_n(\text{due}) \doteq \$500(98.928908)$$

$$S_n(\text{due}) \doteq \$49,464.45$$

At the end of 72 periods, when all deposits of $500 have been made at the beginning of each period, and the interest rate is 10% compounded monthly, Mark will have $49,464.45 in his investment fund.

(ii) Finding the Present Value of an Annuity Due

When we want to figure out the present value of an annuity due we must incorporate that each payment will be discounted one less interest period. The formula we will use to find A_n (due) is:

$$A_n \text{ (due)} = \frac{R(1 + i)[1 - (1 + i)^{-n}]}{i} \qquad \textbf{Formula 9.2}$$

EXAMPLE 9.2

The monthly rent on an apartment is $750 per month, payable at the beginning of each month. If the current interest rate is 12% compounded monthly, what single payment twelve months in advance would be equivalent to a year's rent?

Solution In reading the problem we should note that a single payment, now, will be equivalent to twelve payments made at the beginning of each month. This single payment is simply the present value of the year's payments. Since the payments are made at the beginning of each period we must use Formula 9.2. Defining all the terms we have:

$$R = \$750$$

$$i = \frac{0.12}{12}, \text{ or } 0.01$$

$$n = 12$$

Substituting into Formula 9.2 gives:

$$A_n \text{ (due)} = \frac{\$750(1 + 0.01)[1 - (1 + 0.01)^{-12}]}{0.01}$$

$$A_n \text{ (due)} \doteq \$750(11.3676283)$$

$$A_n \text{ (due)} \doteq \$8,525.72$$

Therefore, a single payment of $8,525.72 is equivalent to twelve monthly payments of $750 made at the beginning of each month.

(iii) Finding the Payment, R, for Annuities Due

As with an ordinary simple annuity, often we need to find R when the interest rate, the number of periods, and either the amount or present value is known. The method we use rearranges the formula for S_n(due) to find R. If the amount, S_n(due), is known then we find R by the formula:

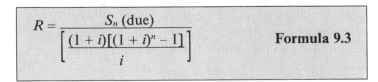

$$R = \frac{S_n \text{ (due)}}{\left[\frac{(1 + i)[(1 + i)^n - 1]}{i} \right]} \qquad \textbf{Formula 9.3}$$

If the present value is known then we simply rearrange Formula 9.2 to find *R*. That is:

$$R = \frac{A_n \text{ (due)}}{\left[\frac{(1 + i)[1 - (1 + i)^{-n}]}{i}\right]} \qquad \textbf{Formula 9.4}$$

EXAMPLE 9.3

Nick Krenshaw wants to accumulate $4,000 in eight months. If the first payment will be made today and the interest rate is 13% compounded monthly, what will be the required size of each monthly payment?

Solution This problem requires us to find *R* when the future amount is known. We can see that the problem tells us the values of *i* and *n* so all that is necessary is to determine which formula for *R* is appropriate. Since the payments are to start at the beginning we know we are working with an annuity due. Turning to Formula 9.3 and substituting would go as follows:

$S_n \text{ (due)} = \$4,000$

$$i = \frac{0.13}{12}, \text{ or } 0.0108333$$

$n = 8$

Applying Formula 9.3:

$$R = \frac{S_n \text{ (due)}}{\left[\frac{(1 + i)[(1 + i)^n - 1]}{i}\right]}$$

$$R = \frac{\$4,000}{\left[\frac{\left(1 + \frac{0.13}{12}\right)\left[\left(1 + \frac{0.13}{12}\right)^8 - 1\right]}{\frac{0.13}{12}}\right]}$$

$$R \doteq \frac{\$4,000}{8.40002}$$

$R \doteq \$476.19$

Payments of $476.19, made at the beginning of each period, for the next eight months, will accumulate to $4,000.

(iv) Finding the Term, *n*, for an Annuity Due

The value of *n* can be found, when we know either the amount or the present value as well as *R* and *i*, by rearranging Formulas 9.1 and 9.2, and then solving for *n*. Since the algebra is somewhat awkward, only the final expressions are provided. If you want to undertake the algebra please review the examples in the logarithm section of Chapter 4, especially parts (b) and (c) of Example 4.22.

$$n = \frac{\ln\left[1 + \dfrac{S_n(\text{due})i}{R(1+i)}\right]}{\ln(1+i)}$$

Formula 9.5

Formula 9.5 calculates the value of n when the amount, R, and i are known for an annuity due.

To compute n when the present value, R, and i are known with an annuity due we use the following formula:

$$n = \frac{-\ln\left[1 - \dfrac{A_n(\text{due})i}{R(1+i)}\right]}{\ln(1-i)}$$

Formula 9.6

Use Formula 9.6 with special caution since people often forget the negative sign that precedes the first **ln**. The following two examples outline how to find n for a given present value or amount for an annuity due:

EXAMPLE 9.4

If $200 is deposited at the beginning of each quarter, how many years will it take to accumulate $12,000 if the interest rate is 16% compounded quarterly?

Solution This problem requires us to accumulate a specific amount, when the payments occur at the beginning of the period. Thus, we would use the formula:

$$n = \frac{\ln\left[1 + \dfrac{S_n(\text{due})i}{R(1+i)}\right]}{\ln(1+i)}$$

Now, defining the terms:

$$R = \$200$$

$$i = \frac{0.16}{4}, \text{ or } 0.04$$

$$S_n(\text{due}) = \$12,000$$

Substituting into our formula yields:

$$n = \frac{\ln\left[1 + \dfrac{\$12,000(0.04)}{\$200(1 + 0.04)}\right]}{\ln(1 + 0.04)}$$

$$n \doteq \frac{\ln[3.30769]}{\ln(1.04)}$$

$$n \doteq 30.50048 \text{ quarters, or dividing by four, 7.63 years}$$

Therefore, if the deposits are made every quarter for 30.50048 quarters, or 7.63 years there will be $12,000 in the account. (The actual number of quarterly payments would be eight, with the first seven at $200, and the last payment being a smaller payment.)

9.2 Deferred Annuities

Deferred annuities refer to annuities whose payments do not begin until some period in the future. A common example is where someone purchases a retirement fund today, but does not receive any payments until retirement at some point in the future. **The term deferred means exactly what it states: deferred until some point in the future.**

Our discussion of deferred annuities focuses on those annuities where the payments come at the **end** of each payment period. There are situations where a deferred annuity could have payments starting at the beginning of each period. However, these are left for you to consider using the procedures of the previous section.

The formulas we use are similar to those in the sections on ordinary simple annuities. The change we build into our old formulas must reflect the period of time for which the payments are deferred. **The deferral period refers to the length of time, in payment periods, that will pass before a payment occurs.** This period is generally represented by d.

Let's begin with the amount of a deferred annuity since it's very straight forward.

(i) Amount of a Deferred Annuity

The amount of a deferred annuity is the same as the amount of an ordinary simple annuity. That is, the deferral period has no influence on a future value.

Consider the situation where someone is making regular deposits to reach an amount of $5,000. If the payments do not commence for five years it simply means that the payments start five years from now. However, this deferral has no influence on the desired sum of $5,000. Thus, there is no need to concern ourselves with the situation of finding the amount of a deferred annuity since it would be dealt with by the formula for the amount of an ordinary annuity.

(ii) Present Value for a Deferred Annuity

The present value of a deferred annuity is found by using the following formula:

$$A_n \text{ (def)} = \frac{R(1+i)^{-d}[1-(1+i)^{-n}]}{i} \qquad \textbf{Formula 9.7}$$

In this formula, we see that the only difference between the ordinary annuity formula and the deferred annuity formula is the $(1 + i)^{-d}$ term. This term is used to discount the value of the annuity over the deferral period. The term d refers to deferral periods — that is, the number of deferral periods.

Also, note that Formula 9.7 is applicable to payments that are at the end of the payment period. If we want a deferred annuity due then we would need to turn to our formula for an annuity due and then add in the deferral factor $-(1 + i)^{-d}$. Let's look at an example to make things a little more clear:

EXAMPLE 9.5

Gordon Investments Ltd. is offering a retirement package that guarantees ten years of end of the month payments of $650. The plan requires the investor to purchase the retirement plan today and not start receiving the payments for five years, with the first payment coming at the end of the first month following the five years. If the interest rate is 8% compounded monthly, what will be the purchase price of the retirement package?

Solution   Since this plan does not provide payments for five years it is a deferred annuity. The most important thing we must do is find the number of payment periods in the deferral period, d. Since the payments are monthly, we must assume that the deferral period is based on five years of monthly payments. Therefore, the deferral period is 12×5, or 60, periods. First let's outline the information we have:

$$R = \$650$$

$$i = \frac{0.08}{12}, \text{ or } 0.00666667$$

$n = 12 \times 10$, or 120   Remember the payments are for ten years once they start.

$d = 12 \times 5$, or 60   This is the number of payment periods that the annuity is deferred.

Turning to our present value formula for a deferred annuity we have:

$$A_n(\text{def}) = \frac{R(1 + i)^{-d}[1 - (1 + i)^{-n}]}{i}$$

Making the appropriate substitutions yields:

$$A_n(\text{def}) = \frac{\$650\left(1 + \dfrac{0.08}{12}\right)^{-60}\left[1 - \left(1 + \dfrac{0.08}{12}\right)^{-120}\right]}{\dfrac{0.08}{12}}$$

$$A_n(\text{def}) \doteq \$650\left(1 + \frac{0.08}{12}\right)^{-60}[82.42148]$$
$$A_n(\text{def}) \doteq \$35{,}959.40$$

Thus, if you were thinking about purchasing this retirement package you would not want to pay any more than $35,959.40 with a five year deferral, if the interest rate is 8% compounded monthly.

EXAMPLE 9.6

What is the present value of an annuity paying $1,300 at the end of each semiannual period for four years if the first payment is to be made in 5.5 years? Assume the interest rate is 12% compounded semiannually and the payments are at the end of each period.

Solution The first thing we must do is find the number of deferral periods. Since the first payment is in 5.5 years there must be five years of deferral. Why only 5 and not 5.5? This is because the first payment occurs at the end of 5.5 years. Thus, since the payments come at the end of each period, only the first five years have no payments. If there were 5.5 years of deferral, then the first payment would occur at year six.

Defining the values for each term:

$$R = \$1,300$$

$$i = \frac{0.12}{2}, \text{ or } 0.06$$

$$n = 4 \times 2, \text{ or } 8 \qquad \text{The payments last for four years.}$$

$$d = 5 \times 2, \text{ or } 10 \qquad \text{Ten deferral periods.}$$

Now substituting into our formula:

$$A_n(\text{def}) = \frac{R(1 + i)^{-d}[1 - (1 + i)^{-n}]}{i}$$

$$A_n(\text{def}) = \frac{\$1,300(1 + 0.06)^{-10}[1 - (1 + 0.06)^{-8}]}{0.06}$$

$$A_n(\text{def}) \doteq \$1,300(3.467516)$$

$$A_n(\text{def}) \doteq \$4,507.77$$

Therefore, the present value of a deferred annuity paying $1,300 semiannually for four years is $4,507.77.

(iii) Finding *R* for a Deferred Annuity

As with the earlier annuities, finding *R* when the present value is known requires us to rearrange Formula 9.7, to solve for *R*. This rearrangement would result in:

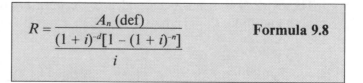

$$R = \frac{A_n(\text{def})}{\dfrac{(1 + i)^{-d}[1 - (1 + i)^{-n}]}{i}} \qquad \textbf{Formula 9.8}$$

EXAMPLE 9.7

Joan and Larry have just bought a new living room suite for $7,500 including taxes. The furniture was purchased at Moe's Low Cost Furniture Mart, which has a special offer of no payments for six months. If Moe's provide furniture loans at a rate of 28.5% compounded monthly, what would be the size of the regular monthly payments if the full amount must be repaid in 36 equal end-of-month payments? What would the size of the monthly payments be if they came at the beginning of each period?

Solution To find the end-of-month payments, the terms must be defined:

$$R = \,?$$
$$A_n \,(\text{def}) = \$7,500$$
$$i = \frac{0.285}{12} \,, \text{ or } 0.02375$$
$$n = 12 \times 3, \text{ or } 36 \text{ payments}$$
$$d = 6 \qquad \text{There are six periods } \underline{\text{without}} \text{ payments, thus six deferral periods.}$$

Applying Formula 9.8:

$$R = \frac{A_n \,(\text{def})}{\dfrac{(1 + i)^{-d}[1 - (1 + i)^{-n}]}{i}}$$

Substituting the terms:

$$R = \frac{\$7,500}{\dfrac{(1 + 0.02375)^{-6}[1 - (1 + 0.02375)^{-36}]}{0.02375}}$$

$$R \doteq \$359.48$$

Beginning of Month Payments:

To find the payments at the beginning of each payment period, Formula 9.8 must be adjusted. As you will recall, the formulas for an annuity due had an extra $(1 + i)$ term. Thus, Formula 9.8 would now look as follows:

$$R = \frac{A_n \,(\text{def})}{\dfrac{(1 + i)(1 + i)^{-d}[1 - (1 + i)^{-n}]}{i}}$$

The extra $(1 + i)$ has been added to account for the payment at the beginning of the period.

Substituting the terms:

$$R = \frac{\$7,500}{\dfrac{(1 + 0.02375)(1 + 0.02375)^{-6}[1 - (1 + 0.02375)^{-36}]}{0.02375}}$$

$$R \doteq \$351.14$$

Therefore, the required end of the month payments are $359.48, providing that they do not commence until seven months after the purchase. When the payments are at the beginning of each period, the size of the 36 regular payments is $351.14.

(iv) Finding *n* for a Deferred Annuity

To find the term or number of payments for a deferred annuity requires re-arranging Formula 9.7, using logarithms, and solving for *n*. As with the formula for *n* when we were dealing with ordinary simple annuities, there will be a negative sign at the beginning of the right side of the formula.

The other feature of this formula is that we must incorporate the value of *d*, reflecting the deferral periods. The formula is:

$$n = \frac{-\ln\left[1 - \dfrac{A_n(\text{def})i}{R(1 + i)^{-d}}\right]}{\ln(1 + i)} \qquad \textbf{Formula 9.9}$$

EXAMPLE 9.8

Julio has $50,000 in a retirement fund. If he plans to make no more contributions to the plan and plans to retire in four years, how long can he draw monthly payments of $500 once he retires? Assume the interest rate on the fund is 6% compounded monthly.

Solution To solve the problem we must first find the value for each term:

$$R = \$500$$

$$i = \frac{0.06}{12}, \text{ or } 0.005$$

$$d = 12 \times 4, \text{ or } 48 \qquad \text{We assume that four years pass and his first payment comes at four years and one month.}$$

$$A_n(\text{def}) = \$50,000$$

Substituting into the formula gives:

$$n = \frac{-\ln\left[1 - \frac{A_n(\text{def})i}{R(1 + i)^{-d}}\right]}{\ln(1 + i)}$$

$$n = \frac{-\ln\left[1 - \frac{\$50,000(0.005)}{\$500(1 + 0.005)^{-48}}\right]}{\ln(1 + 0.005)}$$

$$n \doteq \frac{-\ln(0.364755)}{\ln(1.005)}$$

$$n \doteq 202.21$$

Therefore, if Julio makes no more payments to this retirement fund and retires in four years, he can draw $500 a month for approximately 202 months, and a final smaller payment at month 203.

SUMMARY OF FORMULAS

Simple Annuity Due

Formula 9.1

$$S_n(\text{due}) = \frac{R(1 + i)[(1 + i)^n - 1]}{i}$$

Used to find the amount for an annuity due.

Formula 9.2

$$A_n(\text{due}) = \frac{R(1 + i)[1 - (1 + i)^{-n}]}{i}$$

Used to find the present value for an annuity due.

Formula 9.3

$$R = \frac{S_n(\text{due})}{\frac{(1 + i)[(1 + i)^n - 1]}{i}}$$

Used to find the payment for an annuity due, when the amount, i, and n are known.

Formula 9.4

$$R = \frac{A_n(\text{due})}{\frac{(1 + i)[1 - (1 + i)^{-n}]}{i}}$$

Used to find the payment for an annuity due, when the present value, i, and n are known.

Formula 9.5

$$n = \frac{\ln\left[1 + \frac{S_n(\text{due})i}{R(1 + i)}\right]}{\ln(1 + i)}$$

Used to find the number of payments when the amount, i, and R are known.

Formula 9.6

$$n = \frac{-\ln\left[1 - \frac{A_n(\text{due})i}{R(1 + i)}\right]}{\ln(1 + i)}$$

Used to find the number of payments when the present value, i, and R are known for an annuity due.

Deferred Ordinary Simple Annuity

Formula 9.7

$$A_n(\text{def}) = \frac{R(1+i)^{-d}[1-(1+i)^{-n}]}{i}$$

Used to find the present value of a deferred annuity.

Formula 9.8

$$R = \frac{A_n(\text{def})}{\dfrac{(1+i)^{-d}[1-(1+i)^{-n}]}{i}}$$

Used to find the payment for a deferred annuity when the present value, i, and n are known.

Formula 9.9

$$n = \frac{-\ln\left[1 - \dfrac{A_n(\text{def})i}{R(1+i)^{-d}}\right]}{\ln(1+i)}$$

Used to find the number of payments when the present value, i, and R are known for a deferred annuity.

GLOSSARY OF TERMS

Amortization Period   the time period over which a debt is paid off or retired.

Amount of an Annuity   the sum of the annuity payments plus accumulated interest.

Annuity   a financial instrument that requires periodic payments. In general, the payments are made at the same period in time.

Annuity Due   annuities that have the payments at the beginning of each period.

Complex Annuity   see General Annuity in Chapter 10.

Deferral Period   the number of payment periods that pass without a payment. If a period has a payment, it is not part of the deferral period.

Deferred Annuity   when an annuity does not commence until some point in the future. Deferred annuities are only relevant when dealing with present values, e.g., a deferred loan.

Lease Payment   the payment for use of equipment, real estate, and other types of assets. In general, lease payments occur at the beginning of each period.

Simple Annuity   an annuity that has the interest period (conversion period) and the payment period coinciding.

Term of an Annuity   the term of an annuity refers to the time from the start to the finish of the annuity payments. However, sometimes in business the term of an annuity also refers to the time period that the interest rate is fixed for the annuity.

General Annuities

The material in this chapter is an extension of Chapters 8 and 9. The major distinction among Chapters 8 and 9 and Chapter 10 is that the methods described in this chapter will be applicable to all annuity problems — regardless of whether the interest period and the payment period coincide. Since the methods in this chapter permit us to undertake annuity calculations, irrespective of whether the interest and payment period coincide, we call them **general annuity procedures**. In other texts you may see the name complex annuity methods. A complex annuity is simply another name for a general annuity.

Not only will we be studying annuities that have different interest and payment periods, but we also will learn about a very special type of annuity that has payments that go on forever, called a **perpetuity**.

Included in this chapter is an appendix that provides a brief discussion of the topics of Net Present Value and Discounted Cash Flow. These procedures are designed to provide a framework for using annuity procedures to evaluate business investment decisions.

10.1 General Annuities and the Amount

With the annuities discussed so far, there has been the common feature that the interest period and the payment period coincided. As will be seen, this is not always the case in the real world. The topic of general annuities addresses the circumstance where payments and interest periods are different. Although general annuities allow for different interest and payment periods, the same methods are used to calculate general annuities as ordinary simple annuities, with one slight adjustment for interest rates. Equally important is that the formulas for general annuities can be used for both simple or general annuities. This is the reason for the title general annuities. (Remember that the terms general and complex mean the same.)

General annuities are common in government and corporate finance. Two applications are the retirement of long term debt, where a future sum is required, and a pension plan scheme that requires a future value for someone's retirement.

For example, suppose you are contributing to a pension plan that requires end of the month payments of $200. If the interest rate is 6% compounded semiannually, what is the amount after ten years? The first thing that should be noted is that the interest period and the payment period are different. There are two ways we can approach the problem.

One approach to the general annuity is to calculate an equivalent monthly rate, using the procedures outlined in Chapter 7, then replace *i* in the annuity formulas from Chapter 8 with the equivalent rate.

Another approach is to develop an annuity formula for an ordinary general annuity, which, as part of the calculations, transforms the interest rate to an equivalent rate. This second approach saves one step in the calculations over the first method. However, it can be confusing because of the number of terms in each annuity formula.

The approach taken in this book will be to show you both methods for finding the amount and present value for ordinary general annuities. In the later examples, you will find that the first method (finding the equivalent rate of interest and then substituting it into the annuity formula) is used — but please, use either method. Your choice of method is simply a personal preference. When our attention turns to a general annuity due and general deferred annuity only the first method, using the equivalent rate of interest, will be used.

A. Method 1: Using the Equivalent Rate of Interest

Turning to the problem at hand, we wish to compute the sum of $200 end of the month payments for ten years at an interest rate of 6% compounded semiannually. The formula we would use from Chapter 8 is:

$$S_n = \frac{R[(1 + i)^n - 1]}{i}$$

In this problem we know:

$$R = \$200$$

$$n = 120$$

$$i = \frac{0.06}{2}, \text{ or } 0.03 \text{ semiannually}$$

The difference in this problem is that the payments are monthly and the interest rate is calculated semiannually. Therefore, to use our S_n formula we must now convert the semiannual rate to a monthly equivalent rate of interest. Using the approach of Chapter 7, the calculation would be:

$$\left[1 + \frac{0.06}{2}\right]^2 = (1 + i)^{12}$$

The above expression states that there is a rate, *i*, that when compounded twelve times a year will yield interest the same as 6% compounded twice a year. Here the unknown value of *i* is the monthly rate of interest, equivalent to 6% compounded semiannually. Now solving for *i* yields:

$$i = (1.03)^{\frac{2}{12}} - 1$$

$$i = (1.03)^{\frac{1}{6}} - 1$$

$$i \doteq 0.0049386$$

Thus, 0.0049386×12, or 5.926% compounded monthly is equivalent to 6% compounded semiannually. To solve our annuity problem, we now substitute the equivalent rate into our amount formula, that is:

$$S_n = \frac{R[(1 + i)^n - 1]}{i} \quad \text{where } i \text{ will be } 0.0049386$$

Substituting the other values yields:

$$S_n \doteq \frac{\$200[(1 + 0.0049386)^{120} - 1]}{0.0049386}$$

$$S_n \doteq \$32,645.19$$

Thus, if we make payments of $200 a month for ten years and the rate of interest is 6% compounded semiannually, the amount will be $32,645.19.

From this last example, it is possible to develop a formula for finding the equivalent rate of interest derived from the $(1 + i)^n$ expression. This formula can be expressed as:

$$f = (1 + i)^c - 1 \qquad\qquad \textbf{Formula 10.1}$$

Where:

$f =$ the equivalent rate of interest
$i =$ the rate of interest per conversion period
$c = \dfrac{\text{(number of interest conversion periods per year)}}{\text{(number of payment periods per year)}}$

In our example, f would have been found as follows:

$i = 0.03$ (compounded semiannually)

$c = \dfrac{2}{12}$, or $\dfrac{\text{2 semiannual conversions per year}}{\text{12 monthly payments per year}}$

$$f = (1 + 0.03)^{\frac{2}{12}} - 1$$

$$f \doteq 1.0049386 - 1$$

$$f \doteq 0.0049386$$

Using the formula for the equivalent rate of interest, we can adjust the amount formula for an ordinary annuity to a general annuity formula as follows:

$$S_n = \frac{R[(1 + f)^n - 1]}{f} \qquad\qquad \textbf{Formula 10.2}$$

B. Method 2: Using the General Annuity Formula

A second formula that could be used to find the amount of an ordinary general annuity would be to substitute the expression for f directly into our annuity formula. Therefore, everywhere f appears in Formula 10.2 substitute $(1 + i)^c - 1$, which yields the following:

$$S_{nc} = \frac{R([1 + (1 + i)^c - 1]^n - 1)}{[(1 + i)^c - 1]}$$

The reason S_{nc} was used instead of S_n was to make it clear that we are now using a general annuity formula that computes the equivalent rate in the process of finding the amount. Reducing the expression yields Formula 10.3, which calculates the amount of a general annuity, including the computation of the equivalent rate.

$$S_{nc} = \frac{R[(1 + i)^{nc} - 1]}{[(1 + i)^c - 1]} \qquad \textbf{Formula 10.3}$$

EXAMPLE 10.1

Find the amount of an annuity that requires payments of $1,000 at the end of each month for six years, if the interest rate is 18% compounded semiannually.

Solution If we apply Formula 10.3 directly we must first determine the value of each term in the expression:

$$R = \$1,000$$

$$i = \frac{0.18}{2}, \text{ or } 0.09$$

$$n = 12 \times 6, \text{ or } 72$$

$$c = \frac{2}{12}$$

$$S_{nc} = \frac{R[(1 + i)^{nc} - 1]}{[(1 + i)^c - 1]}$$

Now substituting:

$$S_{nc} = \frac{\$1,000[(1 + 0.09)^{(72)(\frac{2}{12})} - 1]}{[(1 + 0.09)^{\frac{2}{12}} - 1]}$$

$$S_{nc} \doteq \$1,000[125.3000545]$$

$$S_{nc} \doteq \$125,300.05$$

The amount of the annuity is $125,300.05.

Just to confirm that this result and the method using the equivalent rate of interest produce the same results, you should rework the problem using f and Formula 10.2.

10.2 General Annuities and Present Value

In our discussion above we noted that two methods can be used to compute the value of a general annuity. A similar approach will be used in this section on present value.

Before we get too far along, it is valuable to gain some idea of where one might use the general annuity method for present value in business and personal finance. The most common example that people experience is the standard residential mortgage. If you call your local bank or trust company and ask them how often they calculate the interest on a standard residential mortgage, you will normally find that the interest is compounded semiannually and the payments occur monthly. This is a good example of a general annuity. Other examples include certain consumer loans, credit card charges, and retirement plans.

Using the Equivalent Rate of Interest

As you will recall, the present value of an ordinary simple annuity was found in Chapter 8 by using the formula:

$$A_n = \frac{R[1 - (1 + i)^{-n}]}{i}$$

Using our formula for finding the equivalent rate of interest we can adjust our ordinary simple annuity formula to provide for the difference in payment and interest period. As you will remember, the formula we used for the equivalent rate was:

$$f = (1 + i)^c - 1$$

Where c was defined as follows:

$$c = \frac{\text{The number of interest conversion periods per year}}{\text{The number of payment periods per year}}$$

Substituting f for i into our present value formula, we have the formula for finding the present value of a general annuity.

$$A_n = \frac{R[1 - (1 + f)^{-n}]}{f} \qquad \textbf{Formula 10.4}$$

EXAMPLE 10.2

Ron and Susan have just purchased a house and arranged a mortgage with the Royal Bank. The mortgage is to have monthly payments of $818.15 and will be paid off over 25 years. If the interest rate is 11% compounded semiannually, what is the size of the mortgage?

Solution   To find the size of the mortgage we must find the present value of the monthly payments over the 25 year period. We can see that the payment period and the interest period do not coincide, thus requiring the use of the general annuity formula. The first step is to find f, which is done as follows:

$$f = (1 + i)^c - 1$$

Where:

$$i = \frac{0.11}{2}, \text{ or } 0.055$$

$$c = \frac{2}{12} \qquad \text{This states that there are two interest periods per year divided by twelve payments per year.}$$

Substituting these into our formula for f yields:

$$f = (1 + 0.055)^{\frac{2}{12}} - 1$$

$$\doteq 0.008963394$$

Now substituting the value of f into the annuity formula would go as follows:

$$A_n = \frac{R[1 - (1 + f)^{-n}]}{f}$$

$$R = \$818.15$$

$n - 12 \times 25$, or 300   12 payments per year for 25 years.

$$f = 0.00896339$$

$$A_n = \frac{\$818.15[1 - (1 + 0.00896339)^{-300}]}{0.00896339}$$

$$A_n = \$818.15[103.8929555]$$

$$A_n = \$85,000.02$$

Therefore, the size of the mortgage must be $85,000, with the $0.02 simply occurring through rounding.

10.3 Finding the Payment for an Ordinary General Annuity When the Amount and Present Value Are Known

Finding of the regular payment R, for an ordinary general annuity when the amount or present value is known, uses the methods used in Chapter 8 to find R for an ordinary annuity. The expressions we will use are a rearrangement of the earlier formulas introduced in this chapter. The derivation of the formulas below are shown for Formulas 10.2 and 10.4.

A. Finding *R* When the Amount Is Known

The expression for R, given the amount of an ordinary general annuity is found by rearranging

$$S_n = \frac{R[(1+f)^c - 1]}{f}$$

and solving for R. This gives:

$$R = \frac{S_n}{\dfrac{[(1+f)^n - 1]}{f}} \qquad \textbf{Formula 10.6}$$

B. Finding *R* When the Present Value Is Known

As with finding R when the amount was known, we start with the expression for A_n and rearrange it to find R. Therefore:

$$A_n = \frac{R[(1 - (1+f)^{-n}]}{f}$$

Rearranging for R gives:

$$R = \frac{A_n}{\dfrac{[(1 - (1+f)^{-n}]}{f}} \qquad \textbf{Formula 10.7}$$

These two formulas will find the payment R for an ordinary general annuity when the amount and present value are known.

EXAMPLE 10.3

Sally and Harry have just decided to invest in a fund to save $20,000. They plan to use the money for their child's education and expect to contribute to the fund for fifteen years. What will be the required payment at the end of every two-month period if the interest rate paid by the fund is 10% compounded annually?

Solution Since the amount is known we use Formula 10.6. The value for each term is:

$$S_n = \$20,000$$

$$i = 0.10$$

$$n = 6 \times 15, \text{ or } 90$$

$$c = \frac{1}{6} \qquad \text{One interest period per year divided by six payments per year.}$$

Substituting into our Formula 10.6 gives:

$$f = (1 + 0.1)^{\frac{1}{6}} - 1$$

$$\doteq 0.016012$$

$$R = \frac{S_n}{\dfrac{[(1 + f)^n - 1]}{f}}$$

$$R \doteq \frac{\$20,000}{\dfrac{[(1 + 0.016012)^{90} - 1]}{0.016012}}$$

$$R \doteq \frac{\$20,000}{[198.4322444]}$$

$$R \doteq \$100.79$$

If payments of \$100.79 are made at the end of every two months for the next fifteen years there will be \$20,000 in the fund.

10.4 Finding the Term (Number of Payments) When the Amount or Present Value Is Known

A. Finding *n* When the Amount Is Known

The procedure for finding the number of payments, n, for a general annuity is again similar to the methods presented in Chapter 8. The major difference is that we must be able to accommodate situations where the interest period and the payment period are different. The change required is to modify the formulas from Chapter 8, replacing i with f, the equivalent rate of interest.

From Chapter 8, the formula for n when the amount was known was:

$$n = \frac{\ln\left[1 + \dfrac{S_n i}{R}\right]}{\ln(1 + i)}$$

Substituting f for i yields:

$$n = \frac{\ln\left[1 + \dfrac{S_n f}{R}\right]}{\ln(1 + f)} \qquad \textbf{Formula 10.8}$$

EXAMPLE 10.4

Jill has started depositing money into a retirement fund. Once she has $100,000 accumulated she plans to retire. Jill plans to deposit $500 at the end of every three months to a RRSP that pays interest at 8% compounded annually. When can she retire?

Solution   First, identify the values of the terms for Formula 10.8:

$$R = \$500$$

$$S_n = \$100,000$$

$$i = 0.08$$

$$c = \frac{1}{4} \qquad \text{One interest period per year divided by the number of payments per year.}$$

$$f = (1 + 0.08)^{\frac{1}{4}} - 1 \qquad \text{Finding the equivalent rate.}$$

$$f \doteq 0.01942655$$

Substituting these into our formula:

$$n = \frac{\ln\left[1 + \frac{S_n f}{R}\right]}{\ln(1 + f)}$$

$$n \doteq \frac{\ln\left[1 + \frac{\$100,000(0.01942655)}{500}\right]}{\ln(1 + 0.01942655)}$$

$$n \doteq 82.4434$$

To find the number of years Jill has to wait, we divide the number of payments by four, yielding $\frac{82.4434}{4}$, or 20.611 years.

B. Finding *n* When the Present Value Is Known

The procedure used to find the term or number of payments, when the present value is known, follows the method used for a given amount.

First, we identify the formula we used in Chapter 8 for finding *n* when the present value is known:

$$n = \frac{-\ln\left[1 - \frac{A_n i}{R}\right]}{\ln(1 + i)}$$

Next we modify the formula, replacing i with f:

$$n = \frac{-\ln\left[1 - \dfrac{A_n f}{R}\right]}{\ln(1 + f)} \qquad \textbf{Formula 10.9}$$

EXAMPLE 10.5

Don and Marion Patrick are considering buying a house. At a meeting with their bank manager they are advised that the monthly payment on a $100,000 mortgage is $962.53, based on payments over 25 years and an interest rate of 11% compounded semiannually. Instead, the Patricks decide to make monthly payments of $1,050. If the couple continues to make $1,050 payments over the life of the mortgage, how long will it take to repay it?

Solution The solution involves a direct application of Formula 10.9. Defining the terms gives us:

$$R = \$1{,}050$$

$$i = \frac{0.11}{2}, \text{ or } 0.055$$

$$c = \frac{2}{12}, \text{ or } \frac{1}{6}$$

$$f = (1 + 0.055)^{\frac{1}{6}} - 1, \text{ or } 0.00896339$$

$$A_n = \$100{,}000$$

Using Formula 10.9 and substituting terms we have:

$$n = \frac{-\ln\left[1 - \dfrac{A_n f}{R}\right]}{\ln(1 + f)}$$

$$n \doteq \frac{-\ln\left[1 - \dfrac{\$100{,}000(0.00896339)}{\$1{,}050}\right]}{\ln(1 + 0.00896339)}$$

$$n \doteq \frac{-[-1.92179911]}{[0.00892346]}$$

$$n \doteq 215.36 \text{ payments, or } \frac{215.36}{12}, \text{ or } 17.95 \text{ years}$$

Therefore, if Don and Marion make monthly payments of $1,050 instead of $962.35, they will pay off their mortgage in 17.95 years, or 216 payments. The first 215 payments will be $1,050. The final payment at period 216 will be a slightly smaller payment.

10.5 General Annuity Due

As you may recall, the main feature of an annuity due is that the payments come at the **beginning** of the period. As a result, when compared to an ordinary annuity, there is always one extra period of interest per payment when accumulating and one less discount period per payment.

In Chapter 9 we developed a series of formulas for an annuity due. In this chapter we'll modify our earlier annuity due method to allow for situations where the compound period and the payment period do not coincide. In the discussion that follows, all formula will be developed using the equivalent rate of interest, substituted for i.

A. Finding the Amount of a General Annuity Due

The formula used to find the amount of a simple annuity due in Chapter 9 was:

$$S_n(\text{due}) = \frac{R(1 + i)[(1 + i)^n - 1]}{i}$$

As before, replace i with the equivalent rate f. From our previous discussion of general annuities, f can be found by using the expression:

$f = (1 + i)^c - 1$ Where c refers to the number of interest periods per year divided by the number of payments per year.

Now replacing i with f directly gives the amount formula for a general annuity due as:

$$S_n(\text{due}) = \frac{R(1 + f)[(1 + f)^n - 1]}{f} \qquad \textbf{Formula 10.10}$$

EXAMPLE 10.6

Gates West Electronics has established a fund to replace a piece of equipment. The expected cost of replacement in five years is $65,000. The company is going to set aside $800 a month, starting today (payments are at the beginning of the period). The firm can accumulate money at 7% compounded semiannually. Will the company have enough money in five years to replace the machine?

Solution   Since the payments start today we can see the appropriateness of the annuity due formula. Also, since the interest compounding period is different from the payment period, we use the general annuity method. Let's first identify the known values:

$R = \$800$

$i = \dfrac{0.07}{2}$, or 0.035

$$n = 12 \times 5, \text{ or } 60$$

$$c = \frac{2}{12}$$

$$f = (1 + 0.035)^{\frac{2}{12}} - 1,$$

$$\text{or } 0.00575004$$

The formula we'll use is 10.10.

$$S_n(\text{due}) = \frac{R(1 + f)[(1 + f)^n - 1]}{f}$$

Substituting:

$$S_n(\text{due}) \doteq \frac{\$800(1 + 0.00575004)[(1 + 0.00575004)^{60} - 1]}{0.00575004}$$

$$S_n(\text{due}) \doteq \$800(71.818587)$$

$$S_n(\text{due}) \doteq \$57,454.87$$

Therefore, in five years Gates West won't have enough money in its fund to meet the $65,000 requirement.

B. Finding the Present Value of a General Annuity Due

To find the present value of a general annuity due, modify the simple annuity due formula to include f, the equivalent rate of interest. The f factor allows us to transform the interest rate in our formula to an equivalent rate. In turn, this allows us to compute directly the present value of a general annuity due.

The formula we developed for the present value of a simple annuity due was:

$$A_n(\text{due}) = \frac{R(1 + i)[1 - (1 + i)^{-n}]}{i}$$

Replacing i with f yields:

$$A_n(\text{due}) = \frac{R(1 + f)[1 - (1 + f)^{-n}]}{f} \qquad \textbf{Formula 10.11}$$

EXAMPLE 10.7

What is the present value (buy out value) of a lease that has payments of $1,500 payable at the beginning of each month for five years? Assume the interest rate is 18% compounded semiannually. (Note that lease and rental payments are <u>normally</u> made at the beginning of a period.)

Solution   As with the amount formula the first step is to find f:

$$i = \frac{0.18}{2}, \text{ or } 0.09$$

$$f = (1 + i)^c - 1 \text{ where } c = \frac{2}{12}$$

Therefore:

$$f = (1 + 0.09)^{\frac{2}{12}} - 1$$

$$f \doteq 0.01446659$$

Next we list the known terms and substitute them into Formula 10.11:

$$R = \$1{,}500$$
$$f = 0.01446659$$
$$n = 12 \times 5, \text{ or } 60$$

$$A_n(\text{due}) \doteq \frac{\$1{,}500(1 + 0.01446659)[1 - (1 + 0.01446659)^{-60}]}{0.01446659}$$

$$A_n(\text{due}) \doteq \$1{,}500(40.50332)$$
$$A_n(\text{due}) \doteq \$60{,}754.98$$

If someone wanted to buy out the lease today, it would be worth $60,754.98.

C. Finding the Payment for a General Annuity Due

(i) Finding the Payment When the Amount Is Known

To find the payment for an amount of a general annuity due we must rearrange Formula 10.10 and solve for R. This yields:

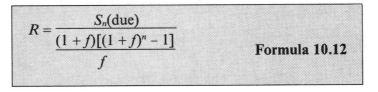

$$R = \frac{S_n(\text{due})}{\dfrac{(1 + f)[(1 + f)^n - 1]}{f}}$$

Formula 10.12

EXAMPLE 10.8

A local government has a debt of $75,000 that comes due in five years. How much does the municipality need to set aside, at the beginning of each month, to have the required funds to repay the debt when it comes due? The municipality can earn 9% compounded annually.

Solution   As with our previous examples, the first step is to find f, the equivalent rate of interest.

$$f = (1 + i)^c - 1$$

Where:

$$i = 0.09$$

$$c = \frac{1}{12}$$

Therefore, the value of f will be:

$$f = (1 + 0.09)^{\frac{1}{12}} - 1$$

$$f \doteq 0.007207323$$

Now defining the other values of the problem:

$$S_n(\text{due}) = \$75,000$$

$$n = 12 \times 5, \text{ or } 60$$

Substituting all the knowns into Formula 10.12 yields:

$$R = \frac{S_n(\text{due})}{\dfrac{(1 + f)[(1 + f)^n - 1]}{f}}$$

$$R \doteq \frac{\$75,000}{\dfrac{(1 + 0.007207323)[(1 + 0.007207323)^{60} - 1]}{0.007207323}}$$

$$R = \frac{\$75,000}{(75.27149373)}$$

$$R \doteq \$996.39$$

If the municipality sets aside \$996.39 at the beginning of each month, it will have the required \$75,000 in five years.

(ii) Finding the Payment When the Present Value Is Known

To find the payment of a general annuity due, we rearrange the present value formula for a general annuity due (Formula 10.11) and solve for R. The algebra is the same as that used to find R for an annuity due in Chapter 9. The expression for R is:

$$R = \frac{A_n(\text{due})}{\dfrac{(1 + f)[1 - (1 + f)^{-n}]}{f}}$$

Formula 10.13

EXAMPLE 10.9

Margaret Pearson has just arranged a mortgage that requires payments at the beginning of each month. The mortgage is $87,000 and the interest is compounded semiannually at 12%. What will be the size of the monthly payments if Margaret wants to repay the mortgage in ten years?

Solution Defining the value for each term:

$$A_n(\text{due}) = \$87,000$$

$$i = \frac{0.12}{2}, \text{ or } 0.06$$

$$c = \frac{2}{12}$$

$$n = 12 \times 10, \text{ or } 120$$

$$f = (1 + 0.06)^{\frac{2}{12}} - 1, \text{ or } 0.009758794$$

Substituting these into our formula we have:

$$R = \frac{A_n(\text{due})}{\dfrac{(1 + f)[1 - (1 + f)^{-n}]}{f}}$$

$$R \doteq \frac{\$87,000}{\dfrac{(1 + 0.009758794)[1 - (1 + 0.009758794)^{-120}]}{0.009758794}}$$

$$R \doteq \$1,221.76$$

The value of each payment will be $1,221.76, when the mortgage is repaid over 10 years with beginning of the month payments.

D. Finding the Number of Payments for a General Annuity Due

To find the number of payments for a general annuity due, we adjust our expressions for finding n for an ordinary annuity due to reflect a general annuity.

(i) Finding n for a Known Amount Given R and i

When $S_n(\text{due})$ is known, and the payments and compound period do not coincide, it is possible to find n by inserting f, the equivalent rate, into the formula for n given the amount of a simple annuity due (see Chapter 9). This would give:

$$n = \frac{\ln\left[1 + \dfrac{S_n(\text{due})f}{R(1 + f)}\right]}{\ln(1 + f)} \qquad \text{(from Formula 9.5)} \qquad \textbf{Formula 10.14}$$

(ii) Finding *n* for a Known Present Value Given *R* and *i*

As with the amount, to find an expression for the number of payments for a general annuity due, we simply replace *i* with *f* in the ordinary annuity due formula for *n*. This yields:

$$n = \frac{-\ln\left[1 - \dfrac{A_n(\text{due})f}{R(1 + f)}\right]}{\ln(1 + f)} \qquad \text{(from Formula 9.6)} \qquad \textbf{Formula 10.15}$$

10.6 General Deferred Annuity

A general deferred annuity can be handled by modifying the formulas developed in Chapter 9 for a deferred annuity. We just incorporate the equivalent rate of interest, *f*, for *i*.

Remember, deferring an annuity makes no difference to the amount of an annuity. That is, only present value is affected by a deferral period.

In addition, there will be a brief discussion of the situation where the payments come at the beginning of each payment period, making the annuity a general deferred annuity due.

A. Present Value of a Deferred General Annuity

The present value of a deferred general annuity can be found by substituting *f* for *i* in the formula:

$$A_n(\text{def}) = \frac{R(1 + i)^{-d}[1 - (1 + i)^{-n}]}{i} \qquad \text{(from Chapter 9)}.$$

Recalling that the formula for *f* is:

$$f = (1 + i)^c - 1$$

Substituting yields:

$$A_n(\text{def}) = \frac{R(1 + f)^{-d}[1 - (1 + f)^{-n}]}{f} \qquad \textbf{Formula 10.16}$$

EXAMPLE 10.10

Julian is buying an income averaging annuity to defer income tax by averaging income over more than one year. The annuity will provide payments of $400 at the end of each month for three years. The payments commence at the end of three years and the interest rate is 9% compounded semiannually. What should he pay today for the annuity?

Solution First we must find the value of each term for the formula. These are:

$$R = \$400$$

$$i = \frac{0.09}{2}, \text{ or } 0.045$$

$$c = \frac{2}{12}, \text{ or } \frac{1}{6}$$

$$n = 12 \times 3, \text{ or } 36$$

$$f = (1 + 0.045)^{\frac{1}{6}} - 1, \text{ or } 0.00736312$$

$$d = 35$$

This value results from the understanding that the <u>first payment</u> occurs at the end of the <u>third year</u>, or period 36, giving 35 deferral periods, i.e., there is a payment in period 36, therefore, this is not part of the deferral period.

Now substituting we have:

$$A_n(\text{def}) = \frac{R(1 + f)^{-d}[1 - (1 + f)^{-n}]}{f}$$

$$A_n(\text{def}) \doteq \frac{\$400(1 + 0.00736312)^{-35}[1 - (1 + 0.00736312)^{-36}]}{0.00736312}$$

$$A_n(\text{def}) \doteq \$400(24.38440)$$

$$A_n(\text{def}) \doteq \$9,753.70$$

A fair price to pay for the annuity, if it is to be deferred for 35 periods, is $9,753.70.

B. Finding the Payment for a General Deferred Annuity

The formula to find R for a general deferred annuity requires that i in the deferred formula of Chapter 9, be changed to f, the equivalent rate. Thus, rearranging Formula 10.16 and solving for R gives:

$$R = \frac{A_n(\text{def})}{\dfrac{(1 + f)^{-d}[1 - (1 + f)^{-n}]}{f}}$$

Formula 10.17

EXAMPLE 10.11

Andrex Holdings has just borrowed \$300,000 to finance a new land development project. The repayment requires end of quarter payments to begin <u>after</u> three years have passed. The interest charged is 18% compounded monthly. If the loan must be repaid over five years, once the payments begin, what is the size of each quarterly payment?

Solution   Defining the values for Formula 10.17:

$$A_n(\text{def}) = \$300,000$$

$$i = \frac{0.18}{12}, \text{ or } 0.015$$

$$c = \frac{12}{4}$$

$$n = 5 \times 4, \text{ or } 20$$

$$d = 3 \times 4, \text{ or } 12 \qquad \text{Three years pass before payments commence.}$$

$$f = (1 + 0.015)^{\frac{12}{4}} - 1$$

$$f \doteq 0.045678375$$

Now substituting these values yields:

$$R = \frac{A_n(\text{def})}{\dfrac{(1 + f)^{-d}[1 - (1 + f)^{-n}]}{f}}$$

$$R \doteq \frac{\$300,000}{\dfrac{(1 + 0.045678375)^{-12}[1 - (1 + 0.045678375)^{-20}]}{0.045678375}}$$

$$R \doteq \frac{\$300,000}{(7.5662689)}$$

$$R \doteq \$39,649.66$$

Thus, payments of \$39,649.66 will be required every quarter for five years to repay the debt. These payments account for the three year deferral period.

C. Finding the Number of Payments for a General Deferred Annuity

Again, finding the term or number of payments, n, relies on an expression developed in Chapter 9. The formula for n with an ordinary deferred annuity was:

$$n = \frac{-\ln\left[1 - \dfrac{A_n(\text{def})i}{R(1 + i)^{-d}}\right]}{\ln(1 + i)}$$

Now replacing i with f, our formula for finding n with a deferred general annuity is:

$$n = \frac{-\ln\left[1 - \dfrac{A_n(\text{def})f}{R(1+f)^{-d}}\right]}{\ln(1+f)} \qquad \textbf{Formula 10.18}$$

EXAMPLE 10.12

If Andrex Holdings in the previous example decides to increase the payments to $50,000, how long will it take them to repay the debt?

Solution Taking the values from the example above gives us:

$A_n(\text{def}) = \$300,000$

$i = \dfrac{0.18}{12}$, or 0.015

$d = 3 \times 4$, or 12   From previous example.

$f = (1 + 0.015)^{\frac{12}{4}} - 1$, or 0.0456784

$R = \$50,000$

Now substituting these values into Formula 10.18 yields:

$$n = \frac{-\ln\left[1 - \dfrac{A_n(\text{def})f}{R(1+f)^{-d}}\right]}{\ln(1+f)}$$

Substituting:

$$n \doteq \frac{-\ln\left[1 - \dfrac{\$300,000(0.0456784)}{\$50,000(1 + 0.0456784)^{-12}}\right]}{\ln(1 + 0.0456784)}$$

$n \doteq 14.1475$, or approximately 3.54 years

If the owners of Andrex Holdings increase the size of each payment from $39,649.68 to $50,000 they will reduce the term of their loan by almost 1.5 years (i.e., from five years to 3.54 years).

10.7 Perpetuities

The term "in perpetuity" means forever. In the area of business finance, **a perpetuity is an annuity that provides payments indefinitely — that is, never ending**. Since there is no end to this type of annuity, it's not possible to find its sum or future value.

Since you may be wondering where a perpetuity would be used, let's look at a few examples with which you may be familiar:

- A university or college sets up a bursary or scholarship fund that is designed to provide a flow of regular payments indefinitely for students.
- Local governments set aside monies so that funds will be available on a regular basis for cultural or heritage activities.

In each example, the goal of the organization setting up the flow of funds is to avoid having to make any contributions beyond the initial deposit. That is, once the initial fund has been established the payments will flow from the fund indefinitely.

You may have already guessed that these payments are nothing more than annual interest payments. Thus, providing the money paid out in awards each period does not exceed the interest income, the payments can continue indefinitely.

There are two types of perpetuities:

- simple perpetuities
- general perpetuities

A. Simple Perpetuities

When the continuous flow of payments come at the end of each period and the interest conversion period coincides with the payment period we have an ordinary simple perpetuity.

Thus, with perpetuities it is necessary to find a present value based on a series of payments that go on forever. Although this might sound complicated it is very easy to find. The expression we use for the present value looks slightly different in that there is no reference to n, the number of payments.

The term we use for the present value of a simple perpetuity is:

$$A_\infty$$

Since the payment each period is based on the interest collected, the expression used for an ordinary simple perpetuity is:

$$A_\infty = \frac{R}{i} \qquad \textbf{Formula 10.19}$$

Where:

R = the interest payment each period

i = the interest rate per payment period

Formula 10.19 allows us to find what sum of money must be set aside at an interest rate of i to generate a payment of R dollars for an indefinite period.

For example, if you wanted to earn $200 a year in interest from a savings account, how much would you need to place in the account if the interest rate is 8% compounded annually?

Since the payment is $200, this must be the interest earned on the funds in the account. We need to find out what value in a savings account will pay $200 in interest when 8% is applied annually.

First let's use our simple interest method from Chapter 6. That is, principal (P) × interest (i) = $200. Solving for P gives us:

$$P = \frac{\$200}{i}$$

$$i = 0.08$$

$$P = \frac{\$200}{0.08}$$

$$P = \$2,500$$

Consequently, if you have $2,500 in the bank and the interest rate is 8% compounded annually, you will generate $200 in interest each year.

Now let's use our formula for finding the present value of a simple perpetuity:

$$A_\infty = \frac{R}{i}$$

Substituting we get:

$$A_\infty = \frac{\$200}{0.08}$$

$$A_\infty = \$2,500$$

As you can see, the result is the same as using our simple interest method.

EXAMPLE 10.13

Jeremy wants to retire and receive $500 a month. When he dies he wants to pass the monthly payment on to his wife. Upon her death, Jeremy wants to pass it on to their only child, and then pass it on to future generations. Jeremy can earn 7.5% compounded monthly. How much will he need to set aside in a perpetuity to achieve his goal? How would it affect the answer if he wanted the payments to start today?

Solution This qualifies as a simple perpetuity since the payments are to go on forever and the payment and interest period coincide. Therefore, the terms of our annuity formula would be:

$$R = \$500$$

$$i = \frac{0.075}{12}, \text{ or } 0.00625$$

Substituting these into Formula 10.19 yields:

$$A_\infty = \frac{R}{i}$$

$$A_\infty = \frac{\$500}{0.00625}$$

$$A_\infty = \$80,000$$

Thus, if \$80,000 is placed in a fund earning 7.5% compounded monthly, it will produce \$500 a month in payments for his wife, child, and descendants. That is, the payments will continue forever since the fund is paying out money based on interest income only.

To have the payments begin immediately we must increase the size of the fund to handle the first payment. This is accomplished by depositing \$80,500, which provides the immediate payment of \$500 and leaves \$80,000 in the fund to provide the future \$500 payments.

Therefore, when the payments are to begin immediately the formula we use is:

$$A_\infty = R + \frac{R}{i} \qquad \text{Formula 10.20}$$

B. General Perpetuities

The approach to general perpetuities follows the logic of our previous discussion on general annuities. That is, we need only adjust our simple perpetuity formula to incorporate the equivalent rate of interest by substituting f for i. Therefore, to find the present value of a general perpetuity with payments at the end of the period use:

$$A_\infty = \frac{R}{f} \qquad \text{Formula 10.21}$$

Where:

R = the interest payment each period

$f = (1 + i)^c - 1$, the equivalent interest rate

When the payments are to begin immediately the formula for the general annuity is:

$$A_\infty = R + \frac{R}{f} \qquad \text{Formula 10.22}$$

SUMMARY OF FORMULAS

Definition: $c = \dfrac{\text{number of conversion periods per year}}{\text{number of payment periods per year}}$

Formula 10.1 $f = (1 + i)^c - 1$

Used to find the equivalent rate of interest.

Ordinary General Annuities

Formula 10.2 $S_n = \dfrac{R[(1+f)^n - 1]}{f}$

Used to find the amount using the equivalent rate of interest, f.

Formula 10.3 $S_{nc} = \dfrac{R[(1+i)^{nc} - 1]}{[(1+i)^c - 1]}$

Used to find the amount. This formula calculates the effective rate as part of the total calculations.

Formula 10.4 $A_n = \dfrac{R[1 - (1+f)^{-n}]}{f}$

Used to calculate the present value using the equivalent rate of interest.

Formula 10.5 $A_{nc} = \dfrac{R[1 - (1+i)^{-nc}]}{(1+i)^c - 1}$

Finds the present value by including the step of finding the equivalent rate as part of the calculations.

Formula 10.6 $R = \dfrac{S_n}{\dfrac{[(1+f)^n - 1]}{f}}$

Finds the payment when the amount is known, and uses f, the effective rate.

Formula 10.7 $R = \dfrac{A_n}{\dfrac{[1 - (1+f)^{-n}]}{f}}$

Finds the payment when the present value is known, using f, the effective rate.

Formula 10.8 $n = \dfrac{\ln\left[1 + \dfrac{S_n f}{R}\right]}{\ln(1 + f)}$

Finds n, the number of payments, when the amount, R and f, are known.

Formula 10.9 $n = \dfrac{-\ln\left[1 - \dfrac{A_n f}{R}\right]}{\ln(1 + f)}$

Finds n when the present value, R and f, are known.

General Annuity Due

Formula 10.10 $S_n(\text{due}) = \dfrac{R(1+f)[(1+f)^n - 1]}{f}$

Finds the amount for a complex annuity due.

Formula 10.11 $A_n(\text{due}) = \dfrac{R(1+f)[1 - (1+f)^{-n}]}{f}$

Finds the present value of an annuity due.

Formula 10.12

$$R = \dfrac{S_n(\text{due})}{\dfrac{(1+f)[(1+f)^n - 1]}{f}}$$

Finds the payment for a given amount for a complex annuity due.

Formula 10.13

$$R = \dfrac{A_n(\text{due})}{\dfrac{(1+f)[1 - (1+f)^{-n}]}{f}}$$

Finds the payment for a given present value for a complex annuity due.

Formula 10.14

$$n = \dfrac{\ln\left[1 + \dfrac{S_n(\text{due})f}{R(1+f)}\right]}{\ln(1+f)}$$

Finds n for a complex annuity due, given R, i, and $S_n(\text{due})$.

Formula 10.15

$$n = \dfrac{-\ln\left[1 - \dfrac{A_n(\text{due})f}{R(1+f)}\right]}{\ln(1+f)}$$

Finds n for a complex annuity due, given R, i, and $A_n(\text{due})$.

General Deferred Annuity

Formula 10.16

$$A_n(\text{def}) = \dfrac{R(1+f)^{-d}[1 - (1+f)^{-n}]}{f}$$

Used to calculate the present value using the equivalent rate of interest for a complex deferred annuity.

Formula 10.17

$$R = \dfrac{A_n(\text{def})}{\dfrac{(1+f)^{-d}[1 - (1+f)^{-n}]}{f}}$$

Finds the payment when the present value of a complex deferred annuity is known, using f, the equivalent rate.

Formula 10.18

$$n = \dfrac{-\ln\left[1 - \dfrac{A_n(\text{def})(f)}{R(1+f)^{-d}}\right]}{\ln(1+f)}$$

Finds n for complex deferred annuity, given R, i, and $A_n(\text{def})$.

Simple and General Perpetuities

Formula 10.19

$$A_\infty = \dfrac{R}{i}$$

Finds the present value for a simple ordinary perpetuity.

Formula 10.20

$$A_\infty = R + \dfrac{R}{i}$$

Finds the present value for a simple perpetuity due.

Formula 10.21

$$A_\infty = \dfrac{R}{f}$$

Finds the present value for a complex perpetuity.

Formula 10.22

$$A_\infty = R + \dfrac{R}{f}$$

Finds the present value for a complex perpetuity due.

GLOSSARY OF TERMS

General Annuity an annuity that may have different payment and interest periods. General annuities are also called complex annuities.

c the conversion factor used in computing the equivalent rate of interest, f. It is found by dividing the number of interest conversion periods per year by the number of payment periods per year.

General Annuity Due an annuity that has payments at the beginning of each period, as well as the possibility that the interest period and the payment period may be different.

General Deferred Annuity an annuity that has payments that start at some point in the future. In addition, the interest period and the payment period may be different.

Perpetuities an annuity that provides payments indefinitely. Perpetuities may be simple or general (complex); simple means the payment period and the interest period coincide and a complex perpetuity provides for the payment period and the interest period to be different.

Investment Applications of Annuities

10.A.1 Net Present Value

Although not specifically referred to in our earlier discussions, when an investment or an expenditure by a company is being contemplated, often those making the decision will use the **net present value (NPV)** approach. This approach simply requires one to compare the future cash flows to the future cash outlays. The difference between the two is called the net present value.

For example, assume a firm is contemplating the purchase of two types of equipment. The first piece of equipment costs $50,000 and will last five years. The expected savings to the company in terms of its operation costs is estimated to be $1,600 per month. Further, the equipment is expected to last five years, at which time its value is assumed to be zero. Another piece of equipment cost $75,000 and is expected to save $1,750 per month for six years, at which time it would be sold for an estimated scrap value of $1,500. If the firm expects to earn 10% compounded monthly on its money, which piece of equipment is the best investment for the company? Another way this question could have been asked is, which piece of equipment has the highest net present value to the firm?

To compute the net present value of the options facing the firm, the following relation is used:

Net Present Value	=	Present Value of Cash Inflows	−	Present Value of Cash Outflows

For the problem at hand, the choice of equipment would be made based on the equipment with the highest net present value (NPV).

The rule is to choose the option with the highest net present value, all other factors being equal. These other factors would include risk and tax considerations as well as a variety of other factors. If a single option is being evaluated, then, providing it has a positive net present value, it is worth undertaking. If the net present value is zero the firm would be indifferent, and if it is negative, it would suggest the venture is not worthwhile.

Using the NPV approach to the two types of equipment, we compute the NPV for each piece of equipment:

Equipment A

Cost = $50,000	Outlay today.
Scrap Value = 0	
$R = \$1,600$	Monthly inflow of savings.
$n = 12 \times 5$, or 60	
$i = \left(\dfrac{0.10}{12} \right)$	

$$\text{Present value of inflows} = \$1,600 \left[\frac{1 - \left[1 + \dfrac{0.10}{12}\right]^{-60}}{\dfrac{0.10}{12}} \right]$$

$$\doteq \$75,304.59$$

$$\text{Present value of outflows} = \$50,000$$

$$\text{Net Present Value} \doteq \$75,304.59 - \$50,000$$

$$\doteq \$25,304.59$$

Equipment B

Cost = $75,000	Outlay today.
Scrap Value = $1,500	In six years.
$R = \$1,750$	Monthly inflow of savings.
$n = 12 \times 6$, or 72	
$i = \left(\dfrac{0.10}{12} \right)$	

$$\text{Present value of inflows} = \$1,750 \left[\frac{1 - \left[1 + \dfrac{0.10}{12}\right]^{-72}}{\dfrac{0.10}{12}} \right] + \$1,500 \left(1 + \frac{0.10}{12}\right)^{-72}$$

$$\doteq \$95,287.93$$

$$\text{Present value of outflows} = \$75,000$$

$$\text{Net Present Value} \doteq \$95,287.93 - \$75,000$$

$$\doteq \$20,287.93$$

Since the NPV of Equipment A is higher than Equipment B, A would be selected.

EXAMPLE 10.A.1

West Coast Research Ltd. has developed a robotic underwater submarine for exploring the sea bottom at very deep depths. The development is on paper only and to make a prototype requires $150,000, $200,000, and $300,000 over the next three years. If all tests go well, West Coast expects to be able to sell the submarines for a net profit (after all costs) of $50,000 per unit. West Coast estimates it will be able to sell six units per year for the three years following the development of the prototype. All cash needs are assumed to occur at the end of each fiscal year. As well, sales are expected to occur at the end of each year. If the owners of West Coast require a return on investment of 16% compounded annually, is this project viable?

Solution

Cost = $150,000, $200,000, $300,000   Outlays — each outlay will need to be evaluated separately.

R = $50,000 × 6, or $300,000   Inflow of net profit.

$n = 3$

$d = 3$

$i = 0.16$

Since the company does not receive the estimated net profit until after the development of the prototype, this delayed income is treated as an annuity deferred; deferred for the three years until the income commences.

$$\text{Present value of inflows} = \$300,000(1 + 0.16)^{-3}\left[\frac{[1 - (1 + 0.16)^{-3}]}{0.16}\right]$$

$$\doteq \$431,653.91$$

Present value of outflows

$$= \$150,000(1 + 0.16)^{-1} + 200,000(1 + 0.16)^{-2} + 300,000(1 + 0.16)^{-3}$$

$$\doteq \$470,140.23$$

Net Present Value $\doteq \$431,653.91 - \$470,140.23$

$$\doteq -\$38,486.32$$

Since the NPV is negative the project should not be undertaken and therefore it is not viable.

10.A.2 Discounted Cash Flow

If the discounting involves future flows of payments or future fixed sums, the resulting value is sometimes called the **discounted cash flow** (DCF) of future payments. In this case, note that DCF is simply today's value of a future series of payments. A firm using this method of evaluating investment options will select the option that has the highest DCF for those cases where money is flowing to the firm, and the lowest DCF if the firm is making cash outlays. Consider Examples 10.A.2. and 10.A.3., which use DCF as the basis between two options. Example 10.A.2. deals with cash flow to the firm and requires the firm to select the highest DCF, while 10.A.3. is a problem that uses DCF when payments are made by the firm, requiring the firm to choose the option with the lowest DCF.

EXAMPLE 10.A.2

Bayles Holdings is considering two rental investments. The first investment is a building that generates a monthly income of $10,000, paid at the beginning of each month. The building is expected to have a remaining useful life of five years, at which time the building would be demolished and the land sold. The estimated value of the land in five years is $250,000. The second investment is a building that generates a monthly income of $7,000, paid at the beginning of each month. The estimated life of the second building is ten years; at this time the building would be demolished and the land sold. The estimated value of the land in ten years is $150,000. Both buildings are being offered for sale at the same price. Using DCF, which option would be best for Bayles Holdings? Assume that money is worth 12% compounded monthly.

Solution Each option generates a cash flow, thus the choice will be based on the option that has the highest DCF.

OPTION 1 **Building 1**

$R = \$10,000$ Note that the payments are at the beginning of the period, thus, use an annuity due.

$n = 12 \times 5$, or 60

$i = \dfrac{0.12}{12}$, or 0.01

Present Value of the Cash Flow (DCF):

$$DCF = \$10,000(1 + 0.01)\left[\frac{[1 - (1 + 0.01)^{-60}]}{0.01}\right] + \$250,000(1 + 0.01)^{-60}$$

$$DCF \doteq \$591,658.29$$

OPTION 2 **Building 2**

$R = \$7,000$ Payments are at the beginning of the period.

$n = 12 \times 10$, or 120

$i = \dfrac{0.12}{12}$, or 0.01

Present Value of the Cash Flow (DCF):

$$DCF = \$7,000(1 + 0.01)\left[\frac{1 - (1 + 0.01)^{-120}}{0.01}\right] + \$150,000(1 + 0.01)^{-120}$$
$$DCF \doteq \$538,231.91$$

Using DCF as the decision rule, the choice would be Building 1, which has the highest DCF for Bayles.

EXAMPLE 10.A.3

Horizon Technology manufactures special computer equipment. The company has had such an increase in demand for its products that it must increase its production capabilities. One option being considered is to purchase the required equipment for $100,000. If the equipment is purchased it is expected that the maintenance and repair costs will be $10,000 per year for five years — maintenance is assumed to occur at the end of each year. After five years, the equipment will have no salvage value and will need to be replaced. Another option is to lease the equipment for five years for $3,000 per month, paid at the beginning of each month. If money is worth 15% compounded annually, which option is best for the company?

Solution Since each option requires cash outlays, the choice will be based on the option that has the lowest DCF.

OPTION 1 Purchasing the equipment

Present Value of the Purchase option (i.e., DCF):

$$= \$10,000\left[\frac{1 - (1 + 0.15)^{-5}}{0.15}\right] + \$100,000$$
$$DCF \doteq \$133,521.55$$

OPTION 2 Leasing the equipment

Present Value of the Lease option (DCF):

$R = \$3,000$ At the beginning of each month.

$c = \dfrac{1}{12}$

$f = (1 + 0.15)^{\frac{1}{12}} - 1$, or 0.01171492

$n = 12 \times 5$, or 60

Since the payments are at the beginning of each month an annuity due will be required. Therefore the DCF of the lease option is:

$$DCF \doteq \$3,000(1 + 0.01171492)\left[\frac{1 - (1 + 0.01171492)^{-60}}{(0.01171492)}\right]$$
$$DCF \doteq \$130,273.34$$

Based on the DCF, the lease option represents the lowest discounted cash outlay to the firm. Thus, using DCF, the recommendation would be to lease the equipment.

CHAPTER 11

Stocks and Bonds

The topic of "stocks and bonds" is of interest to many people. During the 1980's and early 1990's much attention was focused on the stock market. First, there was the severe decline in October 1987, and then, in 1990, the high interest rates and the Persian Gulf crisis. Since then the market has had its share of ups and downs. After the stock market "crash" of 1987, there was an increase in investor interest in bonds because they offer an alternative to buying shares or stocks in companies as an investment. By late 1990, interest in bonds began to dissipate with the expectation of changing interest rates.

One source of money for businesses is internal, involving the earnings retained after all the "bills" have been paid. In addition, there are two major sources of external corporate financing:

- Equity financing
- Debt financing

Equity financing refers to raising money through the sale of shares or stock. The word equity means ownership. When you hold a share in a company you own a part of that company. In return, the company gets an inward flow of money that can be used to finance operations or assist with a major capital project, such as building a new plant. It's important to note that governments cannot sell equity; they raise money through debt financing or taxes.

Debt financing, on the other hand, implies the borrowing of money. When large sums of money need to be borrowed for long periods of time, corporations and governments often sell bonds or debentures to raise the money. This is called a **bond issue or a debenture issue. A bond refers to a written promise to repay a sum of money at a fixed time in the future. In return, the purchaser of the bond or debenture is paid interest for the use of the money at a rate specified.**

A bond is secured by a pledge of assets, whereas a debenture is similar to a bond except that it's not secured by assets. Since there is more risk with a debenture, there is generally a higher rate of return on this form of investment.

The major emphasis in this chapter will be on the method used to determine bond and debenture prices. We'll examine the relevance of the **yield rate** (the rate of return expected by an investor) in determining the price of both types of instruments. Since this text is an introductory one there won't be a full discussion of the many types of bonds available in the marketplace.

You'll be pleased to know that the technical calculations in this chapter are based on the techniques you've learned in previous chapters.

11.1 Equity Financing

As noted in the introduction, equity financing refers to raising money through the sale of shares, a method used by private businesses. Equity financing has two forms, which are the issuing of:

- **common shares**
- **preferred shares**

Common shares give the holder the right to vote on policy decisions of the company when a general meeting of shareholders is called. This participatory right of common shareholders is a fundamental principle of being a part owner of a company. The ability to influence any decisions is dependent on the number of common shares one owns. In many large companies, individuals holding common shares have only a tiny percentage of all the stock of the company. Therefore, the influence of any single shareholder on policy is minimal. An investor looks for two sources of return when purchasing a common share. The first is the dividend payment. Dividends are paid to common shareholders based on the profits of the company. Since profits go up and down over the business cycle, dividends tend to fluctuate as well. As a consequence, investors interested in dividends look at the long term performance of the company and, in particular, the dividends paid over a number of years. The second component of return on common shares is the expected increase in the share price on the market. When combined, the dividend and the change in the market value of the share determine the return to the investor.

The second type of share or equity in a company is the preferred share. This is a share that guarantees a specific annual return from the company. The holder of a preferred share gets a fixed payment each year as specified at the time of issuing the share by the company. However, preferred shareholders do not normally have any voting privileges on company policy, as do common shareholders, nor do they normally share in profits, as do the common shareholders.

To understand a preferred share, consider the example of a company issuing preferred shares for sale at an issue price (or **par value**) of $50 per share. Assume the company offers a rate of return on the preferred shares of 8% per year. Regardless of what one pays for the stock, whether the shares are purchased at a price per share that is higher or lower than par value, one will still receive a guaranteed return of $4 per year per share ($50 × 0.08).

While preferred shareholders are guaranteed an annual return on their shares, common shareholders only get a return on their investment if the company "declares" a dividend. If the preferred shareholder doesn't enjoy the same voting rights as the common shareholder, why would an investor buy a preferred share? The answer is that the rate of return offered to a preferred shareholder is sometimes higher than that offered on bonds or debentures. Even if the rate of interest is lower, there are often very special tax incentives on the income from a preferred share that increase the effective rate of return to the investor. Also, because there is a guaranteed annual return based on the issue price rather than on market price, the investment is considered less risky than buying common shares.

11.2 Reading and Understanding Stock Market Quotations

Common and preferred shares are traded (bought and sold) on stock exchanges in Vancouver, Toronto, Montreal, and other Canadian cities, in addition to exchanges around the world. The stocks traded can be one of two types:

- **Listed** stocks: the stocks are traded on a recognized exchange.

- **Unlisted** stocks: the stocks are traded on an unlisted market. If you turn to the financial section of your local paper, you will find a section that has a heading "Over the Counter" which refers to unlisted stocks.

Every daily newspaper has some type of summary page of stock market activity. The most common format is that used by *The Globe and Mail* and *The Financial Post*. To help you understand how to read the stock section, shown below is a listing of each column for the Industrial Stocks section of *The Financial Post*. The values were taken from one trading day. The stock examined is MacMillan Bloedel, a B.C. company in the wood industry.

Table 11.1   A Market Quotation of a Stock from the Toronto Stock Exchange: Quotation for April 1, 1991, as it appeared in *The Financial Post*, April 2, 1991. Reprinted with permission of *The Financial Post*.

| 52 Week | | | Div. | | | Close or | Net | Vol | Yield | P/E |
High	Low	Company	Rate	High	Low	Latest	Chg	100's	%	Ratio
$20	14¼	MacMillan Bloedel	0.60	$19.875	$19.625	$19.75	−¼	8,796	3.0	53.4

The interpretation of the headings and values are:

High $20:   the highest price the stock has traded for in the past 52 weeks;

Low 14¼: the lowest price the stock has traded at in the past 52 weeks;

52 Week: the time period for which the high and low price is quoted (week 1 to week 52 **inclusive**);

Company: identifies the company;

Div Rate: $0.60 is the dividend rate on the stock over the latest 12-month trading period and represents $0.60 per share;

High:	for this trading day, this was the highest price the stock traded;
Low:	the lowest the stock traded this day;
Close or Latest:	the closing price for this trading day;
Net Chg.:	the change recorded from the closing price on the previous trading day;
Vol 100's:	the number of shares that traded this day, in 100's;
Yield %:	the annual yield of the stock;
P/E Ratio:	the market price of the stock divided by the earnings per share (earnings per share is not given in the quotation).

When stocks are first brought to the market by a company they are offered at a **par value**, which is the issue price. The issue price is the value per share that the company sets for the stock when it is offered for sale for the first time.

Rarely do stocks ever trade at their par value or issue price. The first day of trading determines the interest in a stock. If there are many buyers the value will rise above the issue price. The opposite trend is generally the case, that is, stock prices tend to fall below their issue price, at least until investors have had a chance to view the potential of the stock.

It's very important to remember that the market price of a stock is the result of the actions of buyers and sellers. If there are more sellers, then the price will fall. If there are more buyers, then the price will rise. The price will only stabilize when the number of buyers and sellers are the same.

The most common calculation that you need to be able to do is determine yield rate for a particular stock. Remember that the yield rate is the rate of return expected by the investor. The following examples are intended to provide you with a simple procedure to compute an approximate return, excluding any commissions that one might pay to a broker. A broker is someone who acts on your behalf in the purchase and sale of your shares.

EXAMPLE 11.1

An investor is trying to decide between two investments. Rolex Inc. common shares are trading at $80½ while Triac Electronic's common shares are trading at $74¼. Rolex has been consistent in paying an annual dividend of $3.50 per common share to shareholders, while Triac has been averaging $2.25 per share. If both investments are over one year, which stock has the best rate of return?

Solution To answer this question we simply need to compare the expected dividend for each company to the current share price:

$$\text{Rolex's rate of return} = \frac{\$\ 3.5}{\$80.5}$$

$$\doteq 0.043478$$

$$\text{Triac's rate of return} = \frac{\$\ 2.25}{\$74.25}$$

$$\doteq 0.030303$$

Based on this simple analysis, the investor would buy Rolex stock.

EXAMPLE 11.2

Suppose you are thinking about buying a MacMillan Bloedel preferred share that is trading at $36¼ ($36.25). If the share pays 7½% annually on a par value of $50, what would be your rate of return each year?

Solution The preferred dividend is based on the rate quoted for dividends on the original issue price. Remember that, even though you may buy the share at less than the par value, you still receive the dividend (7½%) on the basis of the share's issue price. Therefore:

First, figure out the actual amount of interest paid annually on the share:

$$0.075 \times \$50 = \$3.75$$

Next, we divide the interest paid by the purchase price of the stock:

$$\frac{\$3.75}{\$36\frac{1}{4}} = 0.10345$$

If you buy the preferred share for $36\frac{1}{4}$, you will earn 10.345% per annum on your investment.

11.3 Debt Financing

As we noted in the introduction, businesses and governments who need to borrow money for a long period of time often prepare and sell a bond issue. A bond is a written promise to pay to the purchaser a specific sum of money at a specific point in the future. In addition, the issuer promises to pay interest, generally semiannually, for the use of the money.

It was noted earlier that a similar type of instrument to a bond is a debenture. Bonds are secured by a pledge of assets while debentures are simply a legal commitment by the borrower to repay the amount borrowed.

Debt financing can take a variety of forms including bonds, debentures, mortgages, and a range of loans that are available to companies. This type of financing is not limited to corporations. Most newspapers on any given day carry at least one story dealing with government debt. Perhaps more than any other topic, the level of debt for school boards, municipalities, and federal and provincial governments poses concern to many business and government leaders. In order to raise the money to pay for government deficits, bond and debenture issues are common.

Government bonds and debentures are often considered to be a good long term investment. For example, the non-market Canada Savings Bonds issued in October 1987 (shortly after the severe stock market decline) were a great investment compared to other types of bank and credit union investments.

The term **non-market bond** is used to describe Canada Savings Bonds since they are not bought and sold on the bond market. Instead, they are bought and sold through local financial institutions at the value specified on the bond. The seller receives the face value amount even if the bonds are cashed in before the **maturity date** (the time the bond holders are paid back the principal).

Government of Canada bonds, on the other hand, are subject to market conditions. When they are sold before maturity, they must be sold through a broker at whatever the market says the bond is worth.

Bonds and debentures are sold on two markets:

- the primary securities market
- the secondary securities market

Primary markets are where bonds are sold when they are first issued by a company or government agency. A dealer or brokerage house sells the bonds on behalf of the issuing company or government agency.

The **secondary security market** is where bonds are resold after being initially purchased. *The Financial Post* bond quotation is an example of the secondary market. It is this secondary market that provides the means to transfer ownership and set the value of bonds and debentures over time.

There are several terms you need to understand in our discussion of bonds and debentures (note that from here on the term bond will be used since the terms and calculations that apply to bonds in general apply to debentures):

Face Value or Par Value
This is the value stated on the bond or the issue price. In general, the face value is stated in a denomination of $1,000 or higher. However, when the sale is also to appeal to small investors, denominations of $100 sometimes occur.

Maturity Date
This is the date when the bondholder can expect to have the full value of the bond repaid. An equivalent term that is sometimes used is **redemption date**. This refers to the date when the bond is redeemed, that is, when the money is paid back to the bondholder by the company or government agency that issued the bond.

Redemption Value
The value the company or government pays to the bondholder when the bond is redeemed. If a bond is redeemed at face value, then we say the bond is redeemed at **par value**, sometimes referred to as par. It is possible to have a bond redeemed at more than par value to make the bond more attractive to the investor when first offered for sale.

Bond Rate
This is the rate of interest used to determine the interest the bond pays to the bond holder. It is also called the **coupon rate** and the **contract rate**. Those of you who have had a Canada Savings Bond have probably "cut" the coupon

off to collect the interest. (This may date some of us, since coupons have not been used on recent issues.)

Yield Rate

When bonds are sold on the open market the purchaser will want a particular rate of return on their investment. This return is called yield rate and will change over time depending on the current rates of interest being paid when the bond is purchased. The yield rate is the factor that determines the purchase price of the bond when it is sold on the open market.

Interest Dates

This refers to the time periods when interest is paid to the bondholder. Most bonds pay interest semiannually. Often abbreviations are used, such as J-J, for bonds that have interest payable on January 1 and July 1.

Accrued Interest

The interest that has accumulated on a bond since the interest was last paid.

Purchase Price

This is the price of a bond based upon the yield rate, the rate of return expected by an investor, which in turn is based on the prevailing interest rates at the time the bond is purchased. It is important to understand that the purchase price of a bond is not necessarily the price that you read in the paper. The value in the paper is the quoted price and, if there is any accrued interest on the bond, then this interest must be added to the quoted price to get the purchase price.

The discussion that follows uses the following symbols to stand for each of the terms above:

F — face value of the bond
RD — the redemption value of the bond
PP — the purchase price of the bond
r — the bond or coupon rate of the bond
i — the yield rate expected by the purchaser
n — the number of remaining interest periods until the redemption or maturity date
R — the interest payment each period, based on the bond rate ($R = F \times r$)

With these definitions in place, we can now examine how the price of a bond is determined to yield a given return.

11.4 Determining the Purchase Price of a Bond on an Interest Date

Bonds can be purchased at any time. However, the procedures differ depending on whether the bond is purchased on the date interest is regularly paid (interest date) or whether it is purchased "between interest dates". Our discussion in the first section focuses on the purchasing of bonds on an interest date.

At the outset, it is important to understand that when someone purchases a bond there are two payments the buyer will receive:

- the regular interest payments, usually paid every six months;
- the redemption value of the bond when it matures or is redeemed.

Therefore, the price that an investor will be prepared to pay for a bond depends on:

R: the regular interest payment ($F \times r$);

RD: the redemption or maturity value.

What must be done is to compute the present value of the remaining interest payments using the yield rate as the interest rate, then, add this present value of interest payments to the present value of the redemption value, also based on the yield rate. By adding these two present values, one can determine the price an investor would be prepared to pay for a bond to generate the required return. The price paid by an investor will ensure the investor obtains the required yield on the investment, since the basis for the computations was the yield rate expected by the investor.

The sum of these two present values can more clearly be expressed in a formula:

STEP 1   Set up an expression for calculating the present value of the remaining interest periods:

$$\frac{R[1 - (1 + i)^{-n}]}{i}$$

Where:

$R = F \times r$

F = face value

r = bond rate

i = yield rate

n = number of remaining interest periods

STEP 2   Next, develop an expression that will find the present value of the redemption value:

$$RD(1 + i)^{-n}$$

Where:

RD = redemption value

i = yield rate

n = number of interest periods remaining

STEP 3   Adding these two present values together gives a formula for the **purchase price of a bond** on an interest date (remember, an interest date is the date on which the interest is paid):

$$PP = \frac{R[1 - (1 + i)^{-n}]}{i} + RD(1 + i)^{-n} \qquad \textbf{Formula 11.1}$$

In the following examples you will find two terms being used depending upon whether the purchase price is greater than the face value or less than the face value.

If the purchase price is greater than the redemption value, then the bond is said to be purchased at a **premium**. Conversely, when a bond is purchased at a price that is less than the redemption value, the bond is said to be purchased at a **discount**.

What determines whether there is a discount or a premium is the relationship between the yield rate and the bond rate. If the yield rate is higher than the bond rate, then the bond is generally purchased at a discount. If the bond rate is greater than the yield rate, then the bond is generally purchased at a premium.

One exception may arise if the bond is redeemed (RD) at a higher value than the face value. This sometimes occurs to make the bonds more attractive to investors. It also occurs if the bonds may be redeemed before the maturity date by the issuing company — if this is possible, the bond is called a **callable bond**. When the redemption value is greater than the face value, it normally results in a statement that the bond will be redeemed at a value in excess of 100% of the face value. For example, a bond with a face value of $1,000 that is to be redeemed at $1,100 is said to be redeemable at 110 (i.e., 110% of the face value). When this occurs, it complicates the problem sufficiently so that it cannot be said in advance whether a premium or discount will apply.

This special case will be examined in Example 11.4.

EXAMPLE 11.3

A $5,000 Government of Canada bond pays the holder an interest rate of 9.5% payable semiannually. The bond will be redeemed at par in ten years. An investor wants to purchase the bond on the bond market to yield a return of 12% payable semiannually. What would be the purchase price of the bond?

Solution Since the bond pays 9.5% on $5,000 semiannually, the regular interest payment will be:

$$R = F \times r$$

$$= \$5,000 \left[\frac{0.095}{2} \right]$$

$$= \$237.50$$

From the information given, the remaining number of interest periods is:

$$n = 10 \times 2, \text{ or } 20$$

The redemption value of the bond in ten years is the par value or the face value of the bond:

$$RD = \$5,000$$

Now to compute the purchase price, we must calculate the present values of the payments and the redemption value. Since the yield rate is the rate the investor wants to receive, it is the rate we must use to find the present values in determining the purchase price. Substituting the values into our formula, we have:

$$PP = \frac{\$237.50[1 - (1 + i)^{-n}]}{i} + \$5,000(1 + i)^{-n}$$

Substituting the remaining values gives:

$$i = \frac{0.12}{2}, \text{ or } 0.06 \qquad\qquad \text{The yield rate.}$$

$$n = 20$$

$$PP = \frac{\$237.50[1 - (1 + 0.06)^{-20}]}{0.06} + \$5,000(1 + 0.06)^{-20}$$

$$PP \doteq \$2,724.11 + \$1,559.02$$

$$PP \doteq \$4,283.13$$

Therefore, if the investor pays \$4,283.13 for the bond the guaranteed return is 12% compounded semiannually. Since the bond is purchased at a price less than the redemption, it is said to have been bought at a **discount**. The value of the discount is:

$$\$5,000 - \$4,283.13 = \$716.87$$

The most important thing to note about this example is that the yield rate is the rate that must be used to determine the present values, and thus the purchase price. The bond rate is used only to find the regular income payments. The reason for this is that the price must be based on the return the investor wants to receive, in this case, 12% compounded semiannually. Only the yield rate will generate a price that guarantees this return.

EXAMPLE 11.4

A large gas and oil company needs to raise \$10,000,000 for capital expansion of its plant. The company issues fifteen year bonds to raise the money. The bonds are redeemable at 102. The rate of interest on the bond is 9% payable semiannually. If at the time of the bond issue interest rates are 8% compounded semiannually, what amount of money will the company receive from the bond issue?

Solution   We should start by noting an important piece of information in this problem. **We are told that the bonds will be redeemed at 102; this means that for every dollar of face value, \$1.02 will be paid upon redemption.** The reason a company may offer such an arrangement is to encourage people to buy their bond and hold it until it is redeemed. To the investor this represents a slight increase in the return, since upon redemption the bondholder will get an additional $0.02 per $1.

Now turning to the problem at hand, the information given is:

$$r = \frac{(0.09)}{2} \qquad \text{The bond rate.}$$

$$i = \frac{(0.08)}{2} \qquad \text{The yield rate.}$$

$$R = 0.045 \times \$10,000,000$$

$$\doteq \$450,000 \qquad \text{Remember that interest payments are based on the bond rate.}$$

$$RD = \$10,000,000 \times (1.02)$$

$$= \$10,200,000 \qquad \text{Redemption value for the entire bond issue.}$$

$$n = 15 \times 2, \text{ or } 30$$

Substituting into Formula 11.1 gives:

$$PP = \frac{R[1 - (1 + i)^{-n}]}{i} + RD(1 + i)^{-n}$$

$$PP = \frac{\$450,000[1 - (1 + 0.04)^{-30}]}{0.04} + \$10,200,000(1 + 0.04)^{-30}$$

$$PP = \$7,781,414.99 + \$3,144,850.41$$

$$PP = \$10,926,265.40$$

Thus, the company will raise $10,926,265.40 from the bond issue, $926,265.40 more than the initial issue, that is:

$$\$10,926,265.40 - \$10,000,000 = \$926,265.40$$

If the bonds were in denominations of $1,000 an investor would pay $1,092.63 for each $1,000 bond, resulting in the payment of a $92.63 premium. It is important to note that the premium is paid by the purchaser to the seller. That is why the company receives more than the face value of the bonds issued; the total premium is paid to the company as part of the purchase price.

11.5 Purchase Price of Bonds Between Interest Periods

Often bonds are not purchased on the convenient dates when interest is paid. In fact, most bond sales occur at points in time other than the interest date. The method used to compute bond prices between interest periods relies on an approximation using both compound and simple interest procedures.

The first step requires us to compute the purchase price of the bond at the interest date immediately preceding the actual purchase date. Then we accumulate this purchase price to the date when the purchase occurs. The procedure we use to bring the price forward, from the immediately preceding interest period, to the actual date of purchase, uses the simple interest method of Chapter 6. The easiest way to understand the process is to look at an example:

EXAMPLE 11.6

A bond with a face value of $100,000 is purchased on September 4, 1991. The interest is payable on April 1 and October 1 at 11% compounded semiannually. If the bond is redeemable at 102 on October 1, 1993, find the purchase price on September 4, 1991, for an investor who wants to earn 14% compounded semiannually.

Solution From the information in this problem we can see that the interest date that **precedes** the purchase date is April 1, 1991. The time that has elapsed between the interest date and the purchase date is (247 – 91), or 156 days. This was found using the Table of Days of the Year in Chapter 6. We must also determine the number of days between interest dates, that is, between April 1 and October 1. Again using the Table of Days we calculate (274 – 91), or 183 days. Time Diagram 11.1 shows the steps involved.

Let's work through each part of the solution in steps:

STEP 1 Find the purchase price at the interest period immediately preceding the purchase date. Use Formula 11.1:

$$PP = \frac{R[1 - (1 + i)^{-n}]}{i} + RD(1 + i)^{-n}$$

Where:

$$r = \frac{0.11}{2}, \text{ or } 0.055$$

$$F = \$100,000$$

$$R = (0.055) \times \$100,000, \text{ or } \$5,500$$

$$i = \frac{0.14}{2}, \text{ or } 0.07$$

$$RD = \$100,000 \times 1.02, \text{ or } \$102,000$$

$$n = 5 \quad \text{This takes us back to April 1, 1991.}$$

Now substituting into our equation:

$$PP = \frac{\$5,500[1 - (1 + 0.07)^{-5}]}{0.07} + \$102,000(1 + 0.07)^{-5}$$

$$PP \doteq \$22,551.09 + \$72,724.59$$

$$PP \doteq \$95,275.68$$

If the bond was purchased on April 1, 1991, the purchase price would be $95,275.68.

STEP 2 The next step is to bring the purchase price from April 1 forward to the actual purchase date of September 4, 1991. We do this by accumulating the purchase price on April 1 to September 4 using simple interest for the number of days that have elapsed. Remember that the time between these two days is 156 days with 183 days being the total days in the interest period from April 1 to October 1, 1991.

$$PP \doteq \$95,275.68 \left[1 + 0.07 \left(\frac{156}{183} \right) \right]$$

$$PP \doteq \$100,960.98$$

Therefore, the purchase price of the bond on September 4, 1991, is $100,960.98. Diagrammatically the problem looks as follows:

Figure 11.1   Time diagram of a bond purchase *between* interest dates

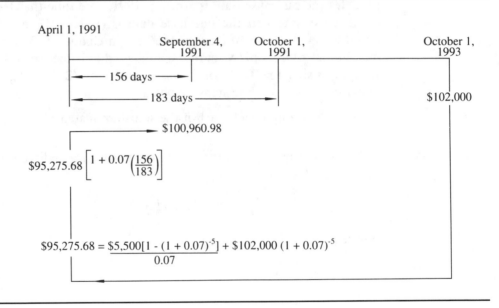

11.6 Flat Price, Quoted Price, and Accrued Interest

In Example 11.6 the purchase price of $100,960.98 is called the **flat price**. What this means is that the price on September 4 includes the **accrued interest** from the last interest period, April 1,1991. More precisely, the accrued interest from April 1 to September 4 is:

$$\$100,000 \left[0.055 \left(\frac{156}{183} \right) \right] \doteq \$4,688.52$$

The bond seller expects to receive the interest upon the sale of the bond. Therefore, when the bond is sold, the price the bondholder considers to be the selling price is:

$$\$100,960.98 - \$4,688.52 = \$96,272.46$$

This price is called the **quoted price**. The relationship between the flat price, quoted price, and accrued interest can be seen in the following expressions:

Quoted Price = Flat Price – Accrued Interest
Flat Price = Quoted Price + Accrued Interest

It is important to note that the accrued interest is accruing at the bond rate, not the yield rate. When you consider what is actually occurring, the bond was accumulating interest to the bondholder from the preceding interest date, April 1 (from Example 11.6) to the purchase date of September 4. Now the price must be adjusted to reflect this interest since the seller of the bond needs to be compensated for the time the bond has been held since the last interest payment.

To get everything straight, let's consider an example:

EXAMPLE 11.7

A $100,000 bond has a bond rate of 12% and will be redeemed on September 1, 1995. Interest is payable semiannually on September 1 and March 1. Find the quoted price, flat price, and accrued interest if the bond is purchased on April 30, 1991. Assume the investor expects to receive 10% payable semiannually.

Solution   To find the purchase price, we must first calculate a price on the interest date preceding the purchase date, March 1. Then this price is accumulated to the point where the purchase occurs on April 30. Following the previous example:

$$r = \frac{0.12}{2}, \text{ or } 0.06$$

$$F = \$100,000$$

$$R = \$100,000 \times 0.06, \text{ or } \$6,000$$

$$i = \frac{0.10}{2}, \text{ or } 0.05$$

$n = 9$ These are the remaining interest periods from March 1, 1991, to September 1, 1995.

Substituting the information in Formula 11.1 gives:

$$PP = \frac{\$6,000[1 - (1 + 0.05)^{-9}]}{0.05} + \$100,000(1 + 0.05)^{-9}$$

$$PP \doteq \$42,646.93 + \$64,460.89$$

$$PP \doteq \$107,107.82$$

Next, accumulate the purchase price on the interest date of March 1, 1991, to the purchase date of April 30, 1991. However, remember that since the computation of the purchase price is based on the yield rate, this is the rate that will be used to move the price on March 1 ($107,107.82) to the purchase date of April 30. To accumulate to April 30, the number of days between the purchase date and the interest payment date must be found. Turning to the Table of Days of the Year.

Purchase date April 30,	120 days
Interest date March 1,	60 days
Total number of days	60 days

The number of days in the interest period between March 1 and September 1 is 184 (244 – 60).

Now, accumulating the interest from the interest date to the purchase date we have the flat price:

$$\text{Flat Price} = \$107,107.82\left[1 + (0.05)\frac{60}{184}\right] \quad \text{Remember to use the yield rate.}$$

$$\doteq \$108,854.14 \quad \text{The purchase on April 30, 1991.}$$

To calculate the quoted price we must subtract the accrued interest **that accrues to the owner of the bond up to the time the bond is sold**. In this problem the interest that belongs to the holder is from March 1 to April 30, and will be paid based on the bond rate. Thus the quoted price will be:

$$\text{Accrued Interest} = \$100,000\left[(0.06)\frac{60}{184}\right], \text{ or } \$1,956.52$$

$$\text{Quoted Price} \doteq \$108,854.14 - \$1,956.52$$

$$\doteq \$106,897.62$$

The purchase price on the interest date is shown below in the time diagram.

Figure 11.2 Time Diagram of the Purchase *between* Interest Dates for Example 11.7

March 1, 1991

April 30, 1991

September 1, 1991

September 1, 1995

60 days

184 days

$100,000

$108,854.14

$$\$107,107.82 \left[1 + 0.05\left(\frac{60}{184}\right)\right]$$

$$\$107,107.82 = \frac{\$6,000\,[1-(1+0.05)^{-9}]}{0.05} + \$100,000\,(1+0.05)^{-9}$$

SUMMARY OF FORMULAS

Formula 11.1
$$PP = \frac{R[1-(1+i)^{-n}]}{i}RD(1+i)^{-n}$$
Finding the purchase price of a bond on an interest date.

GLOSSARY OF TERMS

Accumulation of a Discount the process of adjusting the book value of a bond by accumulating the bond discount over the remaining interest periods on the bond.

Amortization of a Premium the process of adjusting the book value of a bond by amortizing the bond premium over the remaining interest periods on the bond.

Approximate Yield Rate an average yield rate based on a comparison of the annual average income and the average investment.

Bond a debt that is promised to be repaid at a specific point in time called the maturity date. Bonds are secured by a pledge of specific assets of the issuing organization.

Bond Rate the rate of interest paid on a bond. The bond rate determines the regular interest income from the bond. The bond rate is sometimes called the contract rate or the coupon rate on a bond.

Common Stock the manner in which one holds ownership in a company. People who purchase common stock are called common shareholders and receive compensation for the purchase of stock by being paid dividends.

Contract Rate   see Bond Rate.

Coupon Rate   see Bond Rate.

Debenture   a debt that is promised to be repaid at a specific time, called the maturity date. A debenture is not secured by the assets of the company or government who issued the debentures.

Debt Financing   the process of raising money with debt that includes loans, bonds, and debentures. There is no sale of ownership in using debt financing to raise money.

Discount   when a bond is purchased at a price less than the redemption value the bond is said to be purchased at a discount. The discount is the difference between the redemption value and the purchase price.

Equity Financing   raising money for a company by selling some of the ownership. This is accomplished by the sale of stock to investors.

Face Value   the dollar value specified on the bond. Generally, bonds are in denominations (face value) of $1,000, $5,000, and $10,000. When bonds are to be sold to many investors, including very small investors, other denominations may be used — some may be less than $1,000.

Flat Price   the purchase price of a bond that includes any accrued interest on the bond.

Preferred Stock   preferred stock or shares are stocks that have a predefined rate of return based on their par value. Preferred shareholders are paid their income before common shareholders receive any dividends. There are many different types of preferred shares sold in the market.

Premium   when a bond is purchased at a price that is greater than the redemption value the bond is said to be purchased at a premium. The premium is the difference between the purchased price and the redemption value.

Quoted Price   the price of a bond excluding the accrued interest.

Redeemable at > 100 or < 100   when a bond is said to be redeemable at 103, for example, this means that the bond will be redeemed at a rate of $103 for every $100 of the bond's face value, i.e., redeemable at a **premium**. Conversely, if a bond is redeemable at 95, for example, this means that for every $100 of face value only $95 will be paid, i.e., redeemable at a **discount**.

Redeemable at 100   when a bond is said to be redeemable at 100 it is said to be redeemable at par value.

Redeemable Bond   when a bond is said to be redeemable it means that, with proper notice, the bond may be redeemed before the maturity date on the bond.

Redemption Value   the amount paid by the issuer of a bond to the bondholder on or before the maturity date on the bond.

Yield Rate   the rate of interest or return expected by investors when purchasing a bond. The yield rate is determined by the market rate of interest and the degree of risk associated with the investment.

CHAPTER 12

Statistics

A study of recent car purchasers found that 94% of people who had purchased a Japanese automobile were either very or somewhat satisfied with their new car. Of those who had purchased a North American car, 92% were very or somewhat satisfied. Does this mean that buyers of Japanese cars, on average, are more likely to be satisfied with their car purchases, when compared to purchasers of North American cars? The answer is unclear. Although the news media would no doubt jump to this conclusion, additional statistical information is needed to provide an informed opinion about the issue.

Everyday when you pick up the newspaper, there is a good chance that someone is writing about a survey, telling people how the nation's opinion is divided. Not only are people confronted with statistical surveys in the paper, but also people are bombarded with a myriad of statistics from bankruptcy rates and unemployment rates to various economic indicators (the stock market indexes are the most classic). The point is that we cannot escape statistics. Moreover, most business decisions will be based to some extent on statistics.

When you have finished this chapter, you will be able to:

1. explain the meaning of the term statistics;
2. explain the difference between descriptive and inferential statistics;
3 summarize data using frequency distributions and graphical procedures;
4 summarize data using different statistical measures, including central tendency and dispersion; and
5. use statistics to assist with business decision making.

12.1 What Is Statistics?

The need to make informed and accurate decisions in business requires sound information, much of which is based on data collected using the techniques of modern statistics. The term statistics includes the collection, display and analysis of numerical data, including making predictions. When data are collected there are two types — population data and sample data. Population data means data which have been collected using <u>all</u> elements of the population.

For example, if one wished to determine the satisfaction of purchasers of the current years' Rolls Royce it might be possible to speak to all purchasers — or at least send a survey to all purchasers. However, if one wanted to measure the satisfaction of all the purchasers of Ford for this production year, it would not be feasible to try and contact all purchasers since the number would be too large. The cost would be too prohibitive. Therefore we would take a sample of Ford purchasers, where the sample is a subset of all Ford buyers for the current production year. In accounting, auditors do not check all accounts, rather they take a representative sample of accounts, again the reason is cost. Moreover, provided that the sample is selected using the correct statistical methodology, the sample will generally provide a very accurate picture of the population. In most business situations, the data are sample information.

When data are population data, the measures from the population — like an average — are called **parameters**. If the data collected are based on a sample, the measures from the sample — like an average — are called **statistics**.

There are two general areas of statistics — descriptive statistics and inferential statistics. **Descriptive statistics** refers to that part of statistics that deals with the collection, display (e.g., graphical displays), calculations (e.g., finding the average, the midpoint, etc.), and summaries of data. There are no predictions or inferences within descriptive statistics — we simply describe data.

Inferential statistics on the other hand, deals with making inferences and predictions. For example when you read about a poll that states that 58% of those surveyed will be voting for party X, with a maximum margin of error of 3%, 19 times out of 20, an inference can be made. The inference or prediction that can be made is that if the election was held today, party X should receive somewhere between 55% and 61% of the popular vote (58% + 3%), 19 times out of 20. The 19 times out of 20 is saying we are 95% (19/20 = 0.95) confident that the actual votes for party X will fall between 55% and 61% of all votes cast. The + 3% margin of error one is determined using the techniques of inferential statistics. When a researcher is extrapolating from a sample to infer something about the population, from which the sample was drawn, the researcher is said to be applying inferential statistics.

12.2 Using Descriptive Statistics To Summarize Data

Often data is displayed in the form of the Nanaimo real estate example in Table 12.1 below. Here the data is simply displayed in what is called an array of numbers. The problem is that one cannot say very much by looking at the data. One way to summarize the information is to group the data using a series of groups or classes where one can see how many observations fall into each class or group. The advantage of this approach is that it provides an organized way to interpret the market information.

Consider data collected in business and government. Business data often includes hundreds or thousands of observations that record some type of market or economic activity. For example, if a business person wanted to summarize the real estate market in a large Canadian city like Toronto or Vancouver for one month of the year, that person would discover that the number of sales are in the thousands. The sales would include many different types of property, such as residential, commercial or industrial in addition to other types of property sales. To summarize market activity for one type of sale (e.g., residential property), two approaches commonly used are the frequency distribution and the graphical representation. Both methods provide an easy way to summarize and convey information for a large amount of data.

A. Frequency Distributions

A **frequency distribution** is the grouping of a set of data into a series of classes. For each class the number of observations that fall within each class is recorded; the complete listing of the number of observations that fall into each class is called a frequency distribution (i.e., the listings of the class frequencies). To understand how to set up a frequency distribution, consider the data in Table 12.1 for all September sales of single detached homes in the City of Nanaimo, British Columbia.

Table 12.1: Selling Price (in $) of Homes in Nanaimo in September

205,800	210,000	215,300	224,500	224,800
112,000	121,000	**110,500**	135,200	144,800
121,000	125,000	135,400	140,000	149,400
223,000	216,400	217,300	215,000	232,000
230,000	234,200	229,100	248,900	239,450
245,250	249,050	256,250	265,450	274,550
345,000	**374,000**	146,600	154,000	180,000
146,500	147,000	174,500	178,400	188,200
160,400	167,000	199,200	205,000	210,000
183,000	185,800	312,000	324,800	335,000
285,000	297,000	282,100	297,000	281,000
288,400	294,400	179,800	194,500	215,400
195,000	185,500			

In total there are 62 sales recorded in this city, with a low selling price of $110,500 and a high selling price of $374,000. One possible frequency distribution for the data is shown in Table 12.2.

Table 12.2: A Frequency Distribution of Nanaimo Housing Sales for September

Class Limits (in $)	Number of Sales in Each Group *f*	Percentage of Sales in Each Group %	Cumulative Percentage of Sales %
100,000 — 124,999	4	6.5	6.5
125,000 — 149,999	9	14.5	21.0
150,000 — 174,999	4	6.5	27.5
175,000 — 199,999	10	16.1	43.6
200,000 — 224,999	12	19.4	63.0
225,000 — 249,999	8	12.9	75.9
250,000 — 274,999	3	4.8	80.7
275,000 — 299,999	7	11.3	92.0
300,000 — 324,999	2	3.2	95.2
325,000 — 349,999	2	3.2	98.4
350,000 — 374,999	1	1.6	100.0
	62	100.0	

To summarize data in Table 12.1 with a frequency distribution, like the one in Table 12.2, first decide on the number of classes to use. In Table 12.2, eleven classes were selected. The number of classes is to some extent arbitrary, and depends upon who is grouping the data. The general rule is to use five to fifteen classes, depending upon the number of observations. The more observations the more classes (up to fifteen); the fewer the observations, the fewer classes or groups (as low as five).

In Table 12.2, the choice of eleven classes was a value judgement; another researcher might have selected ten or twelve classes. The choice will be based on what seems to describe the data accurately. However, if one uses to many or too few classes it may obscure tendencies in the data. Once the number of classes has been decided upon, the class width, or the size of each class, must be determined. The class width depends upon the number of classes one decides to use, and the range of values from the lowest value to the maximum value of the data. To approximate the class width, find the range by subtracting the minimum value from the maximum value of the data, and then divide this range by the number of classes. For the Nanaimo data we have:

$$\frac{\$374,000 - \$110,500}{11} = \$23,955 \text{ (the approximate width for each class)}$$

The reason $23,955 is referred to as the <u>approximate</u> width is that one normally rounds up to a convenient number for the class width. Normally a researcher would round up to $24,000 or even $25,000, a more convenient width. The width of $25,000 is used for grouping this set of data.

Once the class width is determined, set up the classes by defining the **class limits**. The class limits are minimum and the maximum values of the original data that can fall into a particular class. Once the first class lower limit is decided upon, the width will determine the remaining class limits, since the difference between successive lower limits (or upper class limits) will equal the class width. For example, the first and second lower limits were $100,000 and $125,000, their difference is $25,000, the class width. The choice to start at $100,000 was because it was a convenient number that would be easy for interpretation.

Once the classes are determined, the number of sales that fall within each class is recorded under the column with the *f*, called the **class frequency**. The next column, the **relative frequency**, reports each class frequency as a percentage of the total frequency; the third column is the **cumulative percentage** and records the percentage of the data up to and including the class for which the cumulative percentage is reported.

We can now observe that with the groupings it is possible to see the nature of the market activity for the month of September, and in particular, within what price range the majority of the sales are to be found.

Summarizing the frequency distribution for Nanaimo housing sales:

1. The symbol $ makes it clear to the reader that the groupings are in dollars. The values at the bottom and top of each class are known as the class limits. For example, $175,000 is called the lower limit of the fourthclass, while $199,999 is called the upper limit of the fourth class.
2. The symbol f is used to denote the frequency for each class. In this example the frequency refers to the number of sales in each group.
3. The % heading reports the class frequency as a percent of the total, as well as the cumulative percentages.

One should follow these guidelines when preparing a frequency distribution:

1. The classes must avoid any overlapping, that is each class must be mutually exclusive . The characteristic of <u>mutually exclusive</u> (a sale can fall in one class or the other, but not both) is very important in grouping of data. For example, if a home sold for $179,900 it clearly falls in the $150,000 — $179,999 group — no sale is allowed to fall within two groups.

2. The classes are the same width. This feature is not absolutely necessary, but it makes interpretation of the data much easier.

3. There is an ending to the last class, i.e., the last class is not left at $375,000 or larger, rather it has a maximum. It is important to understand that this last feature, having all the groups closed (having both upper and lower limits) is not followed by researchers. Imagine if there had been a sale of a property at $1,500,000. If this occurred, here are two possibilities for presentation. First one might leave the groupings as above and specify as a footnote that there had been one sale of $1,500,000 and that it has been excluded from the groupings since it was so unusual; and second, is to add a twelfth class, that is an open class by stating a lower limit of $375,000 and simply to state "and over" (i.e., $375,000 and over). The choice depends upon the researcher. However, this writer would use a footnote, since the Table with the closed classes provides the best information on the majority of the data.

EXAMPLE 12.1

The share value for Neon Tristar, a computer software company, has been recorded for twenty five consecutive trading days in November and December. The prices are the closing price of the stock for each trading day. The closing price is the trading price in the market at the end of a trading day. Summarize the market activity showing how the share closing value has fluctuated over the period. Use six classes and construct the frequency distribution showing the relative frequency and the cumulative percentages.

Closing Market Price (in $) of Neon Tristar for Twenty Five Trading Days During the Month of November and December

Day	Value	Day	Value	Day	Value	Day	Value	Day	Value
1	$2.24	6	$2.25	11	$2.10	16	$2.35	21	$2.15
2	2.40	7	2.42	12	2.32	17	2.51	22	2.45
3	2.54	8	2.50	13	2.70	18	2.65	23	2.56
4	2.80	9	2.70	14	2.75	19	2.70	24	2.89
5	2.90	10	2.85	15	2.92	20	2.80	25	2.90

Solution

STEP 1   Find the range in the share values: $2.92 – $2.10 = $0.82

STEP 2   Determine the class width: divide the range of the data by the number of classes and rounding up to a convenient number:

$$\frac{0.82}{6} = 0.1366667$$

<u>Always</u> choose a convenient width by rounding up — never down, since this may result in classes that will not accommodate all the data.

Rounding to $0.15 would yield a class width that is convenient.

STEP 3 Determine the lowest class limit: since the minimum value of the data is $2.10, this would be a convenient place to start. Thus, the first class would be $2.10–$2.24. Since the class width is $0.15, the next class would be $2.25–$2.39. Note that the width of each class is measured from the lower limit of one class to the lower limit of the next class. Thus, $2.10 is the first lower limit and $2.25 is the lower limit of the second class — the difference is $0.15.

STEP 4 Set up the classes, assign the frequencies, and compute the relative frequency (percentage of prices in each group) and the cumulative percentages.

Class Limits (in $)	Number of Prices in Each Group	Percentage of Prices in Each Group	Cumulative Percentage of Prices
	f	%	%
2.10–2.24	3	12	12
2.25–2.39	3	12	24
2.40–2.54	6	24	48
2.55–2.69	2	8	56
2.70–2.84	6	24	80
2.85–2.99	5	20	100
	25	100	

From the frequency distribution it can be seen that the share price closed most often between $2.40 and $2.54 and between $2.70 and $2.84, each grouping occurring 24% of the time. As well, the stock did close at a price of $2.40 or higher 76% of the time.

B. Describing Data with a Graph

Another way of describing data is with a graph. The frequency distribution can be displayed with a bar graph, a line graph or a pie chart. The choice of the type of graph (line, bar or pie) depends on what one wishes to highlight, as well as the level of sophistication of the audience that will be viewing the graph.

(i) A Line Graph

Consider the data presented on housing sales in Nanaimo. To construct a line graph for the number of sales, place the price on the horizontal axis and the frequency on the vertical axis. Plotting grouped data poses a small problem — what value of price would go on the horizontal scale? Since each class has a range of values, a "representative" value for the sales in each price class must be found. The best measure of selling price is the midpoint of each class. This midpoint is used as the representative value of the price for the sales in each group. The class midpoint, the middle value of each class, is found by dividing the sum of the lower (or upper) class limits of consecutive classes by two. For example, the midpoint of the first class is found by finding the value halfway between $100,000 and $125,000 or:

$$\frac{\$125,000 + \$100,000}{2} = \$112,500$$

Table 12.3 shows the computed class midpoints. The symbol X is used to denote the value of the midpoint of each class.

Table 12.3: Class Midpoints

Classes Limits (in $)	Number of Sales in Each Group	Class Midpoint (in $)
	f	X
100,000–124,999	4	112,500
125,000–149,999	9	137,500
150,000–174,999	4	162,500
175,000–199,999	10	187,500
200,000–224,999	12	212,500
225,000–249,999	8	237,500
250,000–274,999	3	262,500
275,000–299,999	7	287,500
300,000–324,999	2	312,500
325,000–349,999	2	337,500
350,000–374,999	1	362,500
Total Frequency	62	

Plotting the data using the class midpoints yields the line graph in Figure 12.1. When examining the graph note that the axes are clearly labeled and the graph is labeled. It is important to make the information easy to interpret.

Figure 12.1 Line Graph for Nanaimo Housing Sales in September

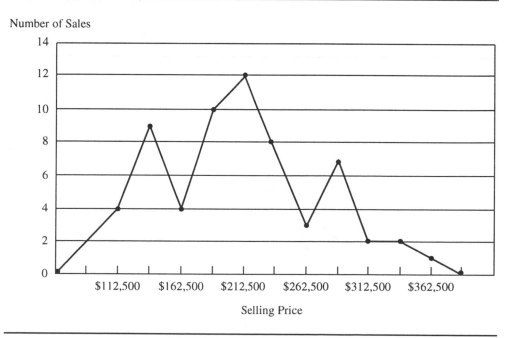

Note that the selling price is "anchored" at the two ends of the graph. This anchoring simply completes the graph.

The reason the frequency distribution is used to construct the line graph is that the original data would not plot as easily. Using the grouped data makes the graph a useful means of summarizing large amounts of data when the values of the variable (price, in this case) are not repeated with any regularity.

To see how a line graph is helpful in showing the daily variation, which may reveal a trend in the data measured over time, consider Example 12.2.

EXAMPLE 12.2

Below are the closing share prices for Neon Tristar was recorded for 25 consecutive trading days, starting on November 1 and ending on December 4, 1992. Plot the closing prices using a line graph to show how the price of the share has changed over the period.

Closing Market Price (in $) of Neon Tristar for Twenty Five Trading Days During the Months of November and December

Day	Value	Day	Value	Day	Value	Day	Value	Day	Value
1	2.24	6	2.25	11	2.10	16	2.35	21	2.15
2	2.40	7	2.42	12	2.32	17	2.51	22	2.45
3	2.54	8	2.50	13	2.70	18	2.65	23	2.56
4	2.80	9	2.70	14	2.75	19	2.70	24	2.89
5	2.90	10	2.85	15	2.92	20	2.80	25	2.90

Solution

STEP 1 Label the vertical axis closing share price and decide on the values for the axis. In this case the share value has been started at $2.00, with increments

Figure 12.2 Line Graph of Neon Tristar Share Prices for 25 Consecutive Trading Days

Closing Share Price

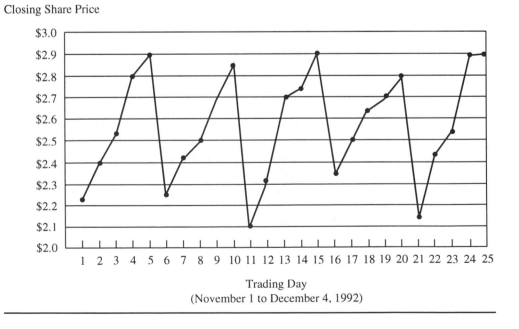

Trading Day
(November 1 to December 4, 1992)

of 0.10. The choice of 0.10 was to provide for a fairly detailed description of price.

STEP 2 Label the horizontal axis as the Trading Day: start with trading day 1 (November 1) and ending at trading day 25 (December 4), 1992;

STEP 3 Plot the daily closing price and join the points;

STEP 4 Label the graph with a title to make it easy for the reader to know what the graph is describing.

(ii) Describing Data with a Bar Graph

Another type of graph used to describe data is the bar graph. Bar graphs are most commonly used for grouped data (in statistics, a bar graph of grouped data is called a frequency histogram). There are two types of bar graphs: horizontal and vertical. Figures 12.3 and 12.4 show the graphed data for Nanaimo housing sales using horizontal and vertical bar graphs for the Nanaimo data from Table 12.2. When presenting information to an audience that may not understand graphs well, bar graphs are generally best, since the information conveyed is easy to understand. The choice of horizontal versus vertical bar graphs is a matter of personal preference, since the same information is conveyed.

Figure 12.3 Vertical Bar Graph for Nanaimo Housing Sales in September

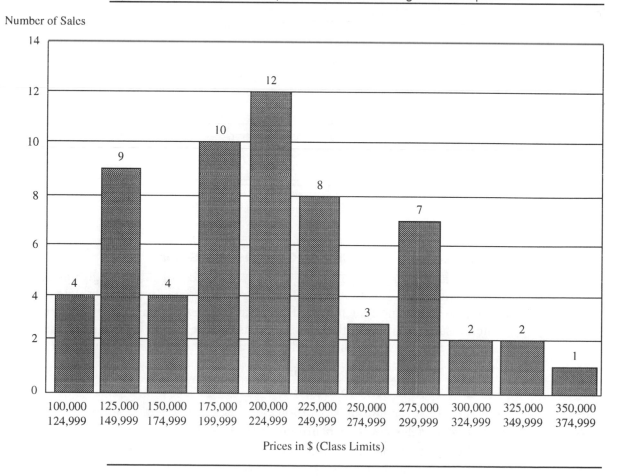

Prices in $ (Class Limits)

In the Figure 12.3 bar graph, the frequencies are plotted on the vertical axis, and the price ranges (class limits) are plotted on the horizontal axis; in Figure 12.4 the vertical and horizontal axes are reversed. Notice that the class frequency (number of sales) has been shown with each bar. This is not necessary, but it does assist in the reading of the graph.

One thing to note is that there is a space between each bar. This space occurs because the scale with the price groupings is not continuous (i.e., there is a $1 gap between upper and lower limits). This is not a problem, however, since the information conveyed does accurately reflect the frequency distribution of the data.

Figure 12.4 Horizontal Bar Graph for Nanaimo Housing Sales in September

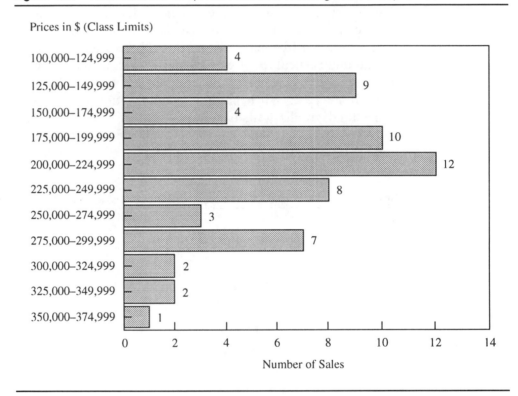

(iii) Describing Data with a Pie Chart or Circle Graph

When it is important to highlight the relative size of different groups or measurements, a pie chart is one of the best graphs to use. In our real estate example, suppose someone had reviewed that data with the objective of describing the home sales by the number of bedrooms for the homes sold during the month of September. After reviewing the records of the sales it was found that:

- 4% of sales had one bedroom
- 20% of sales had two bedrooms
- 40% of sales had three bedroom
- 18% of sales had four bedrooms
- 12% of sales had five bedrooms
- 6% of sales had six or more bedrooms

Figure 12.5 summarizes the above information in a pie chart. To construct the pie chart partition the area of the pie (360 degrees) according to the percentages in the data. In the example below, 40% (0.4) of the area, or 144 degrees, is allocated to sales of three-bedroom homes, while 20% (0.2), or 72 degrees, is allocated to sales of two-bedroom homes and so forth.

Figure 12.5   Housing Sales by Number of Bedrooms Nanaimo in September

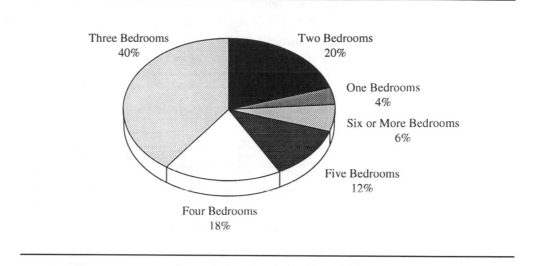

Another example of where a pie chart would be preferred would the displaying of budget expenditures as a percent of the total budget. For example, if it was necessary to show how a provincial government spends its money each year — what percentage of all monies go to education, health and so forth — then a pie chart would depict the information, with each slice of the pie showing the expenditures for each ministry of the government.

12.3 Summarizing Data Using Measures of Central Tendency

Although a frequency distribution and graph of data may be quite descriptive, there is often a need to describe data in terms of where the data cluster or the central point of the data. This measure of the centre point is called a **measure of central tendency**. In statistics there are three common measures of central tendency.: the **mean** (what you know as the arithmetic average); the **median** (the middle value) and the **mode** (the most frequently occurring value). Each of these measures of central tendency is useful in summarizing data.

A. The Mean

(i) The Arithmetic Mean

The mean or arithmetic average is one of the most commonly used measures to describe data. It is a computed measure that uses every observation —

nothing is excluded. This last feature has one good point in that the mean does not waste any information; but this feature of including all the data can have its problems. For example, suppose within the 62 observations of the Nanaimo real estate example either a very low value, say $35,000 or a very high value of $1,500,000 had occurred. These values would tend to distort the value of the mean: e.g., if there was one unusually high value of $1,500,000, this would pull up the value of the mean.

In statistics we have two symbols we use for the mean; μ (pronounced "mu") and $\bar{x}$. The symbol μ is used to describe the **population mean**, and $\bar{x}$ *is used to describe the* **sample mean**. Both measures are computed using the same procedure, as illustrated in Formulas 12.1.A and 12.1.B.

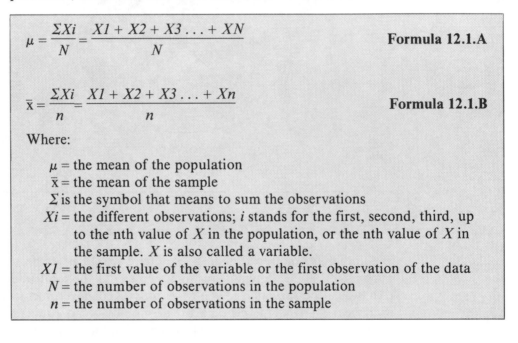

$$\mu = \frac{\Sigma Xi}{N} = \frac{X1 + X2 + X3 \ldots + XN}{N} \qquad \textbf{Formula 12.1.A}$$

$$\bar{x} = \frac{\Sigma Xi}{n} = \frac{X1 + X2 + X3 \ldots + Xn}{n} \qquad \textbf{Formula 12.1.B}$$

Where:

μ = the mean of the population
$\bar{x}$ = the mean of the sample
Σ is the symbol that means to sum the observations
Xi = the different observations; i stands for the first, second, third, up to the nth value of X in the population, or the nth value of X in the sample. X is also called a variable.
$X1$ = the first value of the variable or the first observation of the data
N = the number of observations in the population
n = the number of observations in the sample

A variable in statistics is what is being measured. In our example of house sales in Nanaimo, the variable is the selling price of houses for the month of September and has 62 values The symbol ΣXi, tells one to add up all the X's (add all the selling prices). The term variable is used to describe the fact that the value of X can be different for each sale, as in this real estate example.

EXAMPLE 12.3

John Anderson has been asked to determine the average value of the inventory for each store in a chain of four sporting goods stores. After reviewing the accounting records John found the following:

Store Number	Inventory Values
1	$150,600
2	$123,500
3	$145,400
4	$136,200

Compute the average inventory value of the four stores.

Solution Find ΣXi: In this problem the values of *X1, X2, X3,* and *X4* are $150,600, $123,500, $145,400, and $136,200, respectively. Therefore, ΣX is:

$$\Sigma Xi = \$150,600 + \$123,500 + \$145,400 + \$136,200 = \$555,700$$

$$N = 4$$

In this problem the chain has only four stores, and since John has <u>all</u> the possible values of the variable, this is the population of inventory values.

Therefore, the population mean μ is:

$$\frac{\Sigma Xi}{N} = \frac{\$555,700}{4} = \$138,925$$

For convenience, the subscript *i* in the expression ΣXi is normally dropped and understood to be present; thus, when you see ΣX it will mean the same as ΣXi.

The reason the distinction between sample and population means is made is that a sample mean is only an "estimate" of the population mean since not all the values of the variable in the population are used to measure the sample average. Moreover, in business a researcher is generally working with a sample rather than the population.

To emphasize the distinction between the sample and population mean, consider Example 12.4, which uses the real estate data for Nanaimo housing sales introduced earlier in the chapter.

EXAMPLE 12.4

Marilyn, an analyst with a major land development firm, needs to measure the average selling price of homes for Nanaimo for the month of September. Assist Marilyn in computing the population mean for the average price of homes for the Nanaimo in September. Also, suppose Marilyn had decided that she only needed a sample of thirteen of the sales for the month of September to estimate the population mean. What is the sample mean of a randomly selected sample? The sample consists of the 13 values with an asterisk (*) beside them.

Selling Price of Homes in Nanaimo for the Month of September				
205,800	*210,000	215,300	*224,500	224,800
*112,000	121,000	110,500	135,200	144,800
121,000	*125,000	135,400	*140,000	149,400
223,000	216,400	217,300	215,000	232,000
230,000	234,200	*229,100	248,900	239,450
*245,250	249,050	256,250	265,450	*274,550
345,000	374,000	146,600	154,000	180,000
146,500	147,000	*174,500	178,400	188,200
160,400	167,000	199,200	205,000	210,000
183,000	185,800	312,000	*324,800	335,000
285,000	*297,000	282,100	297,000	281,000
288,400	294,400	179,800	194,500	*215,400
*195,000	185,500			

Solution   (a) The population mean:
Find ΣX. In this problem, the values of X are:

$$\Sigma X = \$205{,}800 + \$112{,}000 + \ldots + \$281{,}000 + \$215{,}400 = \$13{,}262{,}100$$

$$N = 62$$

Therefore, the population mean μ is:

$$\frac{\Sigma X}{N} = \frac{\$13{,}262{,}100}{62} = \$213{,}904.84$$

(b) The sample mean:

Find ΣX. For the sample, the values of X are the values with an asterisk:

$$\Sigma X = 112{,}000 + 245{,}250 + 195{,}000 + 210{,}000 + 125{,}550 + 297{,}000 + 229{,}100$$
$$+\ 174{,}500 + 224{,}500 + 140{,}000 + 324{,}800 + 274{,}550 + 215{,}400$$

$$\Sigma X = \$2{,}767{,}100$$

$n = 13$, the sample size

Therefore, the sample mean x is:

$$\frac{\Sigma X}{n} = \frac{\$2{,}767{,}100}{13} = \$212{,}853.85$$

What is of interest in Example 12.4 is the difference between the sample mean and the population mean. Although there is a slight difference it is quite small, just over $1,000 which is less than ½%. It is important to note that 13 observations out of a population of 62 is a very large sample, relative to the size of the population. What the sample results highlight is the value of taking a sample, which produce a statistic that is a reliable estimate of a population mean. Also taking a sample is quicker, less costly and quite reliable.

To be reliable a sample must be selected in a random fashion, and its size (how many observations) must be sufficiently large to produce representative statistics for the population. Taking a random sample is like selecting numbers from a hat randomly to determine which observations would be included in the sample. In statistics great care is given to how the samples are selected to ensure they are representative of the population.

Before leaving the mean, some of its properties are worth noting:

1. Each sample and population has a mean.
2. All the values of the population or the sample are used in computing the mean.
3. Since the mean uses all the data in its computation it is affected by extreme values. This can be a problem since a few extremely low or high values can influence the value of the mean. This type of influence may distort the summary of data if only a mean is used. Thus when extreme values are present, it may be necessary to use a different measure like the median or the mode to describe the data with a measure of central tendency.
4. The mean is the only measure of central tendency where the sum of the differences between each observation and the mean is zero. For example if you sum the difference between each of the 13 observations for the sample mean in Example 12.4, the differences will sum to zero:

X	$\bar{x}$	$(X - \bar{x})$
112,000	− 212,853.85 =	−100,853.85
195,000	− 212,853.85 = −	17,853.85
215,400	− 212,853.85 =	2,546.15
245,250	− 212,853.85 =	32,396.15
274,550	− 212,853.85 =	61,696.15
125,000	− 212,853.85 = −	87,853.85
140,000	− 212,853.85 = −	72,853.85
210,000	− 212,853.85 = −	2,853.85
224,500	− 212,853.85 =	11,646.15
297,000	− 212,853.85 =	84,146.15
324,800	− 212,853.85 =	111,946.15
174,500	− 212,853.85 = −	38,353.85
229,100	− 212,853.85 =	16,246.15

Sum of the differences: $\Sigma(X-\bar{x}) =$ 0

(ii) The Weighted Mean

Sometimes it is necessary to find the mean for a set of data where each observation is not of the same importance. For example, an apartment building has three one bedroom suites that rent for $600 a month; five two bedroom suites that rent for $700 a month and two three bedroom suites that rent for $850 per month, what is the average revenue per suite, regardless of the suite size?

In this type of problem one cannot simply add up the rents and divide by three, since this method would give equal weight to the rent from each suite and ignore how many suites of each type there are. In this case it is necessary to reflect the number of each type of suite; that is, weigh each rent by the number of suites producing that rent. To find the average revenue we must use the formula:

$$\bar{x}w = \frac{\Sigma wiXi}{\Sigma wi}$$

Formula 12.2

$$\frac{\Sigma wiXi}{\Sigma wi} = \frac{w1 \cdot X1 + w2 \cdot X2 + w3 \cdot X3 + \ldots + wn \cdot Xn}{w1 + w2 + w3 + \ldots + wn}$$

Where:

$\bar{x}w$ = weighted average
Xi are the different values of X (rents)
wi are the different weights for X (the number of each type of suite)

The subscripts in Formula 12.2 can be dropped, giving:

$$\bar{x}w = \frac{\Sigma wX}{\Sigma w}$$

Now turning to our apartment problem, the number of suites with one, two, and three bedrooms are the weights, and the monthly rent for each type of suite is the value of X. For this problem the values of w and X are:

$$\bar{x}w = \frac{\Sigma wX}{\Sigma w} = \frac{3 \cdot \$600 + 5 \cdot \$700 + 2 \cdot \$850}{10} = \$700$$

Therefore, the average monthly revenue per suite is $700.

EXAMPLE 12.5

Venture Research pays its polling and market research interviewers different hourly rates depending on how long the person has worked with the company. Presently Venture has four interviewers who earn $11.50 per hour, three who earn $10.00 per hour, and two who earn $13.00 per hour. What is Venture's average hourly cost for the current group of interviewers?

Solution   Define the values of w and X:

w = 4, 3, and 2
X = $11.50, $10.00, and $13.00

Now applying Formula 12.2:

$$\bar{x}w = \frac{\Sigma wX}{\Sigma w} = \frac{4 \cdot \$11.5 + 3 \cdot \$10.00 + 2 \cdot \$13}{9} = \$11.33 \text{ (repeating)}$$

Based on the weighted mean it is possible to say that on average the hourly cost for a current interviewer is $11.33 per hour.

(iii) The Mean for Grouped Data

The weighted mean is also used for grouped data, where the weights are the class frequencies and the values of X are the class midpoints. The only occasion where one would want to compute the mean from grouped data is when one does not have original data. That is, with today's access to computers, a researcher would always use the original data for computing the arithmetic mean of a set of data. However, if one is reading a report and only tables of grouped data are provided, then there may be a need to compute the mean for grouped data. If so, simply use the formula for the weighted mean, replacing the w's with f's to denote the class frequency, and the X's would be the class midpoints. Doing this gives:

$$\bar{x} = \frac{\Sigma f_i X_i}{\Sigma f_i}$$ **Formula 12.3**

$$\frac{\Sigma f_i X_i}{\Sigma f_i} = \frac{f_1 \cdot X_1 + f_2 \cdot X_2 + f_3 \cdot X_3 + \ldots + f_n \cdot X_n}{f_1 + f_2 + f_3 + \ldots + f_n}$$

Where:

$\bar{x}$ = mean of the grouped data
X_i = the midpoints for each class
f_i = the different class frequencies

Now suppose you had only the frequency distribution for the data on Nanaimo house sales (i.e., assume you did not have the raw data). Estimating the mean of the data using only the classes given in Table 12.2 would give:

Class Limits (in $)	Number of Sales in Each Group f	Class Midpoint X	Class Midpoint Multiplied by Class Frequency $f \cdot X$
100,000–124,999	4	112,500	450,000
125,000–149,999	9	137,500	1,237,500
150,000–174,999	4	162,500	650,000
175,000–199,999	10	187,500	1,875,000
200,000–224,999	12	212,500	2,550,000
225,000–249,999	8	237,500	1,900,000
250,000–274,999	3	262,500	787,500
275,000–299,999	7	287,500	2,012,500
300,000–324,999	2	312,500	625,000
325,000–349,999	2	337,500	675,000
350,000–374,999	1	362,500	362,500
$\Sigma f =$	62	$\Sigma fX =$	13,125,000

To compute the mean for the data, use Formula 12.3:

$$\bar{x} = \frac{\Sigma f_i X_i}{\Sigma f_i}$$

For convenience, drop the subscripts and use:

$$\bar{x} = \frac{\Sigma fX}{\Sigma f}$$

Now, substituting the values gives:

$$\Sigma fX = \$13,125,000 \qquad \Sigma f = 62$$

$$\bar{x} = \frac{\Sigma fX}{\Sigma f} = \frac{\$13,125,000}{62} = \$211,693.55$$

Therefore, the estimated mean for the data using only the groups is $211,693.55, which is lower than the mean found using all the data (i.e., $213,904.84). However, it does provide a good indication of the average for the original data. The point is that it is possible to estimate the mean of a set of data by using a frequency distribution. The value of the mean found by using only the frequency distribution is an estimate of the mean, since it does not use the true values of the original data. The estimate provided is generally a good approximation of the mean.

EXAMPLE 12.6

Venture Research has undertaken a number of research projects for its clients. Table 12.4 shows a sample of twenty projects, and the revenue for each project.

Table 12.4: Revenue (in $) for a sample of 20 projects

3,750	10,500	15,300	19,450
6,500	12,000	16,000	19,750
8,000	12,500	17,500	21,000
9,300	13,250	18,000	22,500
10,000	15,000	19,400	23,000

(a) Group the data using five classes.
(b) Compute the arithmetic mean using the original twenty observations.
(c) Compute the arithmetic mean using the grouped data and compare this measure with the mean based on the original data in part (b).

Solution (a) First, find the width of each class by finding the range from highest value to lowest value. Second, divide this range by the number of required classes. Third, round the computed width to a number that is convenient to use. Since the number of classes required is five we would have:

$$\frac{\$23,000 - \$3,750}{5} = \frac{\$19,250}{5} = \$3,850$$

Now round up to a convenient number, say, $4,000.

Since the lowest value in the data is $3,850, a convenient first lower limit would be $3,500. Remember, the choice of the lower limit must include the lowest value and should be a convenient number. It would have been possible to use $3,850 as the starting point. The choice to use $3,500 as the first lower limit was to make the frequency distribution easy for a reader to understand.

Since we know we will need the class midpoint, average the lower limits of two consecutive classes. Thus if our first class starts at $3,500 and the width is $4,000, the lower limit of the next class will be $7,500. Thus the midpoint of the first class would be:

$$\frac{\$3,500 + \$7,500}{2} = \$5,500$$

Also, since the classes will be the same width, the midpoint of each class will be $4,000 apart. Setting up the groups gives:

Class Limits (in $)	Number of Sales in Each Group f	Class Midpoint X	Class Midpoint Multiplied by Class Frequency $f \cdot X$
3,500– 7,499	2	5,500	11,000
7,500–11,499	4	9,500	38,000
11,500–15,499	5	13,500	67,500
15,500–19,499	5	17,500	87,500
19,500–23,499	4	21,500	86,000
$\Sigma f =$	20		$\Sigma fX = 290,000$

(b) To compute the mean from the <u>original</u> data, use Formula 12.1.B for the sample of projects.

$$\Sigma X = \$3{,}750 + \$6{,}500 + \$8{,}000 + \ldots + \$22{,}500 + \$23{,}000 = \$292{,}700$$

$$\bar{x} = \frac{\Sigma X}{n} = \frac{\$292{,}700}{20} = \$14{,}635 \text{ (remember, } \Sigma X \text{ is based on each observation)}$$

Thus, the mean of the sample is $14,635.

(c) To compute the mean based on the grouped data, use Formula 12.3:

$$\bar{x} = \frac{\Sigma f X}{\Sigma f} = \frac{\$290{,}000}{20} = \$14{,}500$$

From the grouped data, the estimated mean is $14,500, which is slightly lower than the mean based on the original data, but still close enough to provide a good approximation of the sample mean. The point is that it is still possible to estimate the mean from grouped data, when you don't have the original sample data.

B. The Median

(i) The Median for Non-Grouped Data

The second measure of central tendency is the median. The median is the middle point of the data. By saying it is the middle value, one-half of the data are less than or equal to the median, and one-half are greater than or equal to the median.

To find the median, first locate its position using the expression:

$$\frac{n+1}{2} \text{ where } n \text{ is the number of observations}$$

Then, if necessary, compute its value.

Example 12.7 demonstrates how to find the median for a set of data.

EXAMPLE 12.7

Find the median for Venture's sample of projects in Example 12.6, using Table 12.4.

Solution Since the data are already in ascending order in the table locate the position of the median:

$$\text{Position} = \frac{n+1}{2} = \frac{20+1}{2} = 10.5$$

Thus, the median is in the 10.5 position. Find the tenth and eleventh observations and average them:

$$\frac{15{,}000 + 15{,}300}{2} = 15{,}150 = \text{the median value of the projects.}$$

Some things worth noting about the median as a measure of central tendency are:

1. The median uses at most two observations in determining its value. Two observations will generally be used when there are an even number of ob-

servations — the average of the two centre values. When there is an odd number of observations the median observation will be found in the data.

2. The median is unique in the sense that there is only one median for a set of data.
3. Unlike the mean, the median is not affected by extreme values in the data.

The median has a very useful purpose as a measure of central tendency if the data have extreme values. In real estate, the sales of residential properties often include a few extremely high values or some unusually low values. As a consequence, some Real Estate Boards in Canada publish both the mean and the median sale prices on a monthly basis. An informed reader will know that if the mean is considerably higher than the median, there must have been some extremely high-priced sales relative to the majority of sales.

(ii) The Median for Grouped Data

Like the mean for grouped data, the median for grouped data is an approximation. One of the differences in computing the median for grouped data is that it is based on the range from the lowest class limit to the highest class limit. The position of the median for grouped data is found by the expression:

$$\frac{n}{2} \text{ where } n \text{ is the number of observations (total frequency).}$$

Note that the location of the median for grouped data uses only n, not $n +$ 1. The reason is that the median for grouped data is based on a value in the middle of a continuum, starting at the lower class limit and ending at the upper limit. The key is that we are dividing a continuum into two equal parts.

Once the position of the median is located, we need to compute the value of the median. Example 12.8 goes through the step by step procedure to find the median for a set of grouped data.

EXAMPLE 12.8

Using the frequency distribution for Venture Research in Example 12.6, find the median for those data.

Solution

STEP 1 Find the position of the median using:

$\frac{n}{2}$ where $n = 20$. Thus, the position of the median is $20/2$, or the tenth position in the frequency distribution.

STEP 2 Since we require the tenth position, locate the class in which the tenth position of data is located. Starting from the bottom class (3,500–7,499), add the frequencies until the class in which the tenth position is found. For the data, the sum of the first three frequencies (2 + 4 + 5) is 11 and therefore includes the median. In particular, we know that the median falls in the class 11,500–14,499.

STEP 3 Given that the median falls in the class 11,500–14,499 we can safely say that the minimum value of the median is 11,500. However, we know that up to this value, only six observations occurred, leaving four more that we must account for to reach the median.

Therefore, assuming that the data are evenly divided throughout each class, we move four-fifths of the distance (the class width) from the lower limit (11,500) to reach the median. We use four-fifths because we need to move four observations into the third class in which there are five observations. Thus, the median value for the distribution is:

$$11,500 + \frac{4}{5}(4,000) = 14,700$$

Therefore the estimate of the median is 14,700 using thegrouped data. When we review the original data the median was found to be 15,150. Our approximation is quite close.

From Example 12.8, we can say that the median for grouped data can be found as follows:

$$\text{Median for grouped data} = L + \frac{Rf}{fmc} \cdot (\text{class width}) \qquad \text{Formula 12.4}$$

Where:

L = lower class limit of the class in which the median falls.

Rf = required frequency to reach the median position. In all cases it is the number of observations that one must move into the median class to reach the median.

fmc = the number of observations in the class in which the median falls.

class width = the width of the class in which the median falls.

C. The Mode

The third measure of central tendency is called the mode, the observation which occurs most frequently. The mode is used to assist us in understanding the shape of the frequency distribution. For example are the data all clustered at the upper values, the lower values, or are they fairly evenly spread out? The mode can assist in answering this question.

(i) The Mode for Non-Grouped Data

To find the mode of a set of data, one simply looks for the value of the variable that occurs most frequently. For example, if one was interested in determining the mode of the ages of all students in the CGA program, one would ask the computer to sort by the age of students and then count the number of students with the same age. The one that has the highest frequency is the mode. If two ages have the same frequency then we say the data are **bimodal** — there are two modes. If there are three then the data are referred to as **trimodal**. After three modes most researchers would state the mode is not unique. Also, in some instances there may not be a mode for a set of data (i.e., each value occurs only once).

(ii) The Mode for Grouped Data

To find the mode for grouped data, the most frequently used method is to simply state the class with the highest frequency, called the **modal class**. For example, in our real estate data on sales in Nanaimo, the class with the highest frequency was \$200,000–\$224,999, with 12 observations. Thus, this class would be referred to as the modal class.

12.4 Measures of Dispersion

In business, measures of central tendency help us understand the central point of the data. However, not only is the average important, but also it is important to provide a measure of how the data is spread out. The measure that describes the manner in which data is spread out is referred to as **measure of dispersion**. If the data are closely clustered, the measure of dispersion will be small and the mean will be a reliable measure of central tendency. On the other hand, if the dispersion is large, the average will not be reliable. Companies may require knowledge about the dispersion associated with the average defect-free life of their products. Imagine that you purchased a laser printer that was guaranteed for 200,000 pages and that you actually got 250,000 pages out of your printer. This would make you happy. In fact, you were so happy you bought another printer, but its life was only 150,000 pages — now you're unhappy. Imagine how unhappy the users would be if there was that type of variation in the number of pages the printer actually printed. Clearly, knowledge of the dispersion about the average page life of the printer would assist the company in fine-tuning the product and warranties before bringing the printer to the market.

The one measure of dispersion that is most frequently used is the **standard deviation**.

The Standard Deviation

The **standard deviation** is a measure of dispersion that is computed by taking the square root of the average of the squared difference between each observation and the mean. What this really means is that the standard deviation is a measure of how far apart the data are from the average of the data. If all the observations are close to their average then the standard deviation will be small. The only thing that one must be careful about is whether the standard deviation is being computed for sample or population data. If it is sample data, then an important adjustment must be made to the formula.

(i) The Standard Deviation for Non-Grouped Data

Now that we know the standard deviation is a measure of dispersion, the best way to get a feeling for what it measures is with an example. Consider the data below that records all the quarterly sales of passenger aircraft for an aircraft company in 1993:

Quarter	1	2	3	4
Number of Sales	6	3	7	4

Since the data are a listing of <u>all</u> sales for the year, the data are population data. To compute the standard deviation, we must first find the average squared difference of the data about the mean. To do this we must find μ:

$$\mu = \frac{\Sigma X}{N} = \frac{6 + 3 + 7 + 4}{4} = \frac{20}{4} = 5$$

Now finding the squared differences:

	Number of Sales	Difference Between Each Quarterly Sale and the Mean	Difference Between Each Quarterly Sale and the Mean
	X	$(X-\mu)$	$(X-\mu)^2$
Quarter 1	6	$(6-5) = 1$	$(6-5)^2 = 1$
Quarter 2	3	$(3-5) = -2$	$(3-5)^2 = 4$
Quarter 3	7	$(7-5) = 2$	$(7-5)^2 = 4$
Quarter 4	4	$(4-5) = -1$	$(4-5)^2 = 1$
$\Sigma X =$	20	$\Sigma(X-\mu) = 0$	$\Sigma(X-\mu)^2 = 10$

The reason that we compute the squared difference is that the sum of the difference between the mean and each observation will be zero, since the mean is a measure of central tendency. Taking the square of the difference eliminates the negative sign. Once the total squared difference is computed, the average difference is found by dividing the total squared difference by the number of observations. However, since the average of the squared differences are squared numbers, we must take the square root of the average squared difference to get a measure of dispersion that is in the original units of the data (i.e., not squared units).

Now find the average of the squared difference:

$$\frac{\Sigma(X-\mu)^2}{4} = \frac{10}{4} = 2.50$$

To find the standard deviation we must take the square root of the average squared deviation:

$$\sqrt{2.50} = 1.58$$

This measure, 1.58, is called the standard deviation of the population. The formula used for the population standard deviation is:

$$\sigma = \sqrt{\frac{\Sigma(X - \mu)^2}{N}}$$

Formula 12.5

$\sigma =$ the population standard deviation

Generally, in business we are working with sample data, not population data. Recall that the objective of taking a sample is to use sample information to estimate characteristics of the population. For example, if a firm wanted to test a new product, a sample of people might be selected and asked to use the product. From this information it may be possible to generalize about the reaction of the population to the product.

To provide the best estimate of the population standard deviation from a sample, we must adjust the formula we use for the population standard deviation. The adjustment reflects the fact that if the population formula is used on sample data, the result will consistently underestimate the standard deviation of the population. (Remember, our objective is to use a sample to estimate corresponding population parameters.) Formula 12.6 shows how we adjust the formula.

$$s = \sqrt{\frac{\Sigma(X - \bar{x})^2}{n - 1}}$$

Formula 12.6

s = the sample standard deviation

The important differences in the formula used to find the sample standard deviation are:

1. The sum of differences squared is based on the difference between the sample mean and each sample value.
2. The sum of squared differences is divided by ($n - 1$), not n. This adjustment in the denominator corrects for the under estimation that occurs using the population formula on sample data.

Many electronic calculators have preprogrammed functions that compute the standard deviation, for both the population and the sample (e.g., the Sharp EL 733). For those who do not have these preprogrammed calculators, it is still possible to use the formula used by most electronic calculators. Although the formulas may not look easier to use, they save time by reducing the number of calculations. These formulas are often referred to as the short-cut formulas to find the standard deviation.

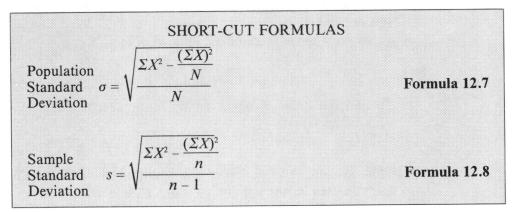

SHORT-CUT FORMULAS

Population Standard Deviation $\sigma = \sqrt{\dfrac{\Sigma X^2 - \dfrac{(\Sigma X)^2}{N}}{N}}$ **Formula 12.7**

Sample Standard Deviation $s = \sqrt{\dfrac{\Sigma X^2 - \dfrac{(\Sigma X)^2}{n}}{n - 1}}$ **Formula 12.8**

The next two examples show how to use the formula, and to demonstrate how accurate sample statistics are in estimating population parameters.

EXAMPLE 12.9

An accountant wishes to determine the average and the standard deviation for the number of pickup truck sales of a national chain of truck dealerships for the month of April. In total there are 60 dealers across the country. The monthly sales (in number of units sold) were:

20	21	21	22	22	11	12	11	13	14
12	12	13	14	14	22	21	21	21	23
23	23	22	24	23	19	18	17	19	21
28	29	31	32	33	28	29	28	29	28
18	18	19	20	21	16	16	17	17	18
24	24	25	26	27	14	14	14	15	18

After you have found the average and standard deviation comment on whether the mean is a reliable measure of central tendency, given the computed dispersion for the data.

Solution   Find the mean and the standard deviation:

$\Sigma X = 20 + 12 + 23 \ldots + 28 + 18 + 18 = 1{,}225$

$\Sigma X^2 = 20^2 + 12^2 + 23^2 \ldots + 28^2 + 18^2 + 18^2 = 26{,}925$

$(\Sigma X)^2 = (20 + 12 + 23 \ldots + 28 + 18 + 18)^2 = (1{,}225)^2 = 1{,}500{,}625$

Compute the population mean using Formula 12.1.A:

$$\mu = \frac{\Sigma X_i}{N} = \frac{1{,}225}{60} = 20.42$$

Compute the population standard deviation using the short-cut Formula 12.7 (note that since we have all the dealers, we have the population):

$$\sigma = \sqrt{\frac{\Sigma X^2 - \dfrac{(\Sigma X)^2}{N}}{N}} = \sqrt{\frac{26{,}925 - \dfrac{(1{,}225)^2}{60}}{60}} = 5.65$$

In terms of how useful the mean is as a measure of central tendency, the standard deviation is quite large relative to the mean. In particular the standard deviation is more than 25% of size the mean (5.65/20.42). This tells us that there is considerable variability in the data, and therefore the mean may not be a reliable measure of central tendency.

Suppose that only a sample had been selected from the 60 dealers across the country in Example 12.9. Would these sample measures provide good estimates of the mean and the standard deviation of the population? Example 12.10 uses a sample to estimate σ and μ with s and $\bar{x}$. A random sample of 12 observation was selected.

EXAMPLE 12.10

A sample of 12 truck dealers was selected at random from the population of 60 dealers. From this sample estimate the population mean and population standard deviation using the sample mean and the sample deviation. The random sample is:

13	12	18	17
19	21	21	22
23	27	27	28

Solution   The calculations necessary for the mean and the standard deviation formula are:

$\Sigma X = 13 + 19 + \ldots + 22 + 28 = 248$

$\Sigma X^2 = 13^2 + 19^2 \ldots + 22^2 + 28^2 = 5{,}424$

$(\Sigma X)^2 = (13 + 19 + \ldots + 22 + 28)^2 = (248)^2 = 61{,}504$

Now apply Formula 12.1.B:

$$\bar{x} = \frac{\Sigma Xi}{n} = \frac{248}{12} = 20.67$$

To compute the sample standard deviation, use short-cut Formula 12.8:

$$s = \sqrt{\frac{\Sigma X^2 - \frac{(\Sigma X)^2}{n}}{n-1}} = \sqrt{\frac{5,424 - \frac{(248)^2}{12}}{12-1}} = 5.21$$

To see how well the sample predicts the population values, consider the data below, which provide a comparison of the findings in Examples 12.9 and 12.10:

	Population (Example 12.9)	Sample Measures (Example 12.10)
	Mean = 20.42	Mean = 20.67
	Standard deviation = 5.65	Standard deviation = 5.21

As can be seen the sample statistics from Example 12.10 are good estimates of the corresponding population parameters. The major determinants of how well the sample statistics estimate the corresponding population parameters are how the sample is selected and the sample size. If the sample is truly a random sample (i.e., each element of the population has the same likelihood of being selected for the sample), and the sample is an appropriate size, then the sample statistics are generally good estimates of the corresponding population parameters. There is always the chance that even when the sample is properly selected and of sufficient size, the data will produce statistics which are "off" by more than one might expect. However, in general, the likelihood of this is quite low.

(ii) The Standard Deviation for Grouped Data

Rarely would one compute the standard deviation based on a grouping of data, since if one has all the observations, a computer can quickly compute the measures for you. The one exception is when you have only the grouped data to view — such as in a report. In this circumstance one might have to compute standard deviation based on a frequency distribution. The method used is similar to computing the mean for grouped data, where the class frequency and the class midpoint are used in the calculations. The formula for the standard deviation for grouped data is:

$$s = \sqrt{\frac{\Sigma f(X - \bar{x})^2}{\Sigma f - 1}} \qquad \textbf{Formula 12.9.A}$$

And the short cut formula is:

$$s = \sqrt{\frac{\Sigma f X^2 - \frac{(\Sigma f X)^2}{\Sigma f}}{\Sigma f - 1}} \qquad \textbf{Formula 12.9.B}$$

The formula for the standard deviation from grouped data assumes that the grouping is of sample data. If the data was population data, then you would simply divide by Σf, and not $\Sigma f - 1$. Example 12.11 reviews the use of the formula for grouped data.

EXAMPLE 12.11

In Example 12.6, Venture Research had undertaken a number of research projects for its clients. Find the standard deviation for the grouped data.

Solution   To use Formula 12.9.A, set up a table like the one below with the computed values as follows:

Class Limits	Class Frequency f	Midpoint X	$\bar{x}$	$f \cdot (X - \bar{x})^2$
$3,500 \leq 7,499$	2	5,500	14,500	162,000,000
$7,500 \leq 11,499$	4	9,500	14,500	100,000,000
$11,500 \leq 15,499$	5	13,500	14,500	5,000,000
$15,500 \leq 19,499$	5	17,500	14,500	45,000,000
$19,500 \leq 23,499$	4	21,500	14,500	196,000,000
Totals	$\Sigma f = 20$			$\Sigma f \cdot (X - \bar{x})^2 = 508,000,000$

$$\bar{x} = \frac{\Sigma f X}{\Sigma f} = \frac{\$290,000}{20} = \$14,500$$

$$s = \sqrt{\frac{\Sigma f (X - \bar{x})^2}{\Sigma f - 1}} = \sqrt{\frac{508,000,000}{20 - 1}} = 5,170.77$$

12.5 Applications of Measures of Central Tendency and Dispersion

Now our interest focuses on the joint use of measures of central tendency and dispersion to describe data. The first joint use is with the coefficient of variation, a measure that assists in comparing the relative variation of two sets of data. The second application outlines how one can describe the proportion of data that are expected to fall within a specified number of standard deviations of the mean, depending upon the shape of the distribution of the data.

A. Coefficient of Variation

Statistics are often used to make a comparison between two sets of data. For example, if one wanted to compare the relative volatility of two stocks, how could one do this, even if the stocks were for companies in different industries? One way is to use the measure called the **coefficient of variation**. The coefficient of variation is a relative measure of comparison, using the mean and standard deviation. It is computed by finding the ratio of the standard deviation to the arithmetic mean. The formula is:

$$CV = \frac{s}{\overline{X}} \qquad CV = \text{coefficient of variation} \qquad \textbf{Formula 12.10}$$

$$CV = \frac{s}{\overline{X}} \cdot 100\% \quad \text{(expressed as a percentage)}$$

The interesting thing about the coefficient of variation is that it is a pure number — there are no units. For example, if the data are measured in dollars the units for the standard deviation and the mean cancel out and one is left with a pure number for comparison. This is the power of the coefficient of variation, it can be used to compare like and unlike types of data.

EXAMPLE 12.12

An investor who dislikes risk has been comparing two stocks, both recommended by a number of investment experts. The first stock has traded over the past six months at an average price of $50.00, with a standard deviation of $4.50. The second stock has traded over the same period at an average price of $78.00 with a standard deviation of $15.00. Given that the investor is going to purchase only one of the stocks, which one should the investor choose if the overriding objective is to minimize risk? (Normally, risk is associated with stocks that have more variability in price.) Use the coefficient of variation and recommend the stock with the least volatility (i.e., lowest relative variation).

Solution   Computing the coefficient of variation for the first stock:

$$CV = \frac{s}{\overline{X}} \cdot 100\% = \frac{\$4.50}{\$50} \cdot 100\% = 9\%$$

Compute the coefficient of variation for the second stock:

$$CV = \frac{s}{\overline{X}} \cdot 100\% = \frac{\$15.00}{\$78} \cdot 100\% = 19.2\%$$

If the investor wishes the lowest volatility and hence the lowest risk, then first stock offers the best option, since the stock with the highest coefficient of variation has had the most volatility.

B. The Empirical Rule

Sometimes the shape of the distribution of the data follows what is referred to as a **symmetrical distribution**. The data are said to be symmetrical when the mean, median, and mode are the same and the shape of the distribution is a bell-shaped curve or a bell shaped bar graph (sometimes called mound-shaped). The importance of this property is that it is possible to predict what proportion of the data will fall within one, two or any number of standard deviations about the mean. Generally, if the data are close to being symmetrical the Empirical Rule works.

Let's summarize the Empirical Rule. If we let k stand for the number of standard deviations, then, providing the data are symmetrical, the proportion of the data that will fall within one, two or three standard deviations (i.e., $k = 1$, $k = 2$ and $k = 3$) of the mean is calculated as follows:

Number of Standard Seviations from the Mean k	Range about the Mean $(\mu \pm k\sigma)$	Percentage of the Data Within the Range
1	$\mu \pm 1\sigma$	68%
2	$\mu \pm 2\sigma$	95%
3	$\mu \pm 3\sigma$	99.7%

What the above tells us is that, providing the data are symmetrical, we should expect to observe 68% of the data values falling within the range ± 1 standard deviation of the mean; 95% within ± 2 standard deviations; and 99.7% within ± 3 standard deviations. Now we have a very useful way of summarizing the data. Figure 12.6 shows the principle of the Empirical Rule.

Figure 12.6

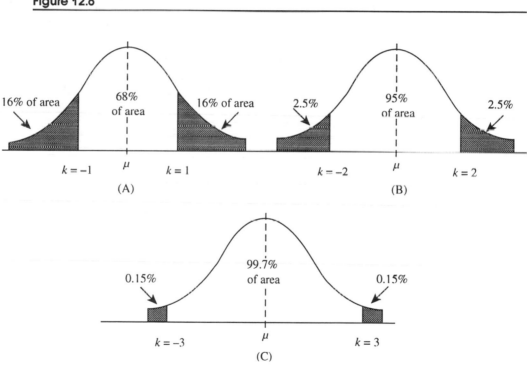

EXAMPLE 12.13

An investor has been reviewing a stock she has in her portfolio. The question is whether to sell or to hold the stock for a while longer. What is known is that the distribution of the stock price is approximately mound shaped (symmetrical) with a mean of $50 and a standard deviation of $5. The current price of the stock is $60. If the investor expects the historical price pattern to continue, what is the likelihood of the share price increasing? What is the likelihood of the stock price declining from its current value?

Solution   Since we know that the distribution of the stock price issymmetrical, first determine how many standard deviations the current price is away from the mean.

Current price = $60   Average price = $50   Standard deviation = $5

Since the current price is $10 higher than the average price, and since the value of one standard deviation is $5, the current price is two standard deviations above the average:

Number of standard deviations, $k = \dfrac{(\$60 - \$50)}{\$5} = 2$

According to the Empirical Rule, 95% of the stock prices are expected to fall within ± 2 standard deviations of the mean. This would suggest that there is a 5% chance that the stock price will fall outside this range (i.e., a 5% chance of being outside the range $40 to $60). Since the data are symmetrical, there will be the same chance that the stock will be above $60 as below $40. Because there is a 5% chance of being outside the $40 to $60 range, and given the data are symmetrical, it follows that there is a 2.5% chance of the price being greater than $60 (i.e., 5%/2). We can conclude that there is a 2.5% chance of the price rising above $60 as well as concluding that the likelihood that the price of the stock declining to below $60 is 97.5% (i.e., 100% – 2.5%). Summarizing, it is possible to state as follows:

There is a 2.5% chance that the stock price will rise above the current price of $60.

There is a 97.5% chance that the stock price will decline below the current $60 price. See Figure 12.7.

Recommendation: The investor should sell the shares.

Figure 12.7

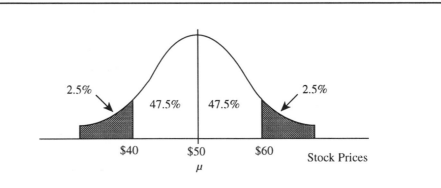

C. Chebyshev's Rule

In the real world not all data are symmetrical. To address this circumstance a Russian mathematician proposed a simple rule to summarize data. The rule is:

Let k be the number of standard deviations, where k must be greater than 1.

Providing $k > 1$, it will be found that no matter how irregular or non-symmetrical the data, the proportion of the data that will fall within k standard deviations of the mean will be at least $[1 - (1/k^2)]$.

For example, if the distribution stock prices in Example 12.13 had not been symmetrical, the proportion of the data that would fall within $k=2$ standard deviations would be:

$1 - \dfrac{1}{2^2} = 0.75$ Thus, <u>at least</u> 75% of the data would fall within two standard deviations of the mean, no matter how irregular the shape of the distribution.

Now let's summarize the proportion of the data that would fall within two and three standard deviations according to Chebyshev's Rule (i.e., $k=2$ and $k=3$):

Number of Standard Deviations from the Mean k	Range About the Mean $(\mu \pm k\sigma)$	Percentage of the Data Within the Range $(1 - 1/k^2)\cdot100\%$
2	$\mu \pm 2\sigma$	at least 75%
3	$\mu \pm 3\sigma$	at least 88.89%
4	$\mu \pm 4\sigma$	at least 93.75%

The power of Chebyshev's rule is that it applies to any distribution of data. However, when we know more about the data — such as when the data are symmetrical — it is better to use the Empirical Rule since it is more precise than Chebyshev's Rule.

EXAMPLE 12.14

Suppose the distribution of stock prices in Example 12.13 was not symmetrical. What would be the likelihood of the share price increasing? What is the likelihood of the stock price declining from its current value?

Solution Since we know that the distribution of the stock price is not symmetrical, we first determine how many standard deviations the current price is away from the mean (as done in Example 12.13).

Number of standard deviations, $k = \dfrac{(\$60 - \$50)}{\$5} = 2$

According to Chebyshev's Rule, at least 75% of the values of the stock price are expected to fall within two standard deviations of the mean. This would imply that there is at most a 25% chance that the stock price will fall outside this range (i.e., at most a 25% chance of being outside the range $40 to $60). Since we know there is at most a 25% chance of being above $60 or below $40, we can say that there is at least at most a 75% chance that the stock will fall below $60. Summarizing, we can state as follows:

There is at most a 25% chance that the stock price will rise above $60.

There is at least a 75% chance that the stock price will decline below $60.

Recommendation: The stock should be sold.

D. The Normal Distribution

The normal distribution is the name given to data that is perfectly symmetrical. Since the distribution is symmetrical (i.e., the mean, median and mode are the same), 50% of the data lies above the mean and 50% falls below the mean (see Figure 12.8). What makes the normal distribution so useful is that it is possible to compute the proportion of data that falls within any number of standard deviations of its mean. The normal distribution is used so frequently that a table of areas under the curve has been produced. One of these tables is shown in Table 12.5. As you can see the table provides area under the curve for only one side of the distribution, because one side of the curve is the mirror image of the other.

Figure 12.8 describes a normal distribution, with the mean, median, and mode in the centre. The values of X, the variable, are along the horizontal axis. The area under the curve is 1 or 100% of the area, with 0.5 or 50% of the area on both sides of the mean. The key to using the normal distribution is to remember that the areas under the curve are based on how many standard deviations X is away from the mean. What is done is to convert the distance that any value of X is away from the mean into standard deviations, called a *z* **value**.

Figure 12.8

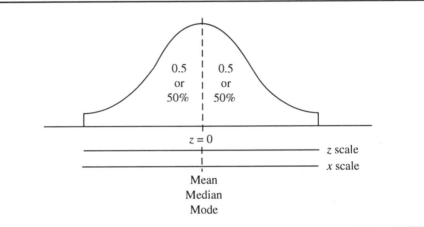

When applying the normal distribution, statisticians have computed the area under the normal curve, dependent upon how many standard deviations one is away from the mean. Since all data are different, statisticians convert all normally distributed data to the Z scale, where Z is the number of standard deviations between a particular value of the variable X and the population mean, μ. The Z values are found using the expression:

$$Z = \frac{X - \mu}{\sigma}$$

Formula 13.11

Where:

X = the value of the variable
μ = the population mean
σ = the population standard deviation
Z = the number of standard deviations between X and the mean, μ

Table 12.5:   Areas under The Standard Normal Curve

Normal Deviate z	.00	.01	.02	.03	.04	.05	.06	.07	.08	.09
0.0	.0000	.0040	.0080	.0120	.0160	.0199	.0239	.0279	.0319	.0359
0.1	.0398	.0438	.0478	.0517	.0557	.0596	.0636	.0675	.0714	.0753
0.2	.0793	.0832	.0871	.0910	.0948	.0987	.1026	.1064	.1103	.1141
0.3	.1179	.1217	.1255	.1293	.1331	.1368	.1406	.1443	.1480	.1517
0.4	.1554	.1591	.1628	.1664	.1700	.1736	.1772	.1808	.1844	.1879
0.5	.1915	.1950	.1985	.2019	.2054	.2088	.2123	.2157	.2190	.2224
0.6	.2257	.2291	.2324	.2357	.2389	.2422	.2454	.2486	.2518	.2549
0.7	.2580	.2612	.2642	.2673	.2704	.2734	.2764	.2794	.2823	.2852
0.8	.2881	.2910	.2939	.2967	.2995	.3023	.3051	.3078	.3106	.3133
0.9	.3159	.3186	.3212	.3238	.3264	.3289	.3315	.3340	.3365	.3389
1.0	.3413	.3438	.3461	.3485	.3508	.3531	.3554	.3577	.3599	.3621
1.1	.3643	.3665	.3686	.3708	.3729	.3749	.3770	.3790	.3810	.3830
1.2	.3849	.3869	.3888	.3907	.3925	.3944	.3962	.3980	.3997	.4015
1.3	.4032	.4049	.4066	.4082	.4099	.4115	.4131	.4147	.4162	.4177
1.4	.4192	.4207	.4222	.4236	.4251	.4265	.4279	.4292	.4306	.4319
1.5	.4332	.4345	.4357	.4370	.4382	.4394	.4406	.4418	.4429	.4441
1.6	.4452	.4463	.4474	.4484	.4495	.4505	.4515	.4525	.4535	.4545
1.7	.4554	.4564	.4573	.4582	.4591	.4599	.4608	.4616	.4625	.4633
1.8	.4641	.4649	.4656	.4664	.4671	.4678	.4686	.4693	.4699	.4706
1.9	.4713	.4719	.4726	.4732	.4738	.4744	.4750	.4756	.4761	.4767
2.0	.4772	.4778	.4783	.4788	.4793	.4798	.4803	.4808	.4812	.4817
2.1	.4821	.4826	.4830	.4834	.4838	.4842	.4846	.4850	.4854	.4857
2.2	.4861	.4864	.4868	.4871	.4875	.4878	.4881	.4884	.4887	.4890
2.3	.4893	.4896	.4898	.4901	.4904	.4906	.4909	.4911	.4913	.4916
2.4	.4918	.4920	.4922	.4925	.4927	.4929	.4931	.4932	.4934	.4936
2.5	.4938	.4940	.4941	.4943	.4945	.4946	.4948	.4949	.4951	.4952
2.6	.4953	.4955	.4956	.4957	.4959	.4960	.4961	.4962	.4963	.4964
2.7	.4965	.4966	.4967	.4968	.4969	.4970	.4971	.4972	.4973	.4974
2.8	.4974	.4975	.4976	.4977	.4977	.4978	.4979	.4979	.4980	.4981
2.9	.4981	.4982	.4982	.4983	.4984	.4984	.4985	.4985	.4986	.4986
3.0	.49865	.4987	.4987	.4988	.4988	.4989	.4989	.4989	.4990	.4990
4.0	.49997									

SOURCE: © 1977 by Harcourt Brace Jovanovich, Inc., and reproduced with their permission from *Statistical Analysis for Decision Making*, 2nd ed., by Morris Hamburg.

Note that the value of the mean on the X scale (the original data scale) cor-responds to the point where $Z = 0$. This is because, when the data are converted from the X scale to the Z scale, the mean is the centre point and values of Z are simply the number of standard deviations between X and the mean. Thus, the value of Z where $X = \mu$ is 0 on the Z scale.

The areas in Table 12.5 start at $Z = 0$, with 0.5 or 50% of the area to the left of the mean, and 0.5 or 50% to the right of $Z = 0$; since one side of the curve is the mirror image of the other, only one side of areas need to be in the table. Figure 12.9 shows the table values of the area under a normal curve for $z = \pm 1, \pm 2$ as well as the areas to the right of $Z = 2$ and to the left of $Z = -2$. From the table, the area under the curve for $Z = 2$ (two standard deviations to the right of the mean) is 0.4772. The area between $Z = 1$ and $Z = 2$ was found by subtracting 0.3413 from 0.4772; the area in the tail (to the right of $Z = 2$ and to the left of $Z = -2$) was found by subtracting 0.4772 from 0.5000, yielding 0.0228.

Figure 12.9

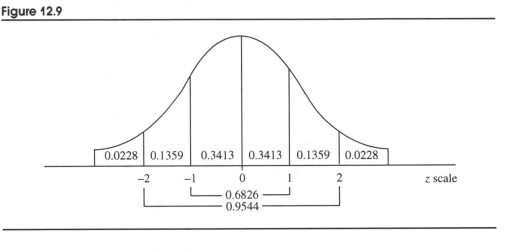

EXAMPLE 12.15

Suppose it is known that the average cost of parts stocked by a large company is $45, with a standard deviation of $5. It is also known that the distribution of costs is approximately normally distributed.
(a) What proportion of the parts have a cost of $40 to $50?
(b) What proportion have a cost of less than or equal to $40?
(c) What proportion of the inventory had a unit cost of $57 or more?
(d) Below what cost are 74.86% of the parts in the inventory?

Solution (a) To determine the proportion of parts that cost $40 to $50, find how many standard deviations these two values are from the mean:

$X = \$40$; $\mu = \$45$; $\sigma = \$5$. Using the Z formula　　**(Formula 12.11)**:

$$z = \frac{X - \mu}{\sigma} = \frac{\$40 - \$45}{\$5} = -1$$

When the value of Z has a negative sign this means X is to the left of the mean.

$X = \$50$; $\mu = \$45$; $\sigma = \$5$. Using the Z formula:

$$z = \frac{X - \mu}{\sigma} = \frac{\$50 - \$45}{\$5} = 1$$

Looking at the table under the Z column for the area to the left of Z = 1, we see that 0.3413 of the area is within one standard deviation of the mean. However, this is only one side of the curve. Therefore, the total area between ± 1 standard deviation is:

$$0.3413 + 0.3413 = 0.6826$$

Thus, the proportion of parts in the price range $40 to $50 is 68.26% (see Figure 12.10).

Figure 12.10

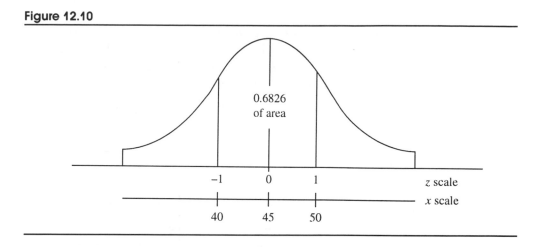

(b) The proportion of parts that cost less than or equal to $40 is found as follows:

$X = \$40$; $\mu = \$45$; $\sigma = \$5$. Use the Z formula:

$$z = \frac{X - \mu}{\sigma} = \frac{\$40 - \$45}{\$5} = -1$$

Since we know the area under the curve is 1 or 100%, and that the proportion of the parts costing between $40 and $45 is 0.3413 (one standard deviation from the mean), the proportion of parts costing less than $40 must be:

$$0.5 - 0.3413 = 0.1587 \text{ or } 15.87\%$$

Note that the solution to this problem uses the knowledge that the area under one side of the curve is 0.5 or 50% of the total (see Figure 12.11).

Figure 12.11

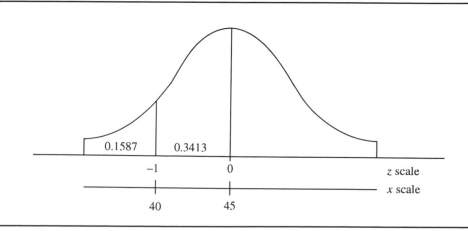

(c) What proportion of the inventory has a cost of $57 or more?

$X = \$57$; $\mu = \$45$; $\sigma = \$5$. Using the Z formula:

$$z = \frac{X - \mu}{\sigma} = \frac{\$57 - \$45}{\$5} = 2.4$$

To find the proportion of the inventory that has a cost of $57 or more, find the area to right of $57, or the area to the right of $Z = 2.4$.

The area in the table up to $Z = 2.4$ is 0.4918; thus, the proportion of the area that is to the right of this value is:

$$0.5 - 0.4918 = 0.0082, \text{ or } 0.82\% \text{ (see Figure 12.12).}$$

Figure 12.12

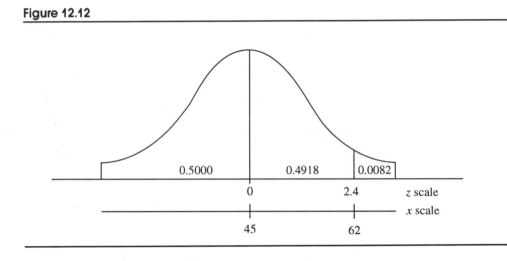

(d) To find what cost 74.86% of the parts in the inventory is below , we must work backwards — that is, we know the area and therefore z, but not X. What we must find is a value of X that is a sufficient nnumber of standard deviations to the right of the mean so that 74.86% of the area lies to its left.

Looking at the table, we search for an area that is as close to 0.2486 as possible. Why 0.2486? Since we know that 0.5 of the area is to the left of the mean, we need only to find the value of Z that corresponds to 0.2486, since the total area to the left of this value will be 0.7486 (0.5 + 0.2486).

The value of Z that has 0.7486 to its left is $Z = 0.67$.

$X = ?$; $\mu = \$45$; $\sigma = \$5$; $Z = 0.67$. We rearrange our Z formula to solve for X:

$$z = \frac{X - \mu}{\sigma}$$

Solve the expression for X:

$$X = \mu + z\sigma$$

Now substitute the values:

$$X = \$45 + 0.67(\$5) = \$48.35$$

Thus, we can conclude that 74.86% of the parts have a cost of $48.35 or less (see Figure 12.13).

Figure 12.13

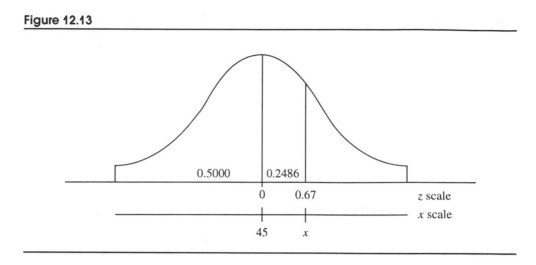

SUMMARY OF FORMULAS

Formula 12.1.A $\mu = \dfrac{\Sigma X}{N}$ Used to find the population mean.

Formula 12.1.B $\bar{x} = \dfrac{\Sigma X}{n}$ Used to find the sample mean.

Formula 12.2 $\bar{x}w - \dfrac{\Sigma wX}{\Sigma w}$ Used to find the weighted average.

Formula 12.3 $\bar{x} = \dfrac{\Sigma fX}{\Sigma f}$ Used to find the average of grouped data.

Formula 12.4 $L + \dfrac{Rf}{fmc} \cdot (\text{class width})$ Used to find the median of grouped data.

Formula 12.5 $\sigma = \sqrt{\dfrac{\Sigma(X - \mu)^2}{N}}$ The standard deviation for the population.

Formula 12.6 $s = \sqrt{\dfrac{\Sigma(X - \bar{x})^2}{n - 1}}$ The standard deviation for a sample.

Formula 12.7 $\sigma = \sqrt{\dfrac{\Sigma X^2 - \dfrac{(\Sigma X)^2}{N}}{N}}$ The short-cut formula for the population standard deviation.

Formula 12.8 $s = \sqrt{\dfrac{\Sigma X^2 - \dfrac{(\Sigma X)^2}{n}}{n - 1}}$ The short-cut formula for the sample standard deviation.

Formula 12.9.A $s = \sqrt{\dfrac{\Sigma f(X - \bar{x})^2}{\Sigma f - 1}}$ The formula for the sample standard for grouped data.

Formula 12.9.B $s = \sqrt{\dfrac{\Sigma fX^2 - \dfrac{(\Sigma fX)^2}{\Sigma f}}{\Sigma f - 1}}$ The short-cut formula for the sample standard deviation for grouped data.

Formula 12.10 $CV = \frac{s}{\bar{X}} \cdot 100\%$ The coefficient of variation formula; used to compare relative variability.

Formula 12.11 $Z = \frac{X - \mu}{\sigma}$ The number of standard deviations between X and the mean for data that are normally distributed.

GLOSSARY OF TERMS

Class Frequency   the number of observations from the data that fall within a particular class.

Class Limit   the lower class limit is the minimum value of the data that can fall within the class and the upper class limit is the maximum value of the data that can fall within the class.

Class Midpoint   the middle value of the class, found by averaging two consecutive lower limits or averaging two consecutive upper limits.

Class Width   the distance from the lower limit to the upper limit, inclusive of the class limits. It is found by subtracting two consecutive lower limits or subtracting two consecutive upper limits.

Coefficient of Variation   a measure of relative variation. It is computed by a ratio of the standard deviation to the mean and is a pure number (i.e., it has no units). The coefficient of variation is used to compare different types of data to provide a measure of relative variation.

Descriptive Statistics   the name given to the body of statistics that involves the collection, display, and calculation of measures of central tendency and dispersion. This is the part of statistics that involves reporting of information.

Frequency Distribution   the listing of the frequencies for each class when data have been grouped.

Inferential Statistics   the name given to the body of statistics that involves making predictions or inferences about a population from sample data.

Mean   a measure of central tendency found by adding all the data and dividing by the number of observations.

Measure of Central Tendency   a measure of the centre point of the data. It is the point where the data tend to cluster. There are three measures of central tendency: the mean (average), the median, and the mode.

Measure of Dispersion   a measure of the spread or variability of the data. Measures of dispersion also tell us how well the mean captures the central point of the data; the more spread out the data, the less reliable is the mean as a measure of central tendency.

Median   the centre point of the data; one-half of the data are less than or equal to the median and one-half of the data are greater than or equal to the median.

Mode   the observation that occurs most frequently in the data.

Parameter   a measure that has been computed on the basis of all the observations in the population. Parameters are always based on population data.

Relative Frequency   the percentage of observations that fall in a particular class relative to the total number of observations. The total of the relative frequencies is 100%.

Standard Deviation   a measure of dispersion, that provides a numerical measure of variability for data.

Statistic   an estimate of a population parameter, based on sample data.

Symmetrical Distribution   distribution in which the mean, median, and the mode are the same. Knowledge of symmetry is of particular importance in applying the Empirical Rule and the normal distribution to summarize data.

Weighted Mean   a mean determined by weighting each observation by an appropriate weight; also known as a weighted average.

Z Value   a measure of the number of standard deviations between a value of the variable and the mean. Z values are used to determine the area, under a normal distribution, between the mean and particular values of the variable.

Index